SCHOLASTIC

100 MATHS LESSONS

Recommended system requirements:

- Windows: XP (Service Pack 3), Vista (Service Pack 2), Windows 7 or Windows 8 with 2.33GHz processor
- Mac: OS 10.6 to 10.8 with Intel Core™ Duo processor
- 1GB RAM (recommended)
- 1024 x 768 Screen resolution
- CD-ROM drive (24x speed recommended)
- 16-bit sound card
- Adobe Reader (version 9 recommended for Mac users)
- Broadband internet connections (for installation and updates)

For all technical support queries, please phone Scholastic Customer Services on 0845 6039091.

Book End, Range Road, Witney, Oxfordshire, OX29 0YD
www.scholastic.co.uk

© 2014, Scholastic Ltd

5 6 7 8 9   6 7 8 9 0 1 2 3

British Library Cataloguing-in-Publication Data
A catalogue record for this book is available from the
British Library.

ISBN 978-1407-12775-0
Printed by Bell & Bain Ltd, Glasgow

Due to the nature of the web we cannot guarantee the
content or links of any site mentioned. We strongly
recommend that teachers check websites before using
them in the classroom.

Extracts from *The National Curriculum in Maths, Maths
Programme of Study* © Crown Copyright. Reproduced
under the terms of the Open Government Licence
(OGL). http://www.nationalarchives.gov.uk/doc/open-
government-licence/open-government-licence.htm

Author
Yvette McDaniel

Series Editor
Ann Montague-Smith

Editorial team
Emily Jefferson, Jenny Wilcox, Penny Nicholson,
Kate Grieg

Cover Design
Andrea Lewis

Design Team
Sarah Garbett, Shelley Best and Andrea Lewis

CD-ROM development
Hannah Barnett, Phil Crothers, MWA Technologies
Private Ltd

Typesetting and illustrations
Ricky Capanni, International Book Management

Contents

Introduction

About the series

The *100 Maths Lessons* series is designed to meet the requirements of the 2014 National Curriculum, Mathematics Programme of Study. There are six books in the series for Years 1–6, and each book contains lesson plans, resources and ideas matched to the new curriculum. These six titles – along with the accompanying *100 Maths Planning Guide* – have been carefully structured to ensure that a progressive and appropriate school curriculum can be planned and taught throughout the primary years.

About the 2014 Curriculum

The curriculum documentation for Mathematics provides a yearly programme for Years 1 to 6 (ages 5 to 11).

The new curriculum goes further than the previous version with times tables to 12 x 12 by Year 4, an early introduction to long division and an increasingly complex understanding of fractions and decimals. The new curriculum also has a strong focus on varied and frequent practice of the fundamentals of maths – mastery of number facts and times tables should be developed throughout the primary phase.

There is a renewed emphasis on reasoning mathematically and solving problems with particular emphasis on multi-step problems and problems in the context of measurement, money and time. The main coverage of the use and application of mathematics however can be found in the aims of the curriculum:

> *The National Curriculum for Mathematics aims to ensure that all pupils:*
> - *become fluent in the fundamentals of mathematics, including through varied and frequent practice with increasingly complex problems over time, so that pupils have conceptual understanding and are able to recall and apply their knowledge rapidly and accurately to problems*
> - *reason mathematically by following a line of enquiry, conjecturing relationships and generalisations, and developing an argument, justification or proof using mathematical language*
> - *can solve problems by applying their mathematics to a variety of routine and non-routine problems with increasing sophistication, including breaking down problems into a series of simpler steps and persevering in seeking solutions.*

Terminology

The curriculum terminology has changed; the main terms used are:
- **Domains:** The main areas of mathematical study, such as Number and Geometry.
- **Topics:** These are identified in each weekly planning grid and drill the domains down into 'Place value', 'Addition and subtraction' and so on.
- **Curriculum objectives:** These are the statutory programme of study statements or objectives.
- **Appendix:** Any reference to an appendix refers to the Mathematics Appendix 1 'Examples of formal written methods for addition, subtraction, multiplication and division.'

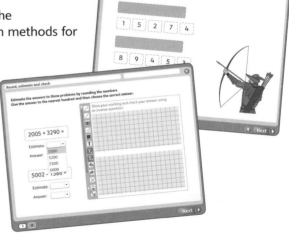

■SCHOLASTIC

About the book

This book is divided by term and week with a summary heading giving an indication of the week's work. Each week follows the same structure:

Weekly overview

At the start of each week you will find a summary of what is covered, which includes:

- **Expected prior learning:** What the children are expected to know before starting the work in the chapter.
- **Weekly planning grid:** A lesson-by-lesson breakdown of the coverage of each week – by 'topic', 'curriculum objectives' and 'expected outcomes'.
- **Oral and mental starters:** Suggested activities that might be used from the bank of starters that follow each half-term's lessons.
- **Overview of progression:** A brief explanation of the expected progress that children should make through each week's work.
- **Watch out for:** Possible mathematical misconceptions with ideas for addressing them.
- **Creative context:** How the week's work could link to other 2014 curriculum areas.
- **Vocabulary:** Key vocabulary to introduce or consolidate. (Words in bold also appear in the glossary, see CD-ROM notes on page 7.)
- **Preparation/You will need:** A full list of resources required from book and CD, as well as any general class resources requiring preparation. (A full resource list is given on page 255.)
- **Further practice:** Ideas for consolidating learning using additional resources or practical activities.

Lessons

Each half term contains six weeks' work. Each week contains five lessons. Each lesson includes the following:

- **Curriculum objectives:** A list of the relevant objectives from the Programme of Study.
- **Success criteria:** Expected outcomes for the lesson written as 'can do' statements.
- **You will need:** List of required resources.
- **Whole-class work:** Ideas for working together as a class.
- **Group/Paired/Independent work:** Teaching notes for paired, groups or independent work.
- **Differentiation:** Ideas to support children who are not sufficiently fluent with concepts or to challenge children to apply their understanding (see 2014 National Curriculum aims for further information on the approach to differentiation).
- **Progress check:** 'Mini-plenaries' to enable teachers to check progress throughout the lesson.
- **Review:** Opportunity to reflect on children's learning, and address any misconceptions.

Assess and review

At the end of each half term are activities designed to assess children's understanding or mastery of key curriculum objectives. These can be conducted during the half-term's lessons or at the end, in an 'assess and review week'.

There are four curriculum objectives covered in each half–term. Each section includes ideas to:

- Check progress using appropriate starter activities.
- Assess children's learning using a mix of activities, problems and puzzles.
- Provide further practice activities to consolidate their understanding.

Oral and mental starter activities

In each half term a bank of oral and mental starters is provided. These can be used flexibly to address particular requirements, though suggestions are made within each weekly overview as to which starters might be used across a week's lessons. Each starter includes modelled teacher questions to probe children's ability to recall facts, rehearse strategies or apply learning.

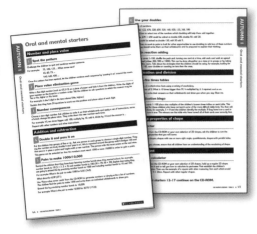

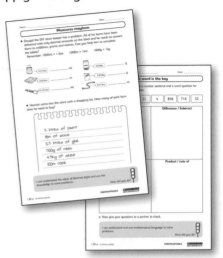

Photocopiable pages

At the end of each chapter, you will find a bank of photocopiable pages linked to the 'Assess and review' section. These sheets offer an 'I can...' statement at the bottom to allow self-assessment of pupil progress towards a particular curriculum objective. Ask the children to colour in the traffic lights next to each statement green, amber or red to reflect their confidence with the objective. There is also space for comments. Additional sheets, linked to the lessons, can be found on the CD-ROM (see page 7 for further information).

Equipment list

This provides an overview of all of the classroom resources required to teach each year's lessons. The resources are broken down by mathematics topic.

Vocabulary list

This provides a list of all key vocabulary to introduce or consolidate over the course of the year. Words appearing in bold type also appear in the glossary (see page 7 for further information).

■SCHOLASTIC

About the CD-ROM

The CD-ROM contains:

- Printable versions of the photocopiable sheets from the book and additional photocopiable sheets as referenced in the lesson plans.
- Interactive activities for children to complete or to use on the whiteboard.
- Interactive teaching resources such as 'Number grids' and 'Pattern squares', designed to support whole–class teaching.
- Printable versions of the lesson plans and the oral and mental starters.
- Digital versions of the lesson plans with the relevant resources linked to them.

Getting started

- Put the CD-ROM into your CD-ROM drive.
  - For Windows users, the install wizard should autorun, if it fails to do so then navigate to your CD-ROM drive. Then follow the installation process.
  - For Mac users, copy the disk image file to your hard drive. After it has finished copying, double-click it to mount the disk image. Navigate to the mounted disk image and run the installer. After installation the disk image can be unmounted and the DMG can be deleted from the hard drive.
- To complete the installation of the program, you need to open the program and click 'Update' in the pop-up. **NB** This CD-ROM is web-enabled and the content needs to be downloaded from the internet to your hard-drive to populate the CD-ROM with the relevant resources. A web connection is only required on first use, after which you will be able to use the CD–ROM without any connection. If at any point any content is updated you will receive a pop-up message upon start–up when you are next connected to the web. You will then have the option to update the content as required.

Navigating the CD-ROM

There are two options to navigate the CD-ROM, either as a Child or as a Teacher.

Child

- Click on the 'Child' button on the first menu screen. In the second menu click on the relevant year group (please note only the books installed on the machine or network will be accessible. You can also rename year groups to match your school's naming conventions via Teacher > Settings > Rename Books area.)
- A list of interactive activities will be displayed; children need to locate the correct class or year group and click 'Go' to launch.
- There is the opportunity to print or save a PDF of the results of each activity on completion.

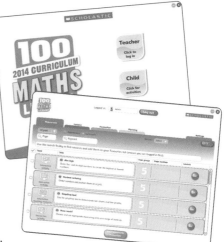

Teacher

- Click on the 'Teacher' button on the first menu screen and you will be taken to a menu showing which of the *100 Maths Lessons* titles you have purchased. From here, you can also access the credits and 'Getting started' information
- To enter the product, click 'Next' in the bottom right of the screen.
- You can then enter a password (the password is: login).
- On first use:
  - Enter as a Guest by clicking on the 'Guest' button.
  - If desired, create a profile for yourself by adding your name to the list of users. Profiles allow you to save favourites and to specify which year group(s) you wish to be able to view.
  - Go to 'Settings' to create a profile for yourself – click 'Add user' and enter your name. Then choose the year groups you wish to have access to (you can return to this screen to change this at any time). Click on 'Login' at the top of the screen to re-enter the CD-ROM with your new profile.
- On subsequent uses you can then select your name from the drop-down list.
- The 'Guest' option will always be available if you, or a colleague, prefer to use this.
- When you have set up your profile, you can then save activities or lessons in 'Favourites'.

For more information about how to use the CD-ROM, please refer to the 'Help' file which can be found in the teacher area of the CD-ROM. It is displayed as a red button with a question mark inside, on the right-hand side of the screen just underneath the 'Settings' tab.

Place value to 1,000,000

Expected prior learning

Children should be able to:

- count from any given number in whole-number steps
- understand the relationship and value of each digit in a number
- use positive and negative numbers in practical contexts and position them on a number line.

Topic	Curriculum objectives	Expected outcomes
Number and place value	**Lesson 1**	
	To read, write, order and compare numbers to at least to 1,000,000 and determine the value of each digit.	Explain what each digit represents in whole numbers and partition and order these numbers.
	Lesson 2	
	To read, write, order and compare numbers to at least to 1,000,000 and determine the value of each digit.	Explain what each digit represents in whole numbers and partition and order these numbers.
	Lesson 3	
	To read, write, order and compare numbers to at least to 1,000,000 and determine the value of each digit.	Explain what each digit represents in whole numbers and partition and order these numbers.
	Lesson 4	
	To count forwards or backwards in steps of powers of 10 for any given number up to 1,000,000.	Count from any given number in whole-number steps, extending beyond zero when counting backwards and relate the numbers to their position on a number line.
	Lesson 5	
	To count forwards or backwards in steps of powers of 10 for any given number up to 1,000,000.	Count from any given number in whole-number steps, extending beyond zero when counting backwards and relate the numbers to their position on a number line.

Preparation

Lesson 1: cut out the 0–9 cards from '0–30 number cards' and 'Place value arrow cards'; for the arrow cards, it will be helpful if the ones, tens, hundreds, and so on, are on different-coloured card to assist with selection and recombining

Lesson 2: make the greater than (>), less than (<) and equals (=) cards from 'Symbol cards'; copy 'Number line shuffle', one per pair

Lesson 3: make some cards showing the numbers 256, 187, 387, 342 and 196; copy 'Greater or smaller?', one per pair

Lesson 4: copy 'Patterns and chains', one per child; copy '100 square' on to card

Lesson 5: label some blank dice, one per pair, as follows: +10, +100, +1000, −10, −100, −1000; copy photocopiable page 'Forwards and backwards, one per pair

You will need

Photocopiable sheets

'Number line shuffle'; 'Greater or smaller?'; 'Greater or smaller? template'; 'Patterns and chains'; 'Forwards and backwards'

General resources

'Place value chart'; '0–30 number cards'; 'Place value arrow cards'; 'Symbol cards'; '100 square'; interactive activity 'Aim high'

Equipment

Calculators; Blu-Tack®; cards showing the numbers 256, 187, 387, 342 and 196; dice; number line which extends into negative numbers or bead string, 100 square; dice marked +10, +100, +1000, −10, −100, −1000

Further practice

The interactive activity 'Aim high' offers the opportunity for further practice of reading and ordering five- and six-digit numbers.

Oral and mental starters suggested for week 1

See bank of starters on page 44. Oral and mental starters are also on the CD-ROM.

1 Spot the pattern

2 Place value elimination game

16 Division lotto

3 Number consequences

Overview of progression

During this week, children will secure their knowledge of place value by comparing the relative size of a number when the digit is moved up and down the place value chart. They will be able to demonstrate this knowledge by creating the smallest and largest numbers possible from given digits.

Watch out for

Children who inaccurately read the place value or do not use the appropriate number of place-holding zeros, thereby misreading the value of the number. The use of a place value chart and place value arrow cards to create larger numbers will give children practise and confidence.

Creative context

Understanding place value is an important mathematical skill which has an impact in many areas of the curriculum, such as using money, counting decades, centuries and millennia in history and working with temperatures and other weather data.

Vocabulary

ascending, between, descending, digit, greater than (>), hundred thousands, hundreds, less than (<), millions, **numeral**, pattern, partition, place value, sequence, ten thousands, tens, thousands, ones

Curriculum objectives
● To read, write, order and compare numbers to at least to 1,000,000 and determine the value of each digit.

Success criteria
● I can count from any given number in whole-number steps, extending beyond zero when counting backwards.

You will need

General resources
'0–30 number cards'; 'Place value arrow cards'; 'Place value chart'

Equipment
Calculators

Differentiation

Less confident learners
These children should make three-digit, or possibly four-digit, numbers.

More confident learners
These children should make six-digit numbers including at least one zero in each number.

Lesson 1
Oral and mental starter 1

Main teaching activities

Whole-class work: Display photocopiable page 'Place value chart' from the CD-ROM and indicate how the place value of each digit moves one place to the left as you move up the chart. Revise the vocabulary of place value to ensure that everyone is clear about it. For example, point to 300 and ask the children to identify the names of all the numbers in that row, then repeat for 30,000 or 3000.

Talk about how digits can be combined to build up any number. Generate a number using 0–9 from the number cards then use the 'Place value arrow cards' to build the number. Start with a four-digit number and invite four children to hold up the correct arrow cards. For example, 2000, 400, 30 and 1 to make 2431. Ask these children to read out each digit individually, then combine the arrows to make the number and read out the whole number together. Invite someone to write it in words on the board. Repeat, choosing different digits. Try a five-digit or six digit number. For each example, pick a digit and ask: *What is the value of the 7 in 37,306? What is the value of the first digit? The last digit?*

Paired work: Give each pair a set of arrow cards. Ask them to select one card from each place value set at random, then record them.

For example: 100,000 + 60,000 + 4000 + 200 + 10 = 64,210 = one hundred and sixty-four thousand, two hundred and ten.

Progress check: Invite pairs to show an example of their recorded numbers on the whiteboard. Ask: *Tell me the value of the largest/smallest digit .What would the number be if we replaced one of the digits with a zero? for example 251, 024. How do we record and say this number?* Explain that sometimes a comma or a space is used when recording numbers larger than a thousand simply to make it easier to read.

Review

Give out calculators and ask the children to put in the number 1024 (say: *one thousand and twenty-four*). Ask them what they have displayed. Ask: *How did you get the 1 into the thousands column? What did you have to remember to put in?* (The zero for no hundreds.) *What would the display have read if you had forgotten the zero?* (One hundred and twenty-four.) Ask the children to clear the display and repeat with 10,046 and 203,402.

Curriculum objectives
● To read, write, order and compare numbers to at least to 1,000,000 and determine the value of each digit.

Success criteria
● I can read whole numbers, explain the value of each digit and use this to partition and order numbers.
● I can relate numbers to their position on a number line.

You will need
Photocopiable sheets
'Number line shuffle'
General resources
'0–30 number cards'; greater than (>) and less than (<) cards from 'Symbol cards'; interactive activity 'Aim high'

Differentiation
Less confident learners
Invite children to work with a more confident talk partner to help explain the place value involved.
More confident learners
Interactive activity 'Aim high' offers an opportunity to read and order five- and six-digit numbers. Alternatively, invite children to repeat the 'Number line shuffle' activity, using six number cards.

Lesson 2 — Oral and mental starter 2

Main teaching activities

Whole-class work: Play 'Human number cards'. Draw a number line on the board. Invite four children to select a number card each. Ask the rest of the class to arrange these children so as to make the smallest possible number. Write this number on the left of the number line. Ask: *What is the largest number possible using the same digits? What do you notice?* (The order is reversed.) Write this number on the right of the number line.

Ask the children to make two more numbers with the same digits. Together, estimate the position of each number on the line by discussing halfway points. Record both numbers on the line.

Finally, using the relevant cards from the 'Symbol cards' set, introduce or revise the symbols < (less than) and > (greater than), and put them between the numbers on the line. For example:

2479   <   2497   <   4297   <   9742

Paired work: Give each pair a set of number cards and ask them to generate four- or five-digit numbers, then record the smallest and greatest possible numbers at either end of the number lines provided on photocopiable page 'Number line shuffle' from the CD-ROM. They then make two more numbers from the same set and estimate their positions. They should use the < symbol to write a number sentence.

Progress check: Ask some of the children to display their number lines and for the others to check that they have correctly placed the numbers. Ask: *Explain how you decided on where to place the other numbers on your number line. How could we calculate the value of the number that is exactly halfway between these numbers?* (Find the difference and halve it.) Beware of those who think that they should halve the larger number.

Review

Draw a number line.

1459   9531

Ask: *How can we find the midpoint of this number line by rounding and estimating?* (From 1500 to 9500 is 8000, so the midpoint is 4000 + 1500 = 5500.) *How could this help us to divide the line into quarters?* (Half of 4000 is 2000, so the quarters are at 3500 and 7500.) Repeat for 2422 and 9470 or for 12,321 and 20,854.

Curriculum objectives
● To read, write, order and compare numbers to at least to 1,000,000 and determine the value of each digit.

Success criteria
● I can write number sentences comparing numbers using the greater than (>) and less than (<) signs.

You will need

Photocopiable sheets
'Greater or smaller?'; 'Greater or smaller? template'

General resources
Greater than (>), less than (<) and equals (=) cards from 'Symbol cards'; interactive activity 'Aim high'

Equipment
Blu-Tack®; cards showing the numbers 256, 187, 387, 342 and 196; dice

Differentiation

Less confident learners
Invite children to work with a more confident talk partner to help explain the place value involved.

More confident learners
Adapt the 'Greater or smaller? template' to extend the initial activity to five- and six-digit numbers where appropriate.

Lesson 3

Oral and mental starter 16

Main teaching activities

Whole-class work: Show the children the greater than (>), less than (<) and equals (=) cards from 'Symbol cards'. Invite children to choose a card and explain what it means. Remind them that the smaller number always goes at the sharp end. Write some number sentences such as: 726 > 290; 3542 < 4687; 10,023 < 10,032.

Explain that these symbols can be useful when ordering numbers. Ask for a volunteer to order the number cards 256, 187, 387, 342 and 196 in ascending order, sticking a less than (<) symbol card in between each number with Blu-Tack®. Ask another child to rearrange these numbers in descending order, using the greater than (>) symbol. Now put the numbers in the original order again and ask a third child to use a mixture of < and > symbols to write an accurate number sentence. (256 > 187 < 387 > 342 > 196).

Paired work: Distribute photocopiable page 'Greater or smaller?' from the CD-ROM, explaining that the children should generate numbers using dice and order them using the < and > symbols.

Progress check: Ask one pair to write up on the board one of their pairs of numbers with the correct symbol. Ask: *If the first number was 10/100/1000 more would the greater/smaller symbol change? What is the value of the first/ second digit? What would I have to add to the smaller number to make this number sentence incorrect?*

Review

Write some pairs of numbers on the board. Invite children to write symbols between them. Include some decimal numbers and some numbers that are equal. For example: 25.6 < 45.6; 0.05 < 0.1; 3809 > 3807; 12,084 > 12,083; 0.3 > 0.03; 3.4 = 3.40; 1.77 < 1.78; 1 < 6; 112 = 112.0. Ask the child as he or she completes each example. Ask: *What part of the number are you using to help you decide which number is larger? Is it the same digit in every example?*

Check further children's understanding using interactive activity 'Aim high' on the CD-ROM. Invite children to write the largest and smallest numbers they can make on their whiteboards before completing each screen.

Curriculum objectives
● To count forwards or backwards in steps of powers of 10 for any given number up to 1,000,000.

Success criteria
● I can recognise a pattern of numbers in steps of 10, 100 and 1000 and continue it for negative and positive numbers.

You will need

Photocopiable sheets
'Patterns and chains'

General resources
'100 square'

Equipment
Number line with negative numbers, or bead string

Differentiation

Less confident learners
Children may need the support of counting apparatus such as 100 squares or number lines to help them.

More confident learners
When they create their own patterns, these children could begin with decimal numbers to challenge their partner.

Lesson 4
Oral and mental starter 3

Main teaching activities

Whole-class work: Explain that the children need to be able to count on and back in steps of 10, 100 and 1000. Write the number 34 on the board, ask: *What is 100 less than this number?* (−66) *How did you work it out?* (Count back or subtract 34 from 100 knowing the result was less than 0 or a negative number.) Explain again about negative numbers being counted as a distance from zero. The larger the digits of a negative number the greater distance it is from zero, therefore making it a much smaller value.

Write the following pattern on the board: __, __, __, 107, __, 307, __, __, 607.

Ask the children to identify the pattern and to complete the missing numbers. Ask: *What is the number before 107?* (7) *And before that?* (−93). *How did you work that out?*

Independent work: Distribute photocopiable page 'Patterns and chains' from the CD-ROM. Explain that some numbers have been placed in the chain and they must first work out the pattern of 'jumps' and then complete the pattern, which may involve extending beyond zero. The children should complete their patterns and then check their answers with a partner. As an extension they should use the blank chains to create further patterns for their partner.

Progress check: Watch out for children who simply reverse the pattern without regard for the values of the number when crossing into negative numbers. Ask for some children to demonstrate their patterns using a number line which extends beyond zero or a bead string.

Review

Ask: *Where are the tricky areas when counting on in 'jumps'?* (Bridging the 10s/100s/1000s and crossing zero.) *What patterns did you notice? How do you think this might help your mental calculation?* Share some patterns to help your assessments and correct misconceptions.

Curriculum objectives
● As lesson 4.

Success criteria
● I can count forwards and backwards in steps of 10, 100 and 1000.

You will need

Photocopiable sheets
'Forwards and backwards'

General resources
'0–30 number cards'

Equipment
Dice marked +10, +100, +1000, −10, −100, −1000

Differentiation

Less confident learners
Children might need to check their place value using a calculator.

More confident learners
Players choose which place value to put each digit selected trying to make the largest number possible.

Lesson 5
Oral and mental starter 16

Main teaching activities

Whole-class work: Write up on the board the number 21,007. Ask the children to tell you the value of all the digits in the number. Ask questions such as: *What would the value of this number be if I counted back 100? 10? 1000?* Ask: *Would counting on in ones be a good strategy for this?* (No, it is inefficient but a number of less confident children may try!) Tell the children that you are going to give them a starting number and they are going to count on in given steps until you clap your hands, when they should reverse the process and count back. Listen for problems, particularly when bridging 100 or 1000 or zero.

Paired work: Hand out photocopiable page 'Forwards and backwards' from the CD-ROM. Explain the rules. Children play the game and complete the score card.

Progress check: Ensure that children are changing the correct place value when applying the rule. Display one completed score card and ask the other children if they can work out what operation was applied to the original number.

Review

Divide the class into two teams. Explain to the children that they have to make the largest number possible using five 0–9 digits selected at random. They will not know which digits will come next so must choose their place value wisely. Choose team captains for each team to scribe. Select a number card and ask the children to discuss in their teams where to place it in the five place value spaces available. The scribe records it on the board. It may not be changed. Repeat with successive digits. The discussions should inform you about the children's understanding of place value.

Addition and subtraction

Expected prior learning

Children should be able to:

- add and subtract whole numbers mentally, using and applying their number bonds knowledge to extend to of pairs to make 10, 100 and 1000
- recognise expanded written methods for addition and subtraction
- understand the inverse relationship of addition and subtraction
- understand the relationship between counting on and back and be able to demonstrate both on a number line.

Topic	Curriculum objectives	Expected outcomes
Addition and subtraction	**Lesson 1**	
	To add and subtract numbers mentally with increasingly large numbers.	Extend mental methods for whole number calculations, for example, subtract one near-multiple of 1000 from another (for example 6070 − 4097).
	Lesson 2	
	To add and subtract whole numbers with more than four-digits, including using formal written methods (columnar addition and subtraction).	Use formal written methods to add and subtract whole numbers with up to five digits.
	To add and subtract numbers mentally with increasingly large numbers.	Extend mental methods for whole number calculations, for example, subtract one near-multiple of 1000 from another (for example 6070 − 4097).
	Lesson 3	
	To add and subtract whole numbers with more than four-digits, including using formal written methods (columnar addition and subtraction).	Use formal written methods to add and subtract whole numbers with up to five digits.
	To add and subtract numbers mentally with increasingly large numbers.	Extend mental methods for whole number calculations, for example, subtract one near-multiple of 1000 from another (for example 6070 − 4097).
	Lesson 4	
	To add and subtract whole numbers with more than four-digits, including using formal written methods (columnar addition and subtraction).	Use formal written methods to add and subtract whole numbers with up to five digits.
	To add and subtract numbers mentally with increasingly large numbers.	Extend mental methods for whole number calculations, for example, subtract one near-multiple of 1000 from another (for example 6070 − 4097).
	Lesson 5	
	To solve addition and subtraction multi-step problems in contexts, deciding which operations and methods to use and why.	Solve one-step and two-step problems involving whole numbers and decimals and all four operations, choosing and using appropriate calculation strategies, including calculator use.

Preparation

Lesson 1: write the following calculations on the board: 3004 – 2891; 4003 – 3728; 4011 – 3883; 5001 – 4569; 8002 – 7695; 7003 – 5991. Make copies of 'Number lines', one per child if needed

Lesson 2: copy photocopiable page 'Find the difference', one per child; make copies of 'Number lines', one per child if needed

Lesson 3: write the following calculations on the board: 578 – 243; 659 – 318; 4261 – 2110; 351 – 138; 2422 – 1375; 20,421 – 12,162

Lesson 4: copy 'Work it out', one per child

Lesson 5: write this question on the board: *There were 5019 people at a rock concert. Because it was late, 2476 people left before the encore. How many were still there at the end?*; copy 'Word problems', one per child

You will need

Photocopiable sheets
'Find the difference'; 'Work it out (1) and (2)'; 'Word problems'

General resources
'Number lines'; 'Place value arrow cards'

Further practice
Interactive activity 'Written addition and subtraction'

Oral and mental starters suggested for week 2
See bank of starters on pages 44 to 45. Oral and mental starters are also on the CD-ROM.

4 Double it and pass it on

5 Pairs to make 1000/10,000

6 Use your doubles

7 Chain reaction adding

Overview of progression
By the end of this week the children should have a good understanding that there is more than one strategy for achieving an answer using addition and subtraction and that the choice of method should be the most efficient and reliable for the numbers involved. They should have the mental flexibility to move between strategies accurately.

Watch out for
Some children learn only one calculating strategy and use it exclusively, irrespective of whether it is the most efficient method. For example, 1310 – 998 is better calculated by counting on since 998 is a very close multiple of 1000, however some children will labour using a formal written decomposition method simply because they have got 'stuck' with one method. Encourage them to check their calculations with an alternative method and then evaluate which one is the most efficient.

Creative context
Formal written addition and subtraction is probably a topic best taught in isolation but it is worth explaining to the children that addition and subtraction are fundamental skills which they will use across many other subjects, for example when calculating distances, rainfall, costs and dates. Therefore there are many contexts through which you could reinforce and practise mental and written calculations.

Vocabulary
add, counting back, counting on, difference between, even, formal standard method, hundreds, informal calculations, **inverse**, multiple, odd, ones, place value, subtract, sum, take away, tens, thousands, total

Curriculum objectives
● To subtract numbers mentally with increasingly large numbers.

Success criteria
● I can add and subtract mentally using increasingly large numbers.
● I can decide when a calculation is possible mentally or when I need a written method for accuracy.

You will need
General resources
'Number lines'

Differentiation
Less confident learners
These children can use 'Number lines' to calculate differences between three-digit numbers only, such as 304 − 289; 403 − 372; 401 − 388; 501 − 456; 802 − 769; 703 − 599.

More confident learners
These children will probably not need the visual support of a number line, but should be encouraged to jot down the 'jumps' as they count on in order to avoid mistakes. They could invent some more questions for a partner to solve, finding *small* differences between four-digit or five-digit numbers by counting on.

Lesson 1 — Oral and mental starter 4

Main teaching activities

Whole-class work: Write on the board: 3001 − 2785. Ask the children what they notice about these numbers and the ways in which they suggest it could be solved. Some may suggest that it should be solved by a formal written calculation, some by counting on or back using a number line and others may think that it may be solved mentally. They should be able to tell you that the numbers involved are very close numerically. Talk about what is meant by *efficient* and *reliable* (for example the strategy which can reach the correct answer in the most time- and energy-efficient way). Demonstrate that using a vertical calculation for this would involve some long winded decomposition which, while it might achieve the correct answer is quite time consuming and has many opportunities for error. Therefore the most efficient method is to count on, either mentally or using a number line, since the numbers involved do not have too great a difference.

Draw a number line and demonstrate counting on in 'jumps'.

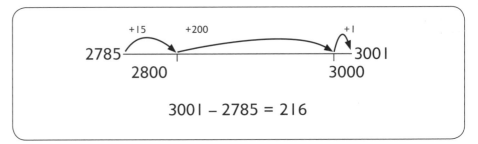

$$3001 - 2785 = 216$$

Demonstrate the method again using 4005 − 3826 and 3012 − 2699. Ask the children to try to solve them using a number line and also whether they can do them mentally, just jotting the 'jumps'. Jotting the 'jumps' allows them to check for errors.

Independent work: Write the following calculations on the board and ask the children to work them out: 3004 − 2891; 4003 − 3728; 4011 − 3883; 5001 − 4569; 8002 − 7695; 7003 − 5991. They should use the counting on method, using jottings or drawing a number line if needed to demonstrate their understanding. (Use photocopiable page 'Number lines' if appropriate.) On completion they should share their strategies and compare their work with a partner.

Progress check: Ask for volunteers to talk through the first few examples explaining their reasons for the 'jumps' they chose. Encourage estimating for a 'reasonable' answer. Discourage those who 'just know' the answer – they need to explain how they arrived at the answer.

Review

Ask individuals to demonstrate on the board how they found some of the differences. Ask: *What clues did you look for when deciding whether you could solve a problem mentally? Were the 'jumps' or steps the same for everybody? Did some children put different 'jumps' together?*

For example: 3001 − 2785 = 200 + 15 + 1 = 216.

Ask: *Could you use this method to find larger differences?* Ask the children when the method might become too cumbersome. (When the difference to be calculated is very big, the steps would be difficult to remember.)

Curriculum objectives

● To subtract numbers mentally with increasingly large numbers.
● To subtract whole numbers with more than four-digit.

Success criteria

● I can use a written method for subtraction which is efficient, accurate and reliable.
● I can use my knowledge of mental strategies to subtract one near-multiple of 1000 from another.

You will need

Photocopiable sheets

'Find the difference'

General resources

'Place value arrow cards'; 'Number lines'

Differentiation

Less confident learners

They can use photocopiable page 'Number lines' for support.

More confident learners

Set some more four-digit by four-digit number sentences extending to five-digit by four-digit (for example, 10007 − 5499 and so on).

Lesson 2

Oral and mental starter 5

Main teaching activities

Whole-class work: Remind the children that we can calculate some differences mentally (such as 50 − 17; 100 − 56 and 1008 − 12) and find others by using informal jottings, either with or without a number line (such as 3004 − 2894; 294 − 177 and 9003 − 8895). Write some similar calculations on the board and ask the children to choose the most efficient method to solve each one. Solve them together, either by counting on out loud or with a volunteer using a number line on the board. If they suggest that a mental method is best ask: *Why is it possible to solve this one mentally? What clues did you look for?*

Write 751 − 239 on the board. Ask whether the children think this might be too difficult to count on. What about 6383 − 2846? Explain that at some point we need a written method to support our calculations because otherwise errors are too likely. Some individuals will still want to calculate mentally, and may be able to do so, but you need to point out that if the risk of error is high, we need a more 'secure', formal method to check with.

Independent work: Distribute photocopiable page 'Find the difference' from the CD-ROM. Explain that the children have to decide which method to use to find each of the differences − either just mentally or with informal jottings to support accuracy. Stress that number lines may be used if they are helpful (you could provide photocopiable page 'Number lines'), but none of the subtractions should require a full written method. The puzzle at the end of the sheet will help them to revise the vocabulary of subtraction.

Progress check: Ask some of the children to demonstrate how they solved one of the difference questions. Ask: *How did you decide whether to count on or back? Did you need to write anything down? Can anybody spot where this person may have made a mistake? What could you have used to help you?*

Paired work: Ask them to discuss how they solved the remaining questions with a partner. If they have different answers, tell them to try an alternative method together to check the calculation.

Progress check: Ask pairs to describe the methods they are using to check answers. Are they using different methods to find the difference?

Review

Ask some of the children to explain their methods, for example with 73 − 38. They might say: *In my head I counted on 2 from 38 to 40, then in tens to 50, 60, 70, then the extra 3, so the difference is 2 + 30 + 3 = 35.* From these explanations, you will be able to judge the children's understanding of informal calculation methods.

Curriculum objectives
● To subtract numbers mentally with increasingly large numbers.
● To subtract whole numbers with more than four-digit, including using formal written methods (columnar addition and subtraction).

Success criteria
● I can use a form of columnar subtraction to help me to subtract more difficult numbers.

You will need
General resources
'Place value arrow cards'

Differentiation
Less confident learners
These children should practise the expanded method without having to redistribute the numbers. It is important that they are able to partition numbers and understand how this can be used for subtraction. They should try 295 − 123; 379 − 245; 664 − 243; 748 − 326; 754 − 513.

More confident learners
Children who are confident using the standard columnar method should be encouraged to answer questions which use decimal numbers in context, for example money, and to interpret the answers.

Lesson 3

Oral and mental starter 6

Main teaching activities

Whole-class work: Explain to the class that they are going to look at how we can use written calculation methods to work out subtraction problems with more complex numbers. Using demonstration and asking volunteers to help, go through the expanded method without decomposition.

For example: 3568 − 1233 might be written:

$$3000 + 500 + 60 + 8$$
$$\underline{- \ 1000 + 200 + 30 + 3}$$
$$2000 + 300 + 30 + 5 = 2335$$

Next demonstrate the expanded method with decomposition using 4512 − 1477.

$4000 + 500 + 10 + 2$ might be redistributed as $\ 4000 + 400 + 100 + 12$

$-1000 + 400 + 70 + 7$ to accommodate $\qquad -\ \underline{1000 + 400 + \ \ 70 + \ \ 7}$

$\qquad\qquad\qquad\qquad\qquad\qquad\qquad\qquad\qquad 3000 + \ \ \ 0 + \ \ 30 + \ \ 5 = 3035$

Finally, work towards the standard vertical method.

You will have to decide the rate at which the children progress through these written methods, according to your school's policy on calculation skills.

Independent and paired work: Write the following calculations on the board and ask the children to use the expanded subtraction method to work them out: 578 − 243; 659 − 318; 4261 − 2110; 351 − 138; 2422 − 1375; 20,421 − 12,162.

When they have finished, they can compare their work with a partner to check that they are using the strategy accurately.

Progress check: Select two or three children who have chosen different versions of written subtraction and ask them to demonstrate to the others, using the same calculation, what they are doing and why. Invite the other children to question the volunteers about their chosen method. Show them again that the expanded version is simply a clearer way to track what they are doing to avoid mistakes. Ask: *When would we know that we needed to redistribute the greater number?* (When the individual digit to be subtracted is larger.) Encourage them to write their calculations out carefully, aligning each place value one under another to avoid errors and to assess before they start which digits will require some redistribution or decomposition, maybe by annotating with a smiley or a sad face.

Review

Ask the children to redistribute the number 342 in a variety of ways. Record each way on the board and ask another child to check that it produces the correct number. For example, the children might suggest: 300 + 40 + 2; 300 + 30 + 12; 200 + 130 + 12.

Write the following calculation on the board and ask what is wrong with it:

$$2\ 6\ 3\ 1$$
$$\underline{-\ 1\ 3\ 4\ 2}$$
$$1\ 3\ 1\ 1$$

Establish that the smaller digit has been taken away from the larger one in each column, whereas the correct method is to subtract the digit below from the one above. You may need to correct misconceptions and focus on a small group who need extra support with decomposition tomorrow.

Curriculum objectives

- To add and subtract numbers mentally with increasingly large numbers.
- To add and subtract whole numbers with more than 4-digits, including using formal written methods (columnar).

Success criteria

- I can select a formal written or mental method to solve addition and subtraction problems.

You will need

Photocopiable sheets

'Work it out (1) and (2)'

Differentiation

Less confident learners

These children should use 'Work it out (2)' which uses smaller numbers and practises the expanded method without the need to redistribute.

More confident learners

These children should use standard written methods and be able to explain the process to an adult.

Lesson 4

Oral and mental starter 7

Main teaching activities

Whole-class work: Distribute photocopiable page 'Work it out (1)' from the CD-ROM. Discuss which of the questions might be calculated mentally, which need informal jottings and which need a written method. Read some of the word questions together and decide how to convert them to calculations. Ask: *Is it an addition or a subtraction problem? Does the calculation require a written method?* Revise columnar addition, both the expanded method and the standard method.

Independent and paired work: Ask the children to work through the mixed addition and subtraction questions on the photocopiable page, using the most appropriate method.

Progress check: Ask some children to report on their progress and the methods they have chosen. Where the children used informal jottings, ask them to explain how they worked out the answer.

Review

Ask some children to explain their answers and the methods they have chosen. Iron out any misconceptions. Write the following calculation on the board.

$$
\begin{array}{r}
2\ 1\ 8 \\
+\ 1\ 3\ 5 \\
\hline
3\ 0\ 0 \\
4\ 0 \\
1\ 7 \\
\hline
3\ 5\ 7
\end{array}
\qquad
\begin{array}{r}
4\ 2\ 6 \\
+\ 2\ 3\ 7 \\
\hline
6\ 1\ 3 \\
\end{array}
$$

Ask: *Is this correct? How can you check? Tell me what this person has done wrong? How can you advise this person how not to make the same mistakes again?*

Curriculum objectives

- To solve addition and subtraction multi-step problems in contexts, deciding which operations and methods to use and why.

Success criteria

- I can choose efficient, accurate and reliable methods to solve problems and calculations.

You will need

Photocopiable sheets

'Word problems'

Differentiation

Less confident learners

Adapt photocopiable page 'Word problems' and fill in appropriate numbers.

More confident learners

Use appropriately challenging five-digit numbers for formal written method practice.

Lesson 5

Oral and mental starter 7

Main teaching activities

Whole-class work: Write this question on the board: There were 5019 people at a rock concert. Because it was late, 2476 people left before the encore. How many were still there at the end? Ask the children to demonstrate a variety of ways to solve this, for example counting on (using informal jottings), such as 2476 + 24 makes 2500, another 2500 makes 5000, add 19. Answer is 2543 people. Alternatively, written subtraction checking with the inverse operation.

$$
\begin{array}{r}
{}^4\!5\ \ {}^9\!0\ \ {}^1\!1\ \ 9 \\
-\ 2\ \ 4\ \ 7\ \ 6 \\
\hline
2\ \ 5\ \ 4\ \ 3
\end{array}
$$

Independent work: Distribute photocopiable page 'Word problems' from the CD-ROM for the children to solve.

Progress check: Ask the children to share their decisions about choice of method. Emphasise that they are looking for a method which is efficient, accurate and reliable for them.

Review

Hear some of the children's answers and explanations. Iron out any misconceptions. Discuss some common errors when subtracting.

Factors of numbers and prime numbers

Expected prior learning

Children should be able to:

- recall multiples to 12 × 12
- understand the place value of whole numbers and the effect of multiplying and dividing by 10.

Topic	Curriculum objectives	Expected outcomes
Multiplication and division	**Lessons 1 and 2**	
	To identify multiples and factors, including finding all factor pairs of a number, and common factors of two numbers.	Identify pairs of factors of two-digit whole numbers.
	To know and use the vocabulary of prime numbers, prime factors and composite (non-prime) numbers.	Use understanding of place value to multiply and divide whole numbers and decimals by 10, 100 and 1000.
	To multiply and divide whole numbers and those involving decimals by 10, 100 and 1000.	Explain the unique nature of a prime number.
		Begin to test numbers to determine whether they are prime numbers or composite numbers.
		Begin to recognise the prime numbers to 19 as a unique set or group.
	Lesson 3	
	To identify multiples and factors, including finding all factor pairs of a number, and common factors of two numbers.	Begin to test numbers to determine whether they are prime numbers or composite numbers.
		Identify pairs of factors of two-digit whole numbers.
	Lesson 4	
	To establish whether a number up to 100 is prime and recall prime numbers up to 19.	Begin to recognise the prime numbers to 19 as a unique set or group.
		Begin to test numbers to determine whether they are prime numbers or composite numbers.
	Lesson 5	
	To solve problems involving multiplication and division including using their knowledge of factors and multiples, squares and cubes.	Begin to recognise the prime numbers to 19 as a unique set or group.
		Begin to test numbers to determine whether they are prime numbers or composite numbers.

■SCHOLASTIC

Preparation

Lesson 1: copy 'Investigating factors', one per child; copy 'Multiplication square' onto card, one per child

Lesson 2: prepare some criteria cards for sorting numbers such as: factors of 48; multiples of 2; even numbers; odd numbers; multiples of 5; multiples of 3; Factors of 21; prime numbers; square numbers; factors of 30; make cards from '0–30 number cards', one set per pair

Lesson 3: copy photocopiable page 'Multiples snap', one per group of four

Lesson 4: copy the photocopiable pages '100 square' and 'Second 100 square' onto card, one per child

You will need

Photocopiable sheets
'Investigating factors';

General resources
'Multiplication square'; '0–30 number cards'; interactive activity 'Factors and multiples'; 'Multiples snap'; '100 square'; 'Second 100 square'

Further practice

Interactive activity 'Factors and multiples' offers further practice of recognising factors and multiples.

Oral and mental starters suggested for week 3

See bank of starters on page 45. Oral and mental starters are also on the CD-ROM.

6 Use your doubles

8 Quick-fire times tables

14 Multiplying and dividing by 10, 100, 1000

Overview of progression

During this week the children will become familiar with the vocabulary and use of factors, multiples and prime numbers and will have an opportunity to investigate systematically how to find and use them. Prime numbers are unique but can be used to form composite numbers. They are a good introduction to 'pure' maths where some numbers have special properties that have fascinated mathematicians for years simply because of their uniqueness.

The starters specifically support the main activity this week.

Watch out for

Some children confuse multiples and factors. It is important to be clear that pairs of factors multiply together to make a product. Multiples are groups of more than one of a number.

Creative context

Creative links can be found through the study of famous mathematicians such as Pythagoras, Euclid, Pierre Fermat, Blaise Pascal, Leonhard Euler, and Alan Turing.

Vocabulary

composite number, digit, even, **factor**, multiple, **numeral**, odd, prime factor, prime number, product, **quotient**, square number

Curriculum objectives

- To identify multiples and factors, including finding all factor pairs of a number, and common factors of two numbers.
- To multiply and divide whole numbers and those involving decimals by 10, 100 and 1000.
- To know and use the vocabulary of prime numbers, prime factors and composite (non-prime) numbers.

Success criteria

- I can find pairs of factors to at least 50.
- I know that a prime number is a unique number divisible only by itself and 1.

You will need

Photocopiable sheets

'Investigating factors'

General resources

'Multiplication square'

Differentiation

Less confident learners

They can use the 'Multiplication square' to help them.

More confident learners

Ask: *From the factors you have found, think of a quick and easy way to find the factors for the even numbers from 50 to 100?* (Halve each number, list the factors of the half, then double these.)

Lesson 1 — Oral and mental starter 14

Main teaching activities

Whole-class work: Explain that this lesson is about factors. Ask: *What is a factor? What are the factors of 12?* (1, 2, 3, 4, 6, 12.) Tell them that factors come in pairs, for example $2 \times 6 = 12$. Remind them that two numbers multiplied together give a product. *Do some numbers have more than two factors?* (Yes) *What do we call a number that is only divisible by itself and 1?* (A prime number) Explain to the children that they are going to make a list of the factors of various numbers. They have to work out all the factors for the numbers given and then circle the prime numbers. Discuss and model how they might do this by working through digits in order and noting the factor pairs of a number, and common factors of two numbers.

Paired work: Distribute photocopiable page 'Investigating factors' from the CD-ROM. Explain that a table has been started on the sheet to list the factors of all numbers from 1 to 50. The children must work together to complete the table.

Progress check: Ask the children: *Are you working systematically? How can you be sure that you haven't missed any factors?* Encourage the children to make jottings which will inform you of their mental dexterity and their understanding of number. Ask: *Do you have knowledge about multiples that will help you to make decisions?* (For example, 5 can only be a factor of a number ending in a 0 or 5.)

Review

Ask: *What is a prime number? What are the prime numbers from 1 to 50?* (2, 3, 5, 7, 11, 13, 17, 19, 23, 29, 31, 37, 41, 43, 47) *Can we make any generalisations about them?* (They are all odd numbers apart from 2.) *What are the factors of 42?... 49?... 36?...*

Curriculum objectives

- To identify multiples and factors, including finding all factor pairs of a number, and common factors of two numbers.
- To multiply and divide whole numbers and those involving decimals by 10, 100 and 1000.
- To know and use the vocabulary of prime numbers, prime factors and composite (non-prime) numbers.

Success criteria

- I can sort numbers by more than one criterion.
- I know the definitions of odd number, even number, prime number, square number, factor and multiple.

You will need

General resources

'0–30 number cards'; interactive activity 'Factors and multiples'

Equipment

Hoops, if needed

Differentiation

Less confident learners

Give children two intersecting hoops and the number cards 1–30 in order to focus their thinking. Give them simpler criteria to sort by, such as 'Multiples of 2', 'Odd numbers'.

More confident learners

Children could have three criteria to sort by such as 'Square numbers', 'Multiples of 7', 'Factors of 48', 'Factors of 72.

Lesson 2
Oral and mental starter 14

Main teaching activities

Whole-class work: Explain to the children that they are going to explore patterns and relationships of numbers, with special reference to factors and multiples. Display the labels you have made and ensure a good understanding of each definition, for example square numbers are created by multiplying a number by itself. Draw a Venn diagram with two intersecting circles on the board. Label one circle, 'Multiples of 5' and the other 'Even numbers'. Tell the children that they may use any number from 1 to 30 to complete the diagram. Discuss what to do with numbers that fit both criteria (they go in the intersection) and numbers, such as 1, which do not fit either criterion (they are recorded outside the circles). Repeat with another example such as 'Factors of 24' and 'Even numbers'.

Paired work: Provide each pair with the ready-prepared criteria cards that you want them to use to make decisions about numbers, for example 'factors of 32', 'multiples of 3', 'odd numbers', 'even numbers', 'multiples of 4'. Explain that you want them to discuss the reasons for placing the numbers between themselves. Once you are confident they can sort and group the numbers according to the criteria given, they should record their work by drawing and labelling the Venn diagrams in their books.

Progress check: To check understanding, ask: *Tell me the numbers that would fit into the intersection of a Venn diagram labelled 'Factors of 16' and 'Square numbers'* (4 and 16). *What about 'Multiples of 5' and 'Prime numbers?'* (only 5)

Review

Draw a Venn diagram on the board. One circle should be labelled 'Multiples of 10' the other labelled 'Numbers greater than 50'. Fill in some numbers on the diagram with the children's help. Also add some incorrect ones and ask the children to spot your mistakes and to explain why they are incorrect. If time allows, go through one or more screens of the interactive activity 'Factors and multiples' on the CD-ROM with the whole class to further check their understanding.

Curriculum objectives
● To identify multiples and factors, including finding all factor pairs of a number, and common factors of two numbers.

Success criteria
● I can identify factors of numbers.
● I can begin to recognise patterns in multiples.

You will need
General resources
'Multiplication square'; 'Multiples snap'

Differentiation
Less confident learners
These children could be asked to look for specific divisors or factors – for example, to look for numbers that are divisible by 2 or 5 and use a multiplication square for reference. They should be able to tell you what they were looking for, for example, multiples of 2 are even.

More confident learners
On completion of the game, the children could use blank cards to create their own number cards, including numbers divisible by 9 (or higher numbers outside the 12 × 12 times tables) to add to the game.

Lesson 3

Main teaching activities

Whole-class work: Explain that this lesson is going to give the children more experience of looking for patterns in multiples and factors. Revise again how to identify factors. Ask: *What are the factors pairs of 30?* (1 and 30, 2 and 15, 3 and 10, 5 and 6). Explain that the product of these pairs of factors is 30.

Next focus on multiples. Ask the children to think of a number that is divisible by both 4 and 2. Ask: *What do you notice?* (Any multiple of 4 is also divisible by 2.) Likewise any multiple of 8 is divisible by both 4 and 2.

Paired work: Play 'Multiples snap' in groups of four. Distribute the cards from photocopiable page 'Multiple snap' from the CD-ROM. Explain that this game will help the children to practise their knowledge of divisibility and also to explore general rules for multiples of 2, 4, 5 and 10.

The cards are shuffled and shared out evenly among the group. Each player in turn places a card face upwards on the discard pile. This continues until two numbers from the same times table appear consecutively. The first player to say 'Snap!' and then to say what both numbers are divisible by wins the whole of the discard pile. The first player to gain all the cards wins. For instance, if 25 and 50 are turned over consecutively, the common factor or divisor is 5 (or 25). The children continue to play and record any rules about multiples/ divisibility they observe.

Progress check: Stop the game and ask the children to explain any rules that they may have already noticed, for example, multiples of 2 and 4 are always even. Write up their observations for reference on the board.

Review

Discuss how we can tell whether a number is divisible by 4. Ask: *Which of your observations about multiples of 4 help us with divisibility? Which ones don't? What about numbers that are divisible by 9? What observations have you made?* (The digits of the numbers in the 9-times table add up to a multiple of 9, so they are easy to spot. For example, 18 ➤ 1 + 8 = 9; 99 ➤ 9 + 9 = 18. Add again! 1 + 8 = 9.) *What did you notice about the number 17?* (It is only divisible by itself and one therefore it is a prime number.)

Curriculum objectives

- To establish whether a number up to 100 is prime and recall prime numbers up to 19.

Success criteria

- I can test numbers with my knowledge of multiples in order to identify prime numbers up to 100 and beyond.
- I can recognise prime numbers to 19 as a set.

You will need

General resources

'100 square'; 'Second 100 square'

Equipment

Calculators

Differentiation

Less confident learners

Provide a list of steps to follow about eliminating numbers.

More confident learners

Ask: *What is the minimum number of tests for divisibility or questions that you need to ask about a number, such as 301, to be sure that it is a prime number?*

Lesson 4

Oral and mental starter 8

Main teaching activities

Whole-class work: Ask the children to refer to their 'Investigating factors' sheet from lesson 1 and to tell you the prime numbers up to 47. Ask them to give you a definition for this unique group of numbers called prime numbers. (A number divisible only by itself and 1.) Tell them that they are going to further investigate prime numbers up to 200, in pairs. Distribute the photocopiable pages '100 square' and 'Second 100 square'. Ask them to suggest ways in which they could eliminate a lot of the numbers straight away (any number ending in 0 or 5 (multiples of 10 and 5) and all even numbers (divisible by 2); anything divisible by 9 is also divisible by 3, and so on).

They can use a calculator to test the remaining numbers to find out if they are indeed part of the group of prime numbers. Remind them that they need to go beyond 10 when exploring divisors for example 11 although some are multiples of known times tables.

Paired work: Investigate together in order to find the prime numbers between 51 and 200. Encourage them to use elimination techniques first in order to reduce the choices before using a calculator.

Progress check: Ask for some volunteers to describe the numbers they were first able to eliminate, using their knowledge of multiples. Ask if anyone has found the first prime number over 50 and how they found it. Check for accuracy.

Review

The bulk of your assessment should be done as the children are working by listening to their discussion and reasoning which will demonstrate their understanding of factors, multiples, divisibility and prime numbers. Ask: *If 9 is not a prime number and nor is 100 why is 109 a prime number?* (100 and 9 have different factors.) Discuss strategies used.

Curriculum objectives

- To solve problems involving multiplication and division where larger numbers are used by decomposing them into their factors.

Success criteria

- I can calculate systematically in order to investigate prime and composite numbers.

You will need

Equipment

Calculators

Differentiation

Less confident learners

Provide a list of prime factors for aid.

More confident learners

What is the minimum number of tests for divisibility or questions needed to ask about a number, e.g. 301, to tell if it is a prime number or not?

Lesson 5

Oral and mental starter 6

Main teaching activities

Whole-class work: Explain that they now have a bank of prime numbers from yesterday. Tell them that a prime number used as a factor is called a prime factor. For example, 2 and 3 are prime factors. When multiplied together they make 6, which is not a prime number but is known as a composite number (it has more factors than just itself and 1). Give a few more examples of multiplying two prime numbers to make a composite number.

Paired work: Explain to the children that today's investigation is to make as many numbers as they can using only prime factors. Encourage them to work systematically to create the numbers in order if possible. Give them the following as a model starting point: $1 \times 1 = 1$; $1 \times 2 = 2$ (prime); $1 \times 3 = 3$ (prime); $2 \times 2 = 4$ (composite) and ask them to continue the pattern. Remind them that they can only use prime factors, so 8 cannot be made by 2×4 as 4 is a composite number.

Progress check: Ask if any pair has made the next five numbers. If so, ask for volunteers to demonstrate how. Check that the children are only using prime factors multiplied together.

Review

Ask the children to give you a definition for prime numbers, prime factors and composite numbers. Ask: *Is it possible to make any of the prime numbers using only prime factors? What about multiplying more than one prime factor together, such as $2 \times 2 \times 3 = 12$.* (No) In fact numbers are either composite or prime. All composite numbers can be made by multiplying prime factors.

Using multiplication and division

Expected prior learning

Children should be able to:

- recall multiples to 12 × 12
- understand the place value of whole numbers and the effect of multiplying and dividing by 10.

Topic	Curriculum objectives	Expected outcomes
Multiplication and division	**Lesson 1**	
	To multiply and divide numbers mentally drawing upon known facts. To multiply and divide whole numbers and those involving decimals by 10, 100 and 1000.	Recall quickly multiplication facts up to 12 × 12 and use them to multiply pairs of multiples of 10 and 100; derive quickly corresponding division facts. Use understanding of place value to multiply and divide whole numbers and decimals by 10, 100 and 1000.
	Lesson 2	
	To multiply and divide numbers mentally drawing upon known facts. To multiply and divide whole numbers and those involving decimals by 10, 100 and 1000.	Recall quickly multiplication facts up to 12 × 12 and use them to multiply pairs of multiples of 10 and 100; derive quickly corresponding division facts. Use understanding of place value to multiply and divide whole numbers and decimals by 10, 100 and 1000.
	Lesson 3	
	To multiply and divide numbers mentally drawing upon known facts. To multiply and divide whole numbers and those involving decimals by 10, 100 and 1000.	Recall quickly multiplication facts up to 12 × 12 and use them to multiply pairs of multiples of 10 and 100; derive quickly corresponding division facts. Use understanding of place value to multiply and divide whole numbers and decimals by 10, 100 and 1000.
	Lesson 4	
	To multiply and divide whole numbers and those involving decimals by 10, 100 and 1000.	Use understanding of place value to multiply and divide whole numbers and decimals by 10, 100 and 1000.
	Lesson 5	
	To solve problems involving multiplication and division, including scaling by simple fractions and problems involving simple rates.	Solve one-step and two-step problems involving whole numbers and decimals and all four operations, choosing and using appropriate calculation strategies, including calculator use.

Preparation

Lesson 1: provide each child with multiplication problems using multiples of 5 or 10 for one of the multiples. Use questions such as: 50 × 5; 60 × 5; 50 × 7; 30 × 5; 32 × 5; 25 × 6; 18 × 5

Lesson 2: copy 'Find the factor', one per child

Lesson 3: prepare some problems using near multiples of 10, such as 22 × 19 or 12 × 21

Lesson 4: copy 'The function machine', one per child; copy 'Place value table' and associated number cards onto card, one per pair; copy 'Place value chart' and 'Multiplication square' onto card, one per pair if needed

Lesson 5: copy 'Place value bingo', one per child

You will need

Photocopiable sheets

'Find the factor'; 'The function machine'; 'Place value bingo'

General resources

'Place value table'; 'Place value chart'; 'Multiplication square'; '0–30 number cards'; interactive teaching resource 'Multiplication square'

Equipment

Counters of at least two different colours, four per child

Further practice

Adapt photocopiable page 'The function machine template' as appropriate to give further practice of multiplying and dividing by 10, 100 or 1000.

Oral and mental starters suggested for week 4

See bank of starters on page 45. Oral and mental starters are also on the CD-ROM.

11 Multiplication bingo

13 Number sentences map

14 Multiplying and dividing by 10, 100 and 1000

15 Place value shuffle

Overview of progression

During this week the children will extend their knowledge of factors to facilitate mental calculations of larger numbers and multiples of 10, 100 and 1000. They should not be expected to do everything in their head, but to make jottings as they factorise larger numbers. They should understand that the broken down factors may then be multiplied in a different order to make the calculation easier.

Watch out for

Some children will simply wish to partition the numbers in tens and ones as they will be attempting vertical written calculations in their head and will miss out some important understanding about multiplying. For example 14 × 22, if simply partitioned as 10 and 4 multiplied by 20 and 1, is more difficult to multiply mentally. It would be more effective to see and calculate it as (14 × 20) + 14.

Creative context

Essentially this is a mathematical skill but, once mastered, it could be used in a variety of contexts for calculating multiple amounts in other areas of the curriculum. A good visual demonstration of multiples and factors are the arrays of soldiers in the Roman army who arranged themselves in legions. Rows and columns of soldiers may be used to demonstrate factorisation of larger numbers.

Vocabulary

decimal place, decimal point, digit, **factor**, factorise, multiple, multiply, place holder, place value

Curriculum objectives
● To multiply and divide numbers mentally drawing upon known facts.
● To multiply and divide whole numbers and those involving decimals by 10.

Success criteria
● I can break larger numbers down into factors for easier mental multiplication.

You will need
General resources
'Multiplication square'

Differentiation
Less confident learners
Provide simplified questions with only multiples of 10 to be factorised, for example, 50×5; 60×5; 30×5; 20×5; 40×5, and so on, and multiples that they are comfortable with.

More confident learners
Provide more challenging questions with mixed multiples to be factorised, for example, 14×5; 18×5; 16×5; 22×5; 28×5, 42×5, and so on.

Lesson 1
Oral and mental starter ⏱

Main teaching activities

Whole-class work: Explain that we can use our knowledge of factors, explored last week, to multiply bigger numbers. For example: $50 \times 6 = 5 \times 10 \times 6$ or $(5 \times 6) \times 10$ or $(10 \times 6) \times 5$ or $(5 \times 10) \times 6$. Write all the variations on the board and ask for volunteers to come and calculate them, demonstrating that factors can be multiplied in any order. Explain that we can rearrange the factors to choose the easiest calculation, and that brackets make the order of multiplication clearer. Repeat the process to solve 60×7 using factors. Ask: *What factors could I use to help me?*

Independent work: Provide each child with multiplication problems using multiples of 5 or 10 (for example, 60×5) for one of the multiples. Explain that the children will be using factors to multiply multiples of 5 and 10. Ask them to explore possible arrangements of factors and choose the easiest order for doing the calculation. Encourage them to write down a variety of arrangements and not just multiply the first order they think of. Use questions such as: 50×5, 60×5, 50×7, 30×5, 32×5, 25×6, 18×5.

Progress check: Ensure that the children are clear about how they are breaking down the larger numbers. Ask some children to share their factorisations and ensure that they are choosing the pairs of factors wisely to make the calculation easier. Ask: *Which factor pair makes multiplying by 36 easier, 12 and 3 or 18 and 2? Why?*

Review

Ask: *What are factors? How can they help us multiply?* (They break down a larger number into more manageable 'chunks'.) Ask the more confident learners: *Were all the numbers you tried to multiply easier when you used factors?* Write an example on the board and demonstrate how factors can be moved around and organised into different pairs in order to make more manageable multiples.

Try finding factors of larger numbers to multiply, for example:

$240 \times 350 = (60 \times 4) \times (7 \times 50)$

Discuss the best order to multiply these and whether to factorise them further.

The important thing is to know the times tables!

Curriculum objectives
- To multiply and divide numbers mentally drawing upon known facts.
- To multiply and divide whole numbers and those involving decimals by 10.

Success criteria
- I can use factors to multiply numbers up to 100 mentally with jottings.
- I can understand that factors may be multiplied in any order, but are made clearer by the use of brackets.

You will need

Photocopiable sheets
'Find the factor'

General resources
Interactive teaching resource 'Multiplication square'

Differentiation

Less confident learners
Work with children using interactive teaching resource 'Multiplication square' to consolidate understanding of the different combinations of factors required for this activity.

More confident learners
Ask children to write problems linked to the number sentences on the photocopiable page.

Lesson 2 — Oral and mental starter 13

Main teaching activities

Whole-class work: Explain that this lesson builds on lesson 1 and today the children are going to use factors to multiply any numbers less than 100. They may have to break a number down into more than two factors in order to find a manageable calculation. Ask the class to find factors to help solve 32×15, using brackets to keep the calculation order clear.

For example: $(16 \times 2) \times (3 \times 5)$ or $(8 \times 4) \times (3 \times 5)$ or $(2 \times 4) \times (3 \times 5) \times 4$

Discuss whether any of these are easier to multiply. Demonstrate multiplying the different combinations and emphasise that the factors may be multiplied in any order, therefore it may be advantageous to look for an opportunity to rearrange the factors in order to multiply by 10.

For example: $(16 \times 2) \times (3 \times 5) = (16 \times 3) \times 10 = (8 \times 2 \times 3) \times 10 = (8 \times 3) \times 2 \times 10 = 24 \times 2 \times 10 = 480$

Repeat this process with several more examples.

Paired work: Distribute photocopiable page 'Find the factor' from the CD-ROM. As the children continue to work through the sheet, listen to the conversations they are having about the reasons for their choices to inform your assessments.

Progress check: Check that the children are factorising accurately, using brackets to help them keep track and are considering the easiest option. Ask: *Think of different ways to factorise 36. Which would you choose if multiplying 36 by 8?*

Review

Write the following calculations on the board: 17×23; 19×9; 12×24. Ask: *Which of these calculations is the easiest to break into factors? Is this method less helpful for some numbers than others? Why?* Discuss why prime numbers and square numbers offer a limited choice of factors. Remind the children that larger numbers may be broken down into more than two factors. Ask for a volunteer to factorise and work out 15×48. Encourage a method such as: $15 \times 48 = (3 \times 5) \times (2 \times 24) = (3 \times 24) \times (2 \times 5) = (3 \times 12 \times 2) \times 10 = 36 \times 2 \times 10 = 720$. Repeat with several more examples, such as, $56 \times 144 = (8 \times 7) \times (12 \times 12)$ or $(8 \times 7) \times (3 \times 4) \times (3 \times 4)$ or $(2 \times 4 \times 7) \times (72 \times 2)$.

Curriculum objectives
● To multiply and divide numbers mentally drawing upon known facts.
● To multiply and divide whole numbers by 10 and 100.

Success criteria
● I can multiply near multiples of 10 and 100 by rounding and adjusting.

Differentiation

Less confident learners
Provide simpler questions using single-digit numbers to be multiplied by 19 or 21.

More confident learners
Provide more challenging questions using numbers to be multiplied by a variety of near multiples of 10 (such as 29 and 31).

Lesson 3

Oral and mental starter 14

Main teaching activities

Whole-class work: Explain that the children are going to explore multiplying by numbers close to multiples of 10, such as 19 or 21. Say: *We can use what we know about place value and factors to help us multiply by multiples of 10.* Demonstrate that $15 \times 20 = (15 \times 2) \times 10 = 30 \times 10 = 300$. We can use this skill to multiply a number like 19 or 21 by rounding it to 20, then adjusting the answer by adding or subtracting the missing amount.

Demonstrate that:

$15 \times 21 = ((15 \times 2) \times 10) + 15 = 300 + 15 = 315$ and
$15 \times 19 = ((15 \times 2) \times 10) - 15 = 300 - 15 = 285$

Repeat using 18×21; 18×19; 24×19; 24×21. Emphasise the importance of the final adjustment: Is it one more 'lot of' or one less?

Paired work: Ask the children to solve problems of near multiples of 10, such as 22×19 or 12×21, using the method they have learned. Make sure they are justifying what they are doing each time.

Progress check: The most common confusion will stem from whether the children should add 'one more lot of' or whether to subtract it. Create a little chant saying: *Rounding down; add one lot back on. Rounding up; subtract one lot off.* Alternatively, liken it to a function machine, if you have rounded up at one end you need to remove it again at the other end of the machine.

Review

Write up 23×31 on the board. Ask: *Which of these numbers is the near multiple of 10? Would you try to round both of the numbers?* Agree that it is only practical to round and adjust using one multiple, as using both would lead to confusion. Ask for a volunteer to come and demonstrate how they work it out, talking through their method: $23 \times 3 \times 10 = 69 \times 10 = 690$. Then add on the extra 'one lot of' $23 = 713$.

Now ask: *If we can do this with near multiples of 10, is it possible to do it with near multiples of 100?* Ask for a volunteer to work out 13×201 on the board: $13 \times 201 = (13 \times 2) \times 100 = 2600$. Then add one extra $13 = 2613$. Use several more examples to consolidate this idea, such as, $81 \times 25 = (25 \times 8) \times 10$ plus another $25 = 2025$; 36×99 could be considered as $36 \times 100 = 3600$ then subtract one lot of $36 = 3564$.

■SCHOLASTIC

Curriculum objectives

● To multiply and divide whole numbers and those involving decimals by 10, 100 and 1000.

Success criteria

● I can use my known times tables and knowledge of place value to multiply and divide by 10, 100 and 1000.

You will need

Photocopiable sheets

'The function machine'

General resources

'Place value chart'; 'Place value table'; 'Multiplication square'; '0–30 number cards'

Differentiation

Less confident learners

Children may benefit from a 'Multiplication square'.

More confident learners

Children should have more challenging numbers to put into the function machine, such as 2.1, 36.4, 1013.

Lesson 4   Oral and mental starter 15

Main teaching activities

Whole-class work: Distribute the photocopiable pages 'Place value table' and a set of 0–9 number cards to each pair. Ask them to place the number 31 correctly on the chart and then to multiply the number by 100, moving the digits and using zeros for place holders. Check accuracy and then ask them to replace the numbers with 0.31. Before they move the digits ask them what they think the answer would be if it were multiplied by 1000. Discuss how to estimate this: 3 × 1000 would be 3000 however this number (rounded down) is 10 times smaller than 3, therefore the estimated answer will be in the region of 300. Now ask the children to check this by moving the digits on the 'Place value chart'. Repeat starting with 38 and dividing by 100. Repeat several times both multiplying and dividing by 10, 100 or 1000.

Independent work: Distribute photocopiable page 'The function machine' from the CD-ROM and ask them to complete it.

Progress check: Ensure that everyone has understood the way the function machine operates, especially for the inverse examples. This can be fun to act out with a child acting as the function machine, writing the expressed answer on an individual whiteboard. Check also the accuracy of place value. Ask: *If I multiplied 0.6 by 100, what should I be thinking to solve this correctly?*

Review

Write the number 62.034 on the board. Ask the children to tell you the value of the individual digits. Ask them to multiply the number by 100 and tell you the value of a given digit now. Repeat with similar numbers, dividing by 100 or 1000. Check the children's understanding of place value. Share some of the function machine answers and encourage children to spot their own mistakes.

Curriculum objectives

● To solve problems involving multiplication and division, including scaling by simple fractions and problems involving simple rates.

Success criteria

● I can solve puzzles and games by combining my known multiples and knowledge of place value.

You will need

Photocopiable sheets

'Place value bingo'

General resources

'Place value table'; 'Place value chart'; 'Multiplication square'

Equipment

Counters of at least two different colours

Differentiation

Less confident learners

Provide a 'Multiplication square' as support.

More confident learners

Play against the clock.

Lesson 5   Oral and mental starter 14

Main teaching activities

Whole-class work: Explain that today's lesson carries on from the oral and mental starter and extends what they have been learning about multiplying during the week. Ask: *If I know 3 × 4 = 12, what is 3 × 40?* (120) Emphasise that the answer is 10 times bigger. Then ask: *What is 30 × 40?* (1200); *0.3 × 4?* (1.2 – 10 times smaller) Explain that a good understanding of place value is important for this activity. Demonstrate using the place value table and number cards to calculate 0.4 × 6. Say: *4 × 6 = 24 but the actual calculation is 10 times smaller.* Place 24 on the place value chart and then move the digits one place to the right, making the answer 10 times smaller. Repeat with more questions.

Paired work: Distribute photocopiable page 'Place value bingo' from the CD-ROM and counters for each pair. Explain the rules and let them begin. An individual whiteboard for jottings may be helpful. Repeat with a new partner. for practice. Children record their calculations so that you can check them for accuracy.

Progress check: Listen to the discussion while children are calculating. Nearly all the numbers have a corresponding product so if they have answers that they cannot find, they should check their calculating. Encourage them to talk through the steps: multiply first and then adjust the place value.

Review

Ask: *I have multiplied 0.02 × 36 but I cannot find my answer of 72 on the grid. What have I done wrong? Talk me through the correct steps again. What about 0.03 × 0.5? How can I decide on the place value?*

Angles

Expected prior learning

Children should be able to:

- understand the concepts of whole turns, half turns and quarter turns
- know the direction of clockwise and anticlockwise
- read and estimate positions on numbered and unnumbered scales.

Topic	Curriculum objectives	Expected outcomes
Geometry: properties of shapes	**Lesson 1**	
	To know angles are measured in degrees; estimate and compare acute, obtuse and reflex angles. To identify: • angles at a point and one whole turn (total 360°) • angles at a point on a straight line and ½ a turn (total 180°) • other multiples of 90°.	Estimate, draw and measure acute and obtuse angles using an angle measurer or protractor to a suitable degree of accuracy; calculate angles on a straight line; calculate reflex angles.
	Lesson 2	
	To know angles are measured in degrees; estimate and compare acute, obtuse and reflex angles. To identify: • angles at a point and one whole turn (total 360°) • angles at a point on a straight line and ½ a turn (total 180°) • other multiples of 90°.	Estimate, draw and measure acute and obtuse angles using an angle measurer or protractor to a suitable degree of accuracy; calculate angles on a straight line; calculate reflex angles.
	Lessons 3, 4 and 5	
	To know angles are measured in degrees; estimate and compare acute, obtuse and reflex angles. To identify: • angles at a point and one whole turn (total 360°) • angles at a point on a straight line and ½ a turn (total 180°) • other multiples of 90°.	Estimate, draw and measure acute and obtuse angles using an angle measurer or protractor to a suitable degree of accuracy; calculate angles on a straight line; calculate reflex angles.

■SCHOLASTIC

Preparation

Lesson 1: copy 'Round the bend', one per child; copy 'Shapes' onto card; one set per pair or assemble a collection of 2D shapes

Lesson 5: copy 'What's the angle?', one per child

You will need

Photocopiable sheets

'Round the bend'; 'What's the angle?'

General resources

'Shapes'

Equipment

2D shapes if not using 'Shapes'; protractors/angle measurers and a large scale version for board use, or ICT equivalent; rulers; calculators if needed; A4 card and coloured pens

Further practice

Give children further practical experience of drawing and measuring angles to specified sizes.

Oral and mental starters suggested for week 5

See bank of starters on page 45. Oral and mental starters are also on the CD-ROM.

9 Shape sorter

10 Perimeter calculator

11 Multiplication bingo

17 Pairs to make 180 and 360

Overview of progression

By the end of the week children should have had plenty of practice at drawing and measuring angles to at least 5° accuracy. They should have a good understanding of the way a protractor may be used to measure angles and they should have started to categorise angles into acute (smaller than 90°) and obtuse (between 90° and 180°). They will have begun to understand the relationship between angles and to calculate missing angles on a straight line or reflex angles of a whole turn. Lessons 4 and 5 use skills of addition and subtraction to find missing angles where lines bisect. This work leads into the next week's work on subtraction.

Watch out for

Some children may read the incorrect scale on the protractor by reading from the wrong side. Spend some time familiarising the children with the fact that protractors can measure from both the left and the right hand side. It is important for them to ensure that they are counting up from 0 either clockwise or anti clockwise in jumps of 10 sequentially.

Creative context

Angles lend themselves to a number of links with art, history and science. Geometrical and symmetrical patterns in nature and buildings are a good starting point and give opportunities for applying the children's understanding of angles.

Vocabulary

acute, angle, angle measurer, anticlockwise, clockwise, degrees (°), horizontal, obtuse, parallel, perpendicular, protractor, reflex angle, right angle, set square, vertical

Curriculum objectives

● To know angles are measured in degrees; measure angles, writing their sizes in degrees (°).

Success criteria

● I can use a protractor to measure a given angle of less than 180°.

You will need

Photocopiable sheets

'Round the bend'

General resources

'Shapes'

Equipment

2D shapes if not using 'Shapes'; protractors/angle measurers and a large scale version for board use

Differentiation

Less confident learners

Organise mixed-ability pairs and ask partners to explain how to use the protractor and how to read the measurements.

More confident learners

Ask children to prepare their own angles to measure, including some adjacent angles to make 180° on a straight line.

Lesson 1   Oral and mental starter 9

Main teaching activities

Whole-class work: Explain to the children that a protractor is used to measure the degrees of turn, about a point. Display a protractor on the whiteboard. Explain that the main divisions are in tens and these are subdivided into fives, and that each small line is worth one degree. Explain that the commonly used semicircular protractors are for measuring angles between 0° and 180°, but a circular one is more useful for measuring up to 360° (a complete turn).

Explain that to measure an angle, you place the 'viewfinder' on the point of the angle and line up the straight line along the bottom of the protractor with one of the angle's lines. The inner and outer scales measure from zero from each end so that you can measure either a 'right-hand' or a 'left-hand' angle.

Paired work: Distribute photocopiable page 'Round the bend' from the CD-ROM and ask the children to measure the angles accurately (to the nearest 1° if possible) and then to check their measurements with a partner. Model how to write the measurement next to the angle.

Progress check: Ask the children how close their measurements have been compared to their partner. Explain that the thickness of a drawn line can make the difference of one degree. Ensure that the children are using the correct scale, depending on the orientation of the angle on the page. Remind them that they can turn the page around for ease of measuring. Offer support to those who are having difficulty.

Review

Draw some angles on the board. Ask for volunteers to come and measure them. Ask the children: *Is the protractor in the correct position? Which scale will we be using? Is the angle an exact measurement in line with the markings on the protractor? Which angle is it nearer? How big is the angle?* Check the children's measurements. Discuss why there are minor variations (variable accuracy of lining up). Repeat using some different angles. Reiterate that they are measuring degrees of turn, about a point. Liken it to clock hands.

Curriculum objectives

- To know angles are measured in degrees; draw a right angle, writing its size in degrees (°).
- To identify multiples of 90° angles at a point and one whole turn (total 360°) reflex angles, and compare different angles.

Success criteria

- I can recognise and draw perpendicular lines and recognise and name acute, reflex and right angles.

You will need

Equipment

Protractors/angle measurers and a large scale version for board use; rulers

Differentiation

Less confident learners

These children may need adult support to draw the diagrams and use the appropriate vocabulary.

More confident learners

Expect more precise diagrams. Ask the children to make a list (with sketches) of acute, obtuse and reflex angles in the school environment.

Lesson 2 — Oral and mental starter 10

Main teaching activities

Whole-class work: Draw a horizontal line on the board. Talk about its properties – horizontal (level with the horizon); the angles from one side to the other are 180°; it will go on to infinity. Draw a line at 90° to the first one. Explain that any lines at right angles to another line or surface is said to be perpendicular to it. In this case, the second line is vertical (at 90° to the horizon). Label the right angles. Now divide one of the right angles using a protractor and label them 45° (in the space not on the line). Explain that two 45° angles make one 90° angle. Discuss acute, obtuse and reflex angles.

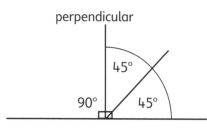

Independent and paired work: Ask the children to draw and label their own perpendicular lines to create and label acute, obtuse and reflex angles. Ask them to write a definition for each of these mathematical terms. Then draw and label another five acute angles and five obtuse angles, label the complementary reflex angle and then check their work with a partner.

Progress check: Ensure that the children have used the correct terminology when labelling their angles by drawing some examples on the board and asking the children to identify them for you.

Review

Draw several pairs of perpendicular lines on the board, using different orientations (so that there is not always a horizontal line). Ask: *What is the difference between a vertical line and a horizontal line? Perpendicular lines are very important for the building industry. Why do you think this is? What special angles are created by perpendicular lines? Who will draw another line on this diagram to make an acute angle? How do we know it is acute? What about an obtuse angle?*

Curriculum objectives

- To know angles are measured in degrees; measure them, writing their sizes in degrees (°).
- To compare different angles.

Success criteria

- I can draw, measure and label acute and obtuse angles accurately.

You will need

Equipment

Protractors/angle measurers and a large scale version for board use; rulers

Differentiation

Less confident learners

Encourage the children to measure angles to the nearest 5°.

More confident learners

Children to create an arrangement of straight lines where all the angles are obtuse.

Lesson 3 — Oral and mental starter 11

Main teaching activities

Whole-class work: Draw two acute angles and two obtuse angles, jumbled up, on the board. Invite the children to identify which is which. Ask for four volunteers, one at a time, to come and measure the angles accurately with a protractor. Ask them to talk through what they are doing as they measure, saying which scale they intend to use (inside or outside) and why.

Independent and paired work: Encourage the children to use a ruler to draw an design of six lines that cross each other. Then they choose at least four angles they think are acute and four they think are obtuse, measure them carefully with a protractor, then label them with their size, in degrees, and the code 'A' or 'O'. They count up the numbers of acute and obtuse angles created. Ask a partner to check their accuracy.

Progress check: Ask the children what they notice about where two lines intersect. (There are two acute and two obtuse angles unless there are four right angles.) Encourage them to self-correct by labelling them as A or O first so that they notice if their measurements are greater or smaller than 90°.

Review

Discuss why a drawing with only obtuse angles is difficult to achieve. (Whenever shapes are joined together, acute angles tend to appear.) Ask: *Do you think it is possible to draw a quadrilateral with only obtuse angles?* (No, because the angles of a quadrilateral add up to 360°, which is 4 × 90°. If you have three angles over 90°, then inevitably the fourth must be acute.)

Curriculum objectives
● To know angles are measured in degrees; measure them, writing their sizes in degrees.
● To identify: angles at a point and one whole turn, angles at a point on a straight line and ½ a turn.

Success criteria
● I can measure and calculate angles on a straight line.
● I know that the angles on a straight line add up to 180°.

You will need
Equipment
Protractors/angle measurers and a large scale version for board use; rulers; calculators

Differentiation
Less confident learners
Children may need adult support when measuring the angles.
More confident learners
Children should measure the minimum numbers of angles to calculate the others.

Lesson 4 — Oral and mental starter 17

Main teaching activities

Whole-class work: Ask a volunteer to draw a horizontal line on the board with two more lines that bisect (see figure). Explain that they will investigate the angles along a straight line. They add up to 180° so the three angles in the diagram must add up to 180°. Ask for a second volunteer to measure the three angles and total them. Measure two of the angles, then calculate the last angle.

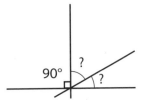

Paired work: The children draw their own three lines to create angles along a straight line and measure them as accurately as possible. Now ask them to add the angles together. Do they make 180°? If not, there has been an inaccurate measurement. Can they identify and correct it? Tell the children that they need to be accurate. When the children have measured the three angles that add up to 180°, ask them to label the angles on their diagram

Progress check: Reassure the children that with standard protractors, absolute accuracy is difficult which is why we allow one or two degrees of accuracy. Ask: *If I know two of the angles can I calculate the last one? How?*

Review

Compare the children's results. Discuss the variations in the angle totals (such as 178° – 182°) as indicating the margin of error. Emphasise that angles on a straight line add up to 180° and that angles in a complete turn total 360°. Demonstrate this by drawing another horizontal line and draw two more lines that intersect the first (see figure). Label the two angles. Ask the children to work out the missing angles without measuring them. Are there any other patterns that the children can observe here? (Opposite angles are equal.)

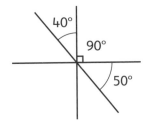

Curriculum objectives
● See lesson 4 above.
Success criteria
● I know that the angles of a complete turn add up to 360°.
● I can use my knowledge to calculate missing angles.

You will need
Photocopiable sheets
'What's the angle?'
Equipment
Protractors and a large scale version for board; rulers; A4 card; coloured pens

Differentiation
Less confident learners
Ask mixed-ability pairs to explain how to calculate the missing angles.
More confident learners
Ask children to prepare their own examples.

Lesson 5 — Oral and mental starter 11

Main teaching activities

Whole-class work: Draw two crossed lines. Label one angle 110°. Ask the children to use their knowledge of angles to complete the labelling of the missing angles. Put in the opposite angle first, then count on to 180° to find the angle along the straight line.

Independent and Paired work: Distribute photocopiable page 'What's the angle?' from the CD-ROM. Ask the children to find the missing angles. Explain they should show how they calculate the angles. When they have completed the task, they compare answers with a partner and discuss and correct discrepancies.

Progress check: Ask: *If I have two intersecting lines, what is the least number of angles I need to know to calculate the rest?* (One) *What about three lines, intersecting at the same point?* (Two)

Review

Compare the children's results. Distribute A4 sheets of card and coloured pens; ask each group to write a different angle fact that they have learned and draw a diagram to show it. For example, they might write 'The angles in a triangle add up to 180°' and draw a triangle with the angles labelled. Ask: *If I didn't have a protractor, how could I identify a right angle? If a straight line is crossed by two lines that are both perpendicular to it, what are the angles?*

■SCHOLASTIC

Length, perimeter and area

Expected prior learning

Children should be able to:

- measure in centimetres and millimetres using a ruler
- convert whole litres, metres, kilometres, kilograms to their corresponding smaller measures, millilitres, centimetres, metres and grams
- measure and calculate perimeters in simple cases.

Topic	Curriculum objectives	Expected outcomes
Measurement	**Lesson 1**	
	To understand and use approximate equivalences between metric units and common imperial units such as inches, pounds and pints.	Represent a puzzle or problem by identifying and recording the information or calculations needed to solve it; find possible solutions and confirm them in the context of the problem.
	Lesson 2	
	To measure and calculate the perimeter of composite rectilinear shapes in centimetres and metres.	Measure and calculate the perimeter of regular and irregular polygons including the perimeter of composite shapes.
	To calculate and compare the area of rectangles (including squares) and including using standard units, square centimetres (cm²) and square metres (m²) and estimate the area of irregular shapes.	Solve one-step and two-step problems involving whole numbers and decimals and all four operations, choosing and using appropriate calculation strategies, including calculator use.
	Lesson 3	
	To calculate and compare the area of rectangles (including squares) and including using standard units, square centimetres (cm²) and square metres (m²) and estimate the area of irregular shapes.	Use the formula for the area of a rectangle to calculate the rectangle's area, using standard units of measure.
	Lesson 4	
	To convert between different units of measure. To calculate and compare the area of rectangles (including squares) and including using standard units, square centimetres (cm²) and square metres (m²) and estimate the area of irregular shapes.	Use the formula for the area of a rectangle to calculate the rectangle's area, using standard units of measure. Solve one-step and two-step problems involving whole numbers and decimals and all four operations, choosing and using appropriate calculation strategies, including calculator use.
	Lesson 5	
	To measure and calculate the perimeter of composite rectilinear shapes in centimetres and metres. To calculate and compare the area of rectangles (including squares) and including using standard units, square centimetres (cm²) and square metres (m²) and estimate the area of irregular shapes. To use all four operations to solve problems involving measure using decimal notation, including scaling.	Represent a puzzle or problem by identifying and recording the information or calculations needed to solve it; find possible solutions and confirm them in the context of the problem.

Preparation

Lesson 1: copy 'Imperial/metric length conversion chart', one per group; assemble a collection of pictures, newspapers and magazines

Lesson 2: copy 'Count the area', one per child

Lesson 4: copy 'Calculate the area', one per child

Lesson 5: write the problem on the board or prepared it as a question to stick into books

You will need

Photocopiable sheets

'Imperial/metric length conversion chart'; 'Count the area'; 'Calculate the area'; 'Calculate the area template'

General resources

'Blank grid paper'

Equipment

Pictures, newspapers, magazines; paper; coloured pens; rulers; metre sticks; tape measures; camera; internet if available; peg boards and elastic bands

Further practice

Give children further practice to reinforce the principles of area and perimeter.

Oral and mental starters suggested for week 6

See bank of starters on pages 44 to 45. Oral and mental starters are also on the CD-ROM.

3 Number consequences

8 Quick-fire times tables

10 Perimeter calculator

12 Equivalent measures

Overview of progression

The majority of this week's lessons are about understanding ways to find perimeter and area and their relationship. The formula area = length × breadth is introduced and applied in order to solve a problem. The first lesson looks at imperial units of measure for length that are still in use and highlights the approximate equivalence with metric measurements. The most important thing is for the children to have an awareness of these in order to be able to compare measurements in a broad sense.

Watch out for

Often children confuse perimeter and area and find it difficult to use the correct unit of measure. This is best overcome by a very practical approach which makes the context real (see below).

Creative context

Area and perimeter lend themselves to practical measuring and problem solving. For children to understand the difference between the two, give them plenty of practice at pacing out the perimeter of the playground, hall or classroom and solving real life problems. If possible, replicate the *Gertie the Goat* investigation linked to some topic work, such as the area covered by a motte and bailey castle or a planned quiet garden for your school. Likewise imperial measures are valuable when they crop up in history topics. The suggested activity lends itself to an art project using collage or as an ideas 'contact sheet' display.

Vocabulary

area, divisor, **factor**, formula, imperial unit of measure, length, measure, measurement, metric unit, **perimeter**, standard unit, units of measurement and their abbreviations

Curriculum objectives

● To understand and use approximate equivalences between metric units and common imperial units such as inches, pounds and pints.

Success criteria

● I can approximate equivalences between metric and common imperial units of length.

You will need

Photocopiable sheets

'Imperial/metric length conversion chart'

Equipment

Pictures, newspapers, magazines; paper; coloured pens; rulers; metre sticks; tape measures; camera; internet if available

Differentiation

Less confident learners

These children may need adult support to organise themselves and their information.

More confident learners

These children should be able to research and present much more background information as well as presenting clear reminders of the equivalents.

Lesson 1 — Oral and mental starter 3

Main teaching activities

Whole-class work: Explain to the children that unusually, compared to many countries in the world the United Kingdom has a dual system of units of measurement. While metric measures are standard in shops, education and commerce, many people still use the imperial units of measure that were in common usage until the 1970s. Explain that it is worth knowing the approximate equivalents in order to make comparisons when presented with imperial measures. The most common imperial measures of length still in use are inch, foot, yard and mile.

Group work: Distribute photocopiable page 'Imperial/metric length conversion chart' from the CD-ROM. Explain to the children that they are going to produce an information sheet or poster to provide a visual reminder about the approximate conversions between the two systems of units and the contexts in which people commonly refer to imperial measurements, for example, signposts give information in miles; cars travel in miles per hour; some people still refer to buying lengths of material in yards. Explain that they can do this in any way they wish but pictures, photos and comparisons as well as the approximate conversion information must be included. The children present their information to the rest of the class. Allow time for questions.

Progress check: Ensure that the children are clear about the approximate equivalents and are representing them accurately.

Review

Share the information sheets or posters and display around school as helpful reminders for others. Discuss some of the equivalents that the children have included in their display and then ask them to calculate the approximate equivalent distances that they may be familiar with, for example, the distance between two nearby towns or how far from school to a nearby landmark.

Curriculum objectives

● To measure and calculate the perimeter of squares and rectangles in centimetres.
● To calculate and compare the area of squares and rectangles including using standard units.

Success criteria

● I understand that area is the space covered by a shape and is measured in cm² and m².
● I understand that perimeter is a linear measure all around a shape and is measured in centimetres or metres.

You will need

Photocopiable sheets
'Count the area'
Equipment
Rulers

Differentiation

Less confident learners
Children will rely on counting the squares.
More confident learners
Children could draw squares and rectangles and measure the sides to calculate the perimeter and area.

Lesson 2

Oral and mental starter 8

Main teaching activities

Whole-class work: Draw a rectangle divided up into centimetre squares. Explain that we can find two pieces of information about this rectangle. *The squares cover the 2D space on the page enclosed by the rectangle. This is known as the area of the rectangle. By counting the squares, we can calculate how much area the rectangle covers. If we also count or measure all the way around the edge, as if it were a fence around the edge of the field, we can find the perimeter.*

Use a number of rectangular shapes, such as book, rulers and paper to emphasise the difference between perimeter and area.

Paired work: Distribute photocopiable page 'Count the area' from the CD-ROM. Ask the children to find the area that each shape covers by counting the squares inside the shape and the perimeter by counting the centimetres (not the squares) around the edge. They must record their answer as Area = ___ cm² and Perimeter = ___ cm.

Progress check: Ask: *What unit of measure do we use for perimeter? Why? What unit for area? Why?*

Review

Draw a rectangle measuring 6cm by 7cm. Ask: *What unit do we use to measure area? Why is area measured in square centimetres? What is its perimeter? What is the area of this shape? How do you know?* (By counting the squares) *Can anybody suggest a quicker way to find the number of squares?* (Multiplying the number of squares across by the number down. So 6cm × 7cm = 42cm².) *How does knowing the perimeter lengths help us find the area? For a rectangle, how could we write a number sentence to represent the perimeter?* (2 × l + 2 × b)

Curriculum objectives

● To calculate the area of rectangles (including squares) and including using standard units, square centimetres (cm²) and square metres (m²).

Success criteria

● I can use the formula length × breadth to calculate the area of a square or rectangle.

You will need

General resources
'Blank grid paper'
Equipment
Rulers

Differentiation

Less confident learners
They may need help drawing the shapes accurately.
More confident learners
Children can draw composite shapes, find the area of each section and add them to find the total area. They should also find the perimeter.

Lesson 3

Oral and mental starter 3

Main teaching activities

Whole-class work: Remind the children of how they found areas by counting centimetre squares. Explain that for squares and rectangles, the area can be calculated as length × breadth. Draw a rectangle and label the sides 2cm and 6cm. Apply the formula: Area = 2cm × 6cm = 12cm². Check your answer by asking the children to count the squares. Repeat using a number of different squares and rectangles.

Independent and paired work: Ask the children to draw some squares and rectangles on 'Blank grid paper' from the CD-ROM, then measure the sides and apply the length × breadth formula to find the area. They should record the area, then check it by counting the squares. When they have finished, they should check their answers with a partner.

Progress check: Tell the children that the length × breadth formula only works for squares and rectangles. Ask: *Why is it not possible to find the area of other quadrilaterals, such as a parallelogram, in this way?* (Diagonal lines cut across whole squares therefore making the calculation incorrect.) Remind the children that it is essential to use the correct unit of measure since otherwise it will be impossible to know whether they are recording an area or a perimeter.

Review

Check children's understanding of how to calculate area by drawing and labelling several rectangles and asking the children to find the area of each. Draw a composite shape such as an 'L' shape, and ask: *How can we find the area if the shape is not a rectangle?* (If it has straight sides, we may be able to divide it into squares and rectangles.) Find the area of each rectangle, then add them together.

■SCHOLASTIC

Curriculum objectives

- To calculate the area of rectangles using standard units.
- To convert between different units of measure.

Success criteria

- I can convert mixed units to a single unit of measure and use these to find areas using the formula length × breadth.

You will need

Photocopiable sheets

'Calculate the area'; 'Calculate the area template'

Equipment

Calculators; dotty paper

Differentiation

Less confident learners

Adapt the 'Calculate the area template' to provide more appropriate number ranges.

More confident learners

Provide dotted paper and challenge children to construct their own area calculations.

Lesson 4
Oral and mental starter 12

Main teaching activities

Whole-class work: Draw a rectangle and explain that it represents a field. Label the sides as 4m and 3m. Ask the children to find the area ($12m^2$). Now label the sides 4m and 300cm. Ask the children whether they can see a difficulty with finding this area. (There are mixed units.) They need to make sure that both sides are measured in the same unit: either 4m × 3m or 400cm × 300cm. Remind the children that they can use factors to help them multiply multiples of 100. Working with the larger units would make the calculation easier. Repeat this, using other mixed units such as cm and mm or km and m.

Independent and paired work: Distribute photocopiable page 'Calculate the area' from the CD-ROM. Ask the children to convert each pair of lengths to the same unit before finding the area of each shape. They check with a partner that all units have been correctly converted and that the answers are expressed in the correct units. Ask them to use a calculator to check the accuracy of the multiplying and attempt to spot where any mistake was made.

Progress check: Ask some of the children to identify the units that they have changed and why to check that they have used equivalents correctly.

Review

Draw a rectangle with the sides labelled 2m and 300cm. Write in the middle: 'Area = $600cm^2$'. Ask: *Is this area correct? Why not? How can we put it right? What tips would you give to someone who wanted to find the area of this shape?* Draw a rectangle and label its area as $12m^2$. Ask: *What lengths might the sides be? Is there more than one possible answer? Why?* List all the possible answers. Repeat with a rectangle with an area of $18cm^2$ and a square with an area of $16cm^2$.

Curriculum objectives

- To solve problems involving addition and subtraction of units of length.
- To calculate the perimeter of squares and rectangles.
- To calculate and compare the area of rectangles and including using standard units, square centimetres and square metres.

Success criteria

- I can apply my knowledge of finding perimeters and areas to investigate a problem, finding all the possible solutions.

You will need

Equipment

Squared paper; rulers; peg boards and elastic bands

Differentiation

Less confident learners

Children could use apparatus to demonstrate their thinking.

More confident learners

Children should produce their findings in a table.

Lesson 5
Oral and mental starter 10

Main teaching activities

Whole-class work: Ask: *If a rectangle has an area of $15cm^2$, what could the sides measure? What would the total perimeter be? Is there more than one possible answer? Would the rectangle look the same in each case?* Draw the rectangles, one measuring 1cm by 15cm and the other 3cm by 5cm. Discuss.

> Gertie the Goat needs a new pen for the winter. Her owner Farmer Thomas only has 64m of fencing for the perimeter of the enclosure but he does not know how to arrange it so that Gertie has the maximum area of grass to eat. Help him and provide all of the possible alternatives for Gertie's new home?

Paired work: Display the above problem which you have prepared. Explain that the children can work together and present their findings to Farmer Thomas in any way they like, including diagrams and number sentences.

Progress check: Listen to the children as they discuss this problem since it will give you a good idea about their understanding. Ask questions such as: *How do you know you have found all the possibilities? Are your findings going to be clear for Farmer Thomas? Have you checked that your perimeter still adds up to 64m? What unit of measure have you used to show the area?*

Review

The children present their ideas to the rest of the class describing any patterns they noticed (the closer the values of the two sides, the greater the area). They should have concluded that the largest area possible for Gertie's pen is a 16m × 16m square, giving her an area of $256m^2$ of grass to eat and play on!

Curriculum objectives
● To read, write, order and compare numbers at least to 1,000,000 and determine the value of each digit.

You will need
1. Check
Oral and mental starter
2 Place value elimination game

2. Assess
'0–30 number cards'; 'Place value arrow cards'; < and > cards from 'Symbol cards'

3. Further practice
Oral and mental starters
5 Pairs to make 1000/10,000
15 Place value shuffle

Photocopiable sheets
'Number builder'

Place value to order and compare numbers to 1,000,000

Most children should be able to identify the value of each digit and use this to order and compare numbers.

Some children will not have made such progress and will require the support of Place value arrow cards to separate a large number into its constituent values.

1. Check

2 Place value elimination game

Encourage the children to ask questions that focus on the place value of each digit and questions which eliminate the greatest number of possibilities. Observe the children who quickly develop a strategy and those who are unable to use the vocabulary of place value and who only use random guesses.

Does your question eliminate the maximum number of possibilities? How has that helped you get closer to the mystery number?

2. Assess

Observe the children describing to a partner a five- or six-digit number, only comparing the place value position of the digits. Children who are unsure could use the 'Place value arrow cards' to create numbers and describe them. Observe the understanding of place value and the vocabulary used. The more confident should then make a number sentence creating a second number with the number cards remaining and the symbols cards. Record the outcomes.

3. Further practice

Use the oral and mental starters to give further practice in using the language of place value and comparing the size of numbers. Photocopiable page 46 'Number builder' provides practice of understanding the place value of each digit.

Curriculum objectives
● To multiply and divide whole numbers and those involving decimals by 10, 100 and 1000.

You will need
1. Check
Oral and mental starter
3 Number consequences

2. Assess
'Place value table'; '0–30 number cards'

3. Further practice
Photocopiable sheets
'Place value function machine'

Multiplying and dividing by 10, 100 and 1000

Most children should be confident multiplying and dividing numbers by 10, 100 and 1000 and should understand the place value, including decimals.

Some children will not have made such progress and will require the support of the 'Place value table' to help them to keep track.

1. Check

3 Number consequences

As the children play, watch for a clear understanding of how digits move up and down the place value, using zeros as place holders.

What is 103 divided by 10? What about by 100? What is the value of the 3? Where is the decimal point? Now multiply by 1000. What do you notice?

2. Assess

As children challenge each other, observe the confident learners who will not need to use the 'Place value table' and will be able to tell you the value of the numbers. Less confident learners may alter the order of the digits, particularly with decimal numbers, and will need reminding that the digits stay the same but move up and down the place value. Record the outcomes.

3. Further practice

Photocopiable page 47 'Place value function machine' gives extra practice to improve dexterity with moving up and down the place value and understanding its effect on the size and value of a number.

Curriculum objectives
● To measure and calculate the perimeter of composite rectilinear shapes in centimetres and metres.

You will need
1. Check

Oral and mental starter

10 Perimeter calculator

2. Assess
Selection of squares and rectangles from 'Shapes'; centimetre-squared paper

3. Further practice

Oral and mental starter

8 Quick-fire times tables

Photocopiable sheets
'Squares and rectangles'

Calculating perimeter

Most children should be able to add the lengths of the sides of squares and rectangles to calculate the perimeter.

Some children will not have made such progress and will require practical experience with measuring and calculating perimeter as a linear measure.

1. Check

10 Perimeter calculator

Concentrating on squares and rectangles, observe the children measuring and calculating the perimeters of individual quadrilaterals and then extend to composite shapes made up of squares and rectangles.

How do we calculate the perimeter? Is there a quicker way? What is the perimeter? What unit of measure do we use? What do we need to remember when calculating the perimeter of composite shapes?

2. Assess

Ask the children to find the perimeters of the given shapes, writing down their calculations as they work. Confident learners will be able to verbalise a formula for individual shapes. Less confident learners may need to draw the shapes on squared paper and count the centimetre squares, especially with composite shapes. Watch out for children confusing perimeter with area. Record the outcomes.

3. Further practice

Photocopiable page 48 'Squares and rectangles' provides further opportunity for understanding how to calculate perimeters for children who are less sure.

Curriculum objectives
● To calculate and compare the area of rectangles (including squares) and including using standard units, square centimetres (cm²) and square metres (m²) and estimate the area of irregular shapes.

You will need
1. Check

Oral and mental starter

11 Multiplication bingo

2. Assess
Squares and rectangles from 'Shapes' and other rectangular shapes, such as an exercise book or A4 piece of paper

3. Further practice

Oral and mental starter

16 Division lotto

Photocopiable sheets
'Squares and rectangles'

Calculate the area of squares and rectangles

Most children should be able to use the formula length × breadth to calculate area in centimetres squared or metres squared.

Some children will not have made such progress and will require practical opportunities to practise measuring and counting the centimetre squares to understand area.

1. Check

11 Multiplication bingo

Use this multiplication game to revise the formula area = length × breadth. Note those children who are still not secure in their recall of multiples.

If a rectangle measures 4cm by 8cm, what is the area? What other measurements could the sides be? How do you know?

2. Assess

Children measure the lengths of the sides of the squares and rectangles from 'Shapes' and the other items and calculate the areas. Observe the children working and recording their areas, especially noting children who forget the unit of measure and those who add the sides together rather than multiplying them. Ask confident learners to order the different shapes by area, smallest first. Record the outcomes.

3. Further practice

Use photocopiable page 48 'Squares and rectangles' and ask the children to find the area of each shape. Less confident learners could count the squares to aid their understanding. The oral and mental starter continues to give practice of multiplying and dividing known number facts, which underpin finding areas.

Oral and mental starters

Number and place value

1 Spot the pattern

Challenge the children to spot and continue number patterns.

For example: 75, 100, 125, ... *What comes next?*

45, 60, 75, ...

440, 420, 400, ...

Once the pattern has been spotted, let the children continue each sequence by 'passing it on' around the room.

2 Place value elimination game

Write a five-digit number (such as 65,213) on a piece of paper and hide it from the children. Write the digits of your number on the board in a random order. Tell the children to ask questions to which the answer may be *Yes* or *No, higher* or *No, lower*.

For example: *Is the 5 digit in the tens column?* (No, higher.)

Explain that they have 20 questions to work out the position and place value of each digit.

3 Number consequences

Choose a two-digit number. Ask children to write it on their whiteboards and apply a set of instructions, some of which change the place value. They write down the new number each time.

For example: 45, ten times bigger, add 100, multiply by 10, add 6, divide by 10 and the answer is ...

Repeat with other numbers and other instructions.

Addition and subtraction

4 Double it and pass it on

Put the children into groups of five or six. Ask one person in each group to choose a single-digit number. They say the number out loud, double it and 'pass it on', this is repeated around the group until it bridges 100 and that person is given a point and begins with a new number. The person with the most points at the end wins.

This game can be extended so that the numbers must reach 1000 or even 10,000 in order to gain a point.

5 Pairs to make 1000/10,000

Remind the children that they have been learning number bonds since they started school, for example, number bonds to 10 (3 + 7; 5 + 5) and number bonds to 100 (30 + 70; 50 + 50). Explain that today they are going to extend this by practising number bonds to 1000 and including number bonds to 10 and 100.

For example: *What is the pair to make 1000 for 455?* (545)

What about for 629? (371)

Use 'Place value arrow cards' from the CD-ROM to generate numbers or simply write a list of numbers. The children find the pairs to make 1000 and write them on individual whiteboards to show you.

Extend this by practising number bonds to 10,000.

For example: *What is the pair to make 10,000 for 8275?* (1725)

■ SCHOLASTIC

6 Use your doubles

Write a set of numbers.

For example: 122, 670, 320, 650, 520, 160, 820, 135, 366, 590

Ask the children to select two of the numbers which doubling will help them add together.

For example: 670 + 650 could be solved as double 600, double 50, add 20.

160 + 135 could be solved as double 130, add 30 add 5.

Ask the children to work in pairs to look for other opportunities to use doubling to add two of these numbers together. They should write them on their whiteboards and be prepared to explain their thinking.

7 Chain reaction adding

Using number cards 1–100, shuffle the pack and, turning one card at a time, add each card until an agreed total is breached (either 200, 500 or 1000). This can be done altogether as a class or in groups or by taking turns around the room. Talk about the strategies that the children should be using, for example, looking for the next 10 or 100, near doubles or counting on tens then the ones.

Multiplication and division

8 Quick-fire times tables

Call out a range of multiplication facts using a variety of vocabulary.

For example: 6 lots of 5; What is 10 times bigger than 9?; 4 multiplied by 3; 3 squared, and so on.

Ask the children to write their answers on their whiteboards and show you when you say: *Show me.*

11 Multiplication bingo

From the number cards 1–100 place nine multiples of the children's known times tables on each table. This can be differentiated for those children who have not learnt some of the more difficult table facts. You then call out assorted table facts, for example, 5 × 9 and the children identify the multiple. If they have it on a card in front of them they turn it over. The winners are the table who have turned all of their cards over correctly first.

Geometry: properties of shape

9 Shape sorter

Using either 'Shapes' from the CD-ROM or your own selection of 2D shapes, ask the children to sort the shapes by common properties that you will name.

For example: regular shapes, shapes with one or more right angle, quadrilaterals, shapes with parallel sides, symmetrical shapes.

Whichever property you choose, ensure that all children have an understanding of the vocabulary of shape.

Measurement

10 Perimeter calculator

From either 'Shapes' from the CD-ROM or your own selection of 2D shapes, hold up a regular 2D shape. Ask the children to name it and to tell you how to calculate its perimeter. First establish the children's understanding of perimeter. Then use the example of a square with sides measuring 5cm each which would have a perimeter of 4 × 5 = 20cm. Repeat with other regular shapes.

Oral and mental starters 12–17 continue on the CD-ROM.

Number builder

■ Use arrow cards to create the following numbers then complete the number sentences for each one.
■ The first one has been done for you.

56,938 = 50,000 + 6000 + 900 + 30 + 8

23,596 =

83,771 =

182,937 =

304,926 =

■ Now write the numbers in order of size, smallest first.

I can understand the place value of digits.

How did you do?

PHOTOCOPIABLE   ⊠ SCHOLASTIC
www.scholastic.co.uk

Place value function machine

- Whatever number is put in at the top of the function machine, the maths rule is applied before the new number falls out of the bottom.
- Complete the functions.

19
387
6
0.3
9.8

9
1.4
960
77.2
1976

- Now choose your own numbers to put into this function machine.

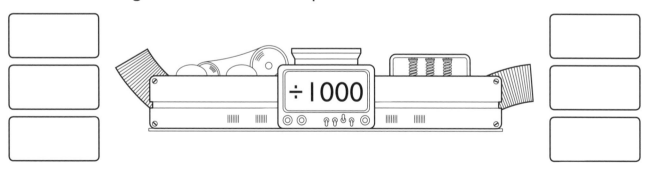

I can multiply and divide whole numbers and decimals.

How did you do?

Squares and rectangles

■ Write the number of squares covered by each shape.

I can calculate area.

How did you do?

Written methods for multiplication

Expected prior learning

Children should be able to:

- recall multiplication facts up to 12 × 12
- multiply using arrays, groups of, multiplying by 10 and partitioning.

Topic	Curriculum objectives	Expected outcomes
Multiplication and division	**Lesson 1**	
	To multiply numbers up to four-digits by a one- or two-digit number using a formal written method, including long multiplication for two-digit numbers.	Recall quickly multiplication facts up to 12 × 12 and use them to multiply pairs of multiples of 10 and 100; derive quickly corresponding division facts.
	To multiply and divide whole numbers and those involving decimals by 10, 100 and 1000.	Refine and use formal written methods to multiply 3-digits × 1-digit and 2-digits × 2-digits up to four digits.
	Lesson 2	
	To multiply numbers up to four-digits by a one- or two-digit number using a formal written method, including long multiplication for two-digit numbers.	Recall quickly multiplication facts up to 12 × 12 and use them to multiply pairs of multiples of 10 and 100; derive quickly corresponding division facts.
	To multiply and divide whole numbers and those involving decimals by 10, 100 and 1000.	Refine and use formal written methods to multiply 3-digits × 1-digit and 2-digits × 2-digits up to four digits.
	Lesson 3	
	To multiply numbers up to four-digits by a one- or two-digit number using a formal written method, including long multiplication for two-digit numbers.	Recall quickly multiplication facts up to 12 × 12 and use them to multiply pairs of multiples of 10 and 100; derive quickly corresponding division facts.
	To multiply and divide whole numbers and those involving decimals by 10, 100 and 1000.	Refine and use formal written methods to multiply 3-digits × 1-digit and 2-digits × 2-digits up to four digits.
	Lesson 4	
	To multiply numbers up to four-digits by a one- or two-digit number using a formal written method, including long multiplication for two-digit numbers.	Recall quickly multiplication facts up to 12 × 12 and use them to multiply pairs of multiples of 10 and 100; derive quickly corresponding division facts.
	To multiply and divide whole numbers and those involving decimals by 10, 100 and 1000.	Refine and use formal written methods to multiply 3-digits × 1-digit and 2-digits × 2-digits up to four digits.
	To solve problems involving multiplication and division, including scaling by simple fractions and problems involving simple rates.	
	Lesson 5	
	To solve problems involving addition, subtraction, multiplication and division and a combination of these, including understanding the meaning of the equals sign.	Solve one-step and two-step problems involving whole numbers and decimals and all four operations, choosing and using appropriate calculation strategies.

Preparation

Lesson 1: copy 'Trying times', one per child

Lesson 2: copy 'Multiplying matters', one per child

Lesson 3: on the board write the following numbers in one colour: 115, 230, 345, 193, 225, and multiples of 10 or 100 in another colour, for example: 20, 40, 80, 300, 400, 500, 90

Lesson 4: copy 'Multiplication word problems', one per child; write the question about the chocolate factory on the board

Lesson 5: write your chosen scenario on the board; collect together the catalogues and reference materials needed to support the scenario you have posed

You will need

Photocopiable sheets

'Trying times (1) and (2)'; 'Multiplying matters'; 'Multiplication word problems'; 'Multiplication word problems template'

General resources

'Multiplication square'; interactive activity 'Trying times'

Equipment

Calculators, catalogues, online resources

Further practice

Following the completion of lesson 1, you could offer individual children further practice of multiplication of three-digit numbers by a single-digit and two-digit by two-digit using the 'Trying times' interactive activity. This also offers similar word problems to further consolidate understanding and apply their use of written methods of multiplication.

Oral and mental starters suggested for week 1

See bank of starters on page 85. Oral and mental starters are also on the CD-ROM.

18 Multiplication sort

21 Quick-fire multiplication and division facts

22 What's the question?

23 What's the question ×10?

Overview of progression

This week's lessons are all about multiplication using both mental and written calculation skills. Children are required to move through the stages of multiplication at a rate that matches their ability and understanding. At each stage they need to estimate and understand the processes. Some children may still need practice using a partitioning method for multiplying leading on, as appropriate, to standard vertical methods of written multiplication. There are opportunities for making decisions about strategies and ways of working and problem solving.

Watch out for

Some children may progress to the vertical written methods without any understanding of the place value of the digits they are multiplying. For these children it is helpful to model the grid method alongside their standard calculation to remind them of the value of each step.

Creative context

There are many occasions when problems need to be solved by multiplying numbers in a real-life context, for example, cooking and baking, team and sporting contexts, planning school social events and gardening.

Vocabulary

answer, calculate, calculation, digit, explain, **factor**, hundred thousands, **inverse**, methods, million, multiple, multiply, operation, place value, problem, reason, reasoning, solution, significant digit, ten thousands, thousands

Curriculum objectives

● To multiply numbers up to four-digits by a one- or two-digit number using a formal written method, including long multiplication for two-digit numbers.
● To multiply and divide whole numbers by 10 and 100.

Success criteria

● I can multiply larger numbers using a formal or informal written method.

You will need

Photocopiable sheets

'Trying times (1) and (2)'

Differentiation

Less confident learners

Provide them with photocopiable page 'Trying times (1)', which involves multiplying two-digit numbers by one-digit numbers.

More confident learners

Ask the children to use the vertical multiplication method throughout 'Trying times (2)'. They may be confident enough to use the standard short multiplication method.

Lesson 1

Oral and mental starter 21

Main teaching activities

Whole-class work: Revise partitioning and the grid method of multiplying. Ask children to solve some multiplication problems. Three examples are shown below. Remind the children to estimate the answer first, so they know its approximate size.

34×8

×	8
30	240
4	32
	272

47×9

×	9
40	360
7	63
	423

123×5

×	5
100	500
20	100
3	15
	615

If a group of your children are very confident with the grid method, you could make them your focus group for this session and teach them vertical multiplication, starting with the most significant digit. The progression you adopt will depend on your individual school calculating policy. The emphasis should be on understanding the process and then choosing the most efficient method.

```
    1 2 4
  ×     6
    6 0 0
    1 2 0
      2 4
    7 4 4
```

Start with the most significant digit: the 100. Remind the children that they are multiplying 20×6, not 2×6. Add using the largest number first: 600, 700, 720, 744.

Independent and paired work: Distribute photocopiable page 'Trying times (2)' from the CD-ROM. The children solve the problems, which involve multiplying three-digit numbers by one-digit numbers, using the multiplication method that each child is most comfortable with. They should check their answers with a partner.

Progress check: Ask the children to tell you which method they have used and to share the answers for one of the questions. Write up on the board a calculation that is incorrect and remind the children where common errors occur (incorrect multiplication fact knowledge, errors with multiplying by powers of 10 and therefore place value problems, errors with adding or recombining). Ask the children to check their calculations very carefully and to look at their resulting answer. Tell them to ask themselves: *Is the answer large enough? What size of number do I expect given these numbers to multiply?*

Review

Ask for two volunteers, one who is confident with the grid method and one who is confident with the vertical method, and ask them to find 206×4. Discuss what needs to be recorded when you multiply no tens by 4 (0). Demonstrate that both methods work. Ask: *How could we check the answer?* (Use the inverse operation, division.) Demonstrate the use of a calculator to divide the answer by 4. Write up the calculation below and ask the children: *Is this correct? How do you know? Estimate what size the answer should be. Will the actual answer be bigger or smaller than that? Correct the errors in this calculation. What advice would you offer this person to help them avoid errors in the future?*

```
    3 1 6
  ×     5
  1 5 0 0   Correct
        5   Incorrect place value
      3 0   Poorly placed, inviting incorrect addition
  1 8 0 5
```

Curriculum objectives

● To multiply numbers up to four-digits by a one- or two-digit number using a formal written method, including long multiplication for two-digit numbers.
● To multiply and divide whole numbers by 10 and 100.

Success criteria

● I can begin to solve larger multiplication problems using a variety of methods.

You will need

Photocopiable sheets
'Multiplying matters'

General resources
Interactive activity 'Trying times'

Equipment
Calculators

Differentiation

Less confident learners

Work through question 1 of the interactive activity 'Trying times' with individuals and small groups. Demonstrate the workings out using the tools provided.

More confident learners

Ask the children to use standard vertical multiplication.

Lesson 2

Main teaching activities

Whole-class work: Write the calculation 215 × 6 on the board. Ask for two volunteers to solve it in different ways, for example the grid method and a vertical method. Remind the children that the inverse of multiplication is division and that calculations can be checked using the inverse.

Provide a number of examples for the children to attempt. Talk them through each stage.

```
  1 1 5
×     4
  4 6 0
    2
```

- *Multiply the ones first (5 × 4 = 20). You cannot put 20 in the ones column, so record the 0 and carry the 2 to be included with the tens.*
- *Multiply the tens (1 × 4 = 4 plus the carried over 2 = 6).*
- *Multiply the hundreds (1 × 4 = 4).*

The inverse calculation for this is 460 divided by 4 = 115.

Repeat using a number of examples.

Independent work: Distribute photocopiable page 'Multiplying matters' from the CD-ROM. Ask the children to complete using a vertical method. They can check the accuracy of their answers by using a calculator and doing the inverse calculation. Where they have made errors, they should highlight them using a different colour and correct them if they can.

Progress check: Ask: *What do you think is the most common mistake made when multiplying like this? Why is it important to carry across? What happens if you forget to count it in?*

Review

Ask for three volunteers to find 107 × 6 using different methods and explaining each step. Discuss and correct any discrepancies. Ask: *Where do you think mistakes are most often made in each of these methods? What effect does this have on the answer? How can you quickly find the approximate size that the answer should be? What do you do first when estimating? Could you suggest any helpful tips for someone who is calculating using your chosen method? How did you decide on the position of the decimal point when you multiplied to solve the money problem?*

Curriculum objectives

● To multiply numbers up to four-digits by a one- or two-digit number using a formal written method, including long multiplication for two-digit numbers.
● To multiply and divide whole numbers and those involving decimals by 10 and 100.

Success criteria

● I can multiply increasingly large numbers by multiples of 10 and 100, recognising when a written calculation is more appropriate.

You will need

General resources

'Multiplication square'

Differentiation

Less confident learners

These children may need support with both the process and the multiplying. A 'Multiplication square' may be helpful and they should multiply two-digit numbers by 20, 30 and 50 only until they become more confident.

More confident learners

As well as attempting to multiply three-digit numbers by multiples of 10, 100 and 1000, they could extend their thinking by considering how they would multiply a decimal number such as 4.7 by multiples of 10 and 100.

Lesson 3 — Oral and mental starter 22

Main teaching activities

Whole-class work: Explain to the children that today's lesson gives them an opportunity to draw together some of the multiplication skills that they have already learned in order to multiply larger numbers. Write up the following question:

125×40

Ask for suggestions as to ways in which this might be solved. Ask for a show of hands to tell you who would prefer to use a written method for this question. Is there anyone who thinks they could solve this mentally?

Encourage the children to look at the numbers to assess how difficult a question is. Remind them about their knowledge of factors. Demonstrate that 40 may be factorised as 4×10. Therefore this calculation is easier to think of as $125 \times 4 \times 10$ which is possible either mentally or with some informal jottings.

$125 \times 4 = 500 \times 10 = 5000$

You might need to revise the place value movement of digits when multiplying by 10, 100 and 1000.

Repeat with a number of different questions, for example, 320×30; 623×500.

Show the children that with more challenging numbers, they might need to use short multiplication for the first part but then can simply multiply by the appropriate power of 10, for example:

$623 \times 5 \times 100 = 3115 \times 100 = 311,500$

Independent and paired work: Ask the children to work in pairs to select a number of each colour from your prepared list and to discuss whether they could multiply these mentally, mentally with jottings or using a short multiplication method and adjusting the place value. The children should then complete the calculations individually, recording the process as they go.

Progress check: Take feedback from the pairs about their decisions and ask them to explain why. From this you will be able to assess their understanding of the process as well as their conceptual understanding about the size and value of numbers. Check also that confident mathematicians aren't overestimating their mental skills and attempting everything in their head, possibly causing avoidable errors.

Review

Write up 746×300. Ask for a volunteer to come and explain the steps they would take to solve this. Suggest that to attempt 746×3 mentally, while not impossible, may offer opportunities for error.

Curriculum objectives

- To multiply numbers up to four-digits by a one- or two-digit number using a formal written method, including long multiplication for two-digit numbers.
- To multiply and divide whole numbers by 10 and 100.

Success criteria

- I can extract relevant information and select appropriate methods to solve multiplication problems.

You will need

Photocopiable sheets

'Multiplication word problems'; 'Multiplication word problems template'

Differentiation

Less confident learners

Provide support with adult help to decipher the relevant information.

More confident learners

Adapt the template version of photocopiable page 'Multiplication word problems'. to include more challenging numbers.

Lesson 4
Oral and mental starter 23

Main teaching activities

Whole-class work: Ask: *A chocolate factory makes 246 chocolates per day. These are packed into boxes of six chocolates. How many boxes can the factory produce each day? The factory is open five days a week. How many boxes can it produce each week?*

Explain that this is a two-step problem. To answer the second question, you need to have answered the first question. Look for clues such as *into boxes of six*: putting a large number into lots of 6 must indicate a division: 246 ÷ 6. The numbers involved are big enough to require a written short division method. Now we can solve the second step. *The factory makes 41 boxes in one day, so how many are made in five days?* This indicates a 2-digit × 1-digit question. Most children should be able to do this mentally or by using jottings: 41 × 5 = (40 × 5) + 5 = 205. A few may need to use the grid method. The answer is 205 boxes of chocolates each week. Remind the children that a word question requires words in the answer, not just a number.

Independent work: Distribute photocopiable page 'Multiplication word problems' from the CD-ROM. The children should solve the word problems on the sheet individually and go on to create one of their own.

Progress check: Ensure that the children are clear about the calculations that they require; while they are mostly multiplying, other operations may be necessary too. Ensure they understand the meaning of the context, for example, it is not possible to have half a person, and so on. Remind them about choosing a formal method for the relative size of the numbers.

Review

Ask: *How did you decipher the relevant information and the operation to use? Which parts could you do mentally and which needed a written calculation? Would you change this next time? Which of the multiplication skills that we have been learning did you use? Is it good to only have one strategy for multiplying?*

Curriculum objectives

- To solve problems involving addition; understanding the meaning of the equals sign.

Success criteria

- I can calculate effectively to find the answer to a practical problem or scenario.

You will need

Equipment

Catalogues; online resources

Differentiation

Less confident learners

Prices in catalogues, such as £8.99, may not be accessible to children. Encourage them to round up the numbers for ease of calculating.

More confident learners

Encourage children to make alternative choices representing value for money.

Lesson 5
Oral and mental starter 18

Main teaching activities

Whole-class work: Explain to the children that they are going to explore the practical uses of being able to multiply in a variety of ways. A real scenario would be most effective but, if not, suggest the following: Your school has been given a grant of £1000 to buy small equipment. You must decide what you would buy. You might choose sports equipment, playtime equipment, books or electronics, stationary or you might have other suggestions.

Provide them with access to catalogues or online resources to choose from and ask them to prepare a proposal for the class to consider. Emphasise that the grant is for small equipment. They may not purchase only one large item.

Paired work: Begin their 'shopping list', working in multiples, for example six footballs, and so on. Then continue to produce their proposals.

Progress check: Use this activity to 'troubleshoot' problems with understanding multiplication and problem solving. Work with individual children looking for errors in the choice of operation, the layout of the calculation, uncertain place value or impossible sized answers in relation to their estimates.

Review

Display the proposals and discuss the choices. Use rounding and estimates to compare each scenario. Ask: *What other operations did you use as well as multiplying? What is the inverse of multiplying? What guidance would you offer to children who find choosing the correct operation tricky?*

Dividing four-digit numbers

Expected prior learning

Children should be able to:

- recall multiplication facts up to 12 × 12
- division by the 'chunking' method.

Topic	Curriculum objectives	Expected outcomes
Multiplication and division	**Lesson 1**	
	To multiply and divide numbers mentally drawing upon known facts.	Refine and use formal written methods to divide 4-digits ÷ 1-digit.
		Recall quickly multiplication facts up to 12 × 12 and use them to multiply pairs of multiples of 10 and 100; derive quickly corresponding division facts.
	Lesson 2	
	To multiply and divide numbers mentally drawing upon known facts.	Refine and use formal written methods to divide 4-digits ÷ 1-digit.
		Recall quickly multiplication facts up to 12 × 12 and use them to multiply pairs of multiples of 10 and 100; derive quickly corresponding division facts.
	Lesson 3	
	To multiply and divide numbers mentally drawing upon known facts.	Refine and use formal written methods to divide 4-digits ÷ 1-digit.
		Recall quickly multiplication facts up to 12 × 12 and use them to multiply pairs of multiples of 10 and 100; derive quickly corresponding division facts.
	Lesson 4	
	To multiply and divide numbers mentally drawing upon known facts.	Refine and use formal written methods to divide 4-digits ÷ 1-digit.
		Recall quickly multiplication facts up to 12 × 12 and use them to multiply pairs of multiples of 10 and 100; derive quickly corresponding division facts.
	Lesson 5	
	To solve problems involving multiplication and division, including scaling and problems involving simple rates.	Solve one-step and two-step problems involving whole numbers and decimals, choosing and using appropriate calculation strategies.

Preparation

Lesson 5: copy 'Written division skills', one per child

You will need

Photocopiable sheets
'Written division skills'
General resources
'Multiplication square'; '0–30 number cards'
Equipment
Bundles of straws in tens plus individual straws

Further practice

Solve simple division problems practically using bundles of straws.

Oral and mental starters suggested for week 2

See bank of starters on pages 85 to 86. Oral and mental starters are also on the CD-ROM.

19 Double and halve

20 Chanting round the room

21 Quick-fire multiplication and division facts

25 Factor pairs

Overview of progression

This week's lessons focus on division, both formal and informal and relate it to known multiplication tables as the 'flip side', or more formally, the inverse of multiplication. There are opportunities to learn and practise short division, as the children are ready, alongside 'chunking' both using addition as well as subtraction.

Watch out for

Some children may be keen to use short division but not have a clear understanding of the place value of each digit. Others may forget to include any remainders as they proceed with their calculations. Demonstrate this with an incorrect calculation which has ignored any remainders as the division is executed and ask the children to spot the mistakes, reminding them that this is a common error which they must avoid.

Creative context

Division is a real-life activity and as such is best used as and when such situations arise.

Vocabulary

answer, approximately, calculate, calculation, digit, divide, estimate, explain, **factor**, hundred thousands, **inverse**, methods, million, multiple, multiply, operation, place value, problem, **quotient**, reason, reasoning, remainder, round, significant digit, solution, ten thousands, thousands

■ SCHOLASTIC

Curriculum objectives

- To multiply and divide numbers mentally drawing upon known facts.
- To divide numbers up to four-digits by a one-digit number using the formal written method of short division and interpret remainders appropriately for the context.

Success criteria

- I can use my known multiplication facts to divide

You will need

General resources

'0–30 number cards'

Equipment

Bundles of straws in tens plus individual straws, if needed

Differentiation

Less confident learners

These children may find the activity very difficult if they do not know many multiplication facts. Try to create some division questions using only divisors 2 and 5 (for example, 27 ÷ 2; 35 ÷ 2; 39 ÷ 5; 68 ÷ 5). Encourage them to use straws to assist them.

More confident learners

Ask these children to attempt 3-digit division, using larger 'chunks'. For example: if 10 × 4 = 40 then 20 × 4 = 80 and 100 × 4 = 400. They could then attempt larger numbers such as, 124 ÷ 8; 229 ÷ 9; 131 ÷ 7; 327 ÷ 8.

Lesson 1   Oral and mental starter 19

Main teaching activities

Whole-class work: Explain that multiplication and division are closely linked – one is the inverse or opposite of the other – and that they are now going to use the multiplication facts they know to help them divide numbers that are bigger than their known table facts. Ask: *What is 62 ÷ 4?* Encourage the children to estimate first: 4 × 10 is 40, too small. 4 × 20 is 80, too big. So we know the answer is between 10 and 20. Go on to demonstrate the 'chunking' method either by subtracting from the starting number or by adding the 'chunks' to make the target number:

$$
\begin{array}{rl}
62 \div 4 & \\
-\underline{40} & (10 \times 4) \\
22 & \\
-\underline{20} & (5 \times 4) \\
2 & \\
\end{array}
$$

Chunking using subtraction

- Write the division question: 62 ÷ 4.
- Find a known × fact (10 × 4).
- Subtract that 'chunk', leaving 22.
- Find the next nearest × fact to 22 (5 × 4).
- Subtract that, leaving a remainder of 2.
- Answer: 15 (lots of 4) remainder 2.

Chunking using addition

- Write the division question: 62 ÷ 4.
- Find a known × fact (10 × 4).
- This is the first 'chunk' toward making 62. There is 22 still to find.
- Find the next nearest × fact to 22 (5 × 4).
- Add 40 + 20 = 60 with remainder 2.
- Answer 15 (lots of 4) remainder 2.

Repeat using other examples, such as 78 ÷ 5 and 56 ÷ 3. Ask the children to show you their preferred version of this method.

Independent and paired work: The children can attempt more examples, such as 59 ÷ 3; 67 ÷ 4; 84 ÷ 5; 76 ÷ 5, individually in their books or on whiteboards, then discuss the results with a partner.

Progress check: Some children may not be able to grasp the concept of either subtracting or adding multiples or 'lots' of a number. It may help these children to jot down key multiplication facts at the side of their page to remind them that they are adding or subtracting groups. This can be easily demonstrated by using straws, ones and bundles of ten to subtract from the starting number or to build to make it.

Review

Check the children's understanding of the method by writing up one of the questions they have attempted on the board. For example, write 59 ÷ 3. Display the number cards 3, 0, 2, 9, 2, 7, 2, 1, 9, 2 close by. Explain that all of these numbers appear in the solution: the children have to decide where they fit and their appropriate place values, using the 'chunking' method of division. So a child might say: *The first chunk is 10 × 3 = 30, so I need the 3 and the zero. Take 30 away from 59 and I'm left with 29, so I need a 2 for the tens and a 9 for the ones. The next chunk is 9 × 3 = 27, so I need the 2 and the 7. Subtracting 27 from 29 leaves a remainder of 2, so the answer is 19 remainder 2.* Ask a volunteer to write up one of his or her calculations on the board, and to choose number cards for the rest of the class to place.

Curriculum objectives

- To multiply and divide numbers mentally drawing upon known facts.
- To divide numbers up to four-digits by a one-digit number using the formal written method of short division and interpret remainders appropriately for the context.

Success criteria

- I know that there is more than one method for dividing and I can select one to use formally to solve problems.

You will need

Equipment

Bundles of straws in tens plus individual straws

Differentiation

Less confident learners

These children may be more confident using additional chunking and could have the support of straws to assist them.

More confident learners

Once you have established that this group are confident using short division they could go on to extend their calculating using four- or five-digit numbers or decimals to divide.

Main teaching activities

Whole-class work: If you have a group who are confident with 'chunking' division, they may be ready to learn short division. Provide a number of examples and demonstrate both methods alongside one another. Talk them through each stage.

For example: 124 ÷ 3

$$\begin{array}{r} 0\ 4\ 1\ \ r1 \\ 3\overline{)1\ ^12\ 4} \end{array}$$

Explain that when doing short division, they should think of the numbers as separate digits: the 1 is worth 100, but can be treated as a single digit. Careful placing of the numbers will give the correct place value. In the example shown:

- *Divide, starting with the most significant digit (the 1 hundred). 1 ÷ 3 is impossible. Mark the place value with a zero.*
- *Move the 1 across to join the tens. Now you have 12 ÷ 3 = 4. Record the 4 in the tens place.*
- *Move across to divide the ones: 4 ÷ 3 = 1 remainder 1.*

Ask: *What is the most common error made in short division? Why can you not afford to forget any numbers that you could not divide? What is the value of the 1 in this calculation?*

Repeat using a number of examples. Explain that sometimes numbers are not precisely divisible and any unused digits are expressed as 'remainders'.

Independent work: Provide some division questions for the children to solve, for example, 369 ÷ 3; 246 ÷ 6; 482 ÷ 3; 304 ÷ 6; 288 ÷ 6. You may wish to guide the children into attempting short division if you believe them to be ready and for others to consolidate their 'chunking' strategy. They complete the questions set and check their work. Remind them that multiplication is the inverse of division, which can be used for checking answers.

Progress check: Ask the children to share their work so far with a partner using the same method as themselves. Ask them to check for the common errors such as, not 'carrying' the unused digits across to the next place value when using short division or errors with multiplying and with subtracting or adding when chunking.

Review

Check answers and ask: *Where do you think mistakes are most often made in each of these methods?* (for example, place value holding zero and placement of answer in short division) *What effect does this have on the answer? How can you quickly find the approximate size that the answer should be? What do you do first when estimating? Could you suggest any helpful tips for someone who is calculating using your chosen method?*

Curriculum objectives
● To multiply and divide numbers mentally drawing upon known facts.
● To divide numbers up to four-digits by a one-digit number using the formal written method of short division and interpret remainders appropriately for the context.

Success criteria
● I can use short division to divide a three-digit number by a one-digit number.

You will need
Equipment
Bundles of straws in tens plus individual straws

Differentiation
Less confident learners
There may be some children for whom short division is a step too far and if they are confident using chunking they should continue to do so.

More confident learners
These children should check their answers using column multiplication.

Lesson 3 — Oral and mental starter 25

Main teaching activities

Whole-class work: Explain that this lesson is to consolidate short division of 3-digits by 1-digit. Explain that they already know many 2-digit ÷ 1-digit facts from the times tables, but having a written method is useful for bigger numbers. Short division assumes that the child is confident with place value. Work through an example such as 128 ÷ 3.

$$\begin{array}{r} 0\ 4\ 8\ \ r2 \\ 3\overline{\smash{)}1\ ^{1}2\ 8} \end{array}$$

- Divide, starting with the most significant digit (the 1 hundred). 1 ÷ 3 is impossible. Mark the place value with a zero.
- Move the 1 across to join the tens. Now you have 12 ÷ 3 = 4. Record the 4 in the tens place.
- Move across to divide the ones: 8 ÷ 3 = 2 remainder 2.

Once the children have grasped this idea, move on to dividing into digits that leave a remainder to be 'transferred along'.

$$\begin{array}{r} 0\ 7\ 9\ \ r1 \\ 3\overline{\smash{)}2\ ^{2}3\ ^{2}8} \end{array}$$

- Divide, starting with the most significant digit (the 2 hundred). 2 ÷ 3 is impossible. Mark the place value with a zero.
- Move the 2 across to join the tens. Now you have 23 ÷ 3 = 7 remainder 2. Record the 7 in the tens place and transfer the 2 across to be divided with the ones number.
- Move across to divide the ones: 28 ÷ 3 = 9 remainder 1.

Emphasise that the remainders must be passed on to the next digit: they cannot be left behind or ignored. For example, discuss 172 ÷ 3. Ask: *What should I put in the hundreds column? If I cannot divide 1 by 3 using whole numbers, what shall I do with the 1 hundred I have not used? Where should I put it so it can be divided? What value have I got in the tens column now? Can I divide it by 3? How much is the remainder? Where shall I put the remainder so it can be divided? How many ones are there now to be divided by 3?*

Independent work: Provide some division questions for the children to solve using short division, for example, 265 ÷ 4; 163 ÷ 4; 257 ÷ 3; 264 ÷ 5; 288 ÷ 6.

Progress check: Since this is consolidation of work begun yesterday, some children may be very confident and others finding short division tricky. It might be helpful at this stage to pair up a less confident child with a confident partner,. Remind them that they are still using known times tables; the place holding zero will help them to put the digits in the correct place and carry unused digits across.

Review

Write this calculation on the board and work through it with the children, asking: *What should I record for the tens column? Why is it important to place the 0 there? What should I do with the 2 tens that have not yet been divided? How many ones are there now to be divided by 4?*

$$\begin{array}{r} 1\ 0\ 6\ \ r2 \\ 4\overline{\smash{)}4\ 2\ ^{2}6} \end{array}$$

Next, write up some examples with incorrect answers (three examples are shown below). Ask for individuals to explain where the calculations have gone wrong and why. Ask: *Is this correct? How do you know? How can we put it right? Think of some hints to stop other people making the same mistakes?* Design and display a 'Division health warning', using the children's suggestions.

$$\begin{array}{r} 0\ 1\ 1 \\ 5\overline{\smash{)}2\ 7\ 5} \end{array} \qquad \begin{array}{r} 1\ 0\ 1\ \ r3 \\ 6\overline{\smash{)}7\ 0\ 9} \end{array} \qquad \begin{array}{r} 1\ 1\ 8 \\ 4\overline{\smash{)}5\ 7\ 2} \end{array}$$

Curriculum objectives
- To multiply and divide numbers mentally drawing upon known facts.
- To divide numbers up to four-digits by a one-digit number using short division and interpret remainders appropriately for the context.

Success criteria
- I can understand division problems in context and solve them to give realistic answers.

You will need

Equipment
Bundles of straws in tens plus individual straws

Differentiation

Less confident learners
Some children may need prompting to suggest ideas and group work to contextualise the numbers. They could use straws to visualise the divisions.

More confident learners
Children may use larger and decimal numbers to suggest problems of their own.

Lesson 4 — Oral and mental starter 20

Main teaching activities

Whole-class work: Write up the following on the board: 372 ÷ 4; 927 ÷ 3; 8240 ÷ 5. Explain to the children that as well as being able to solve the divisions they also need to understand what the numbers might represent. Ask them to put words and a context to the numbers, for example, 372 ÷ 4 might represent a real-life problem such as: A farmer has 372 sheep. He needs to put them into 4 smaller fields. If he divides them equally, how many sheep will be in each field? Now ask the children for alternative suggestions for the same calculation. Repeat with the others including ones with remainders, for example 779 ÷ 4; 218 ÷ 5; 602 ÷ 3.

Paired work: Write up the following number sentences: 8240 ÷ 5; 927 ÷ 3; 218 ÷ 5; 602 ÷ 3; 779 ÷ 4; 7340 ÷ 9. Ask the children to work in pairs to write a word problem that will match the numbers and then find the answers using their preferred division method.

Progress check: Ensure that the children have understood the task by asking for some examples. Ask: *How do you explain any remainders in your answers?*

Review

Hear some examples and discuss how the context has to be taken into account. For example, a restaurant serving 122 people sitting in groups of 5 actually needs 25 tables, that is 24 groups of 5 and one table for the remainder, 2. They could not leave two people standing up!

Curriculum objectives
- To solve problems involving multiplication and division, including scaling and problems involving simple rates.

Success criteria
- I can solve word problems using a written calculation for division.

You will need

Photocopiable sheets
'Written division skills'

General resources
'Multiplication square'

Equipment
Bundles of straws in tens plus individual straws

Differentiation

Less confident learners
These children may continue to need the support of concrete equipment such as straws or a 'Multiplication square'.

More confident learners
Provide these children with more challenging numbers.

Lesson 5 — Oral and mental starter 25

Main teaching activities

Whole-class work: Explain to the children that they will be using pencil and paper methods to solve division word problems. Read the questions on photocopiable page 'Written division skills' from the CD-ROM together. Work through the example on the board with the children's help. Alternatively you may wish to use some of the questions that the children created yesterday for the rest of the class to solve.

Independent and paired work: Ask the children to complete the photocopiable page. When they have finished, they talk through their thinking with a partner, discussing how they deciphered the calculation and the calculating strategy they used. You can use this conversation to assess clarity of understanding.

Progress check: Use this time to work with individuals who still have difficulty decoding number sentences from word problems or are not secure with a written method of division. Ask for volunteers to tell you the number sentences they have created and which method of division they are using to solve them.

Review

Go through some of the questions and discuss the methods used. Ask children to explain which method they chose each time and why. Ask: *Is there someone who used a different method? How can you explain it?* Write up a calculation that has been solved incorrectly. Ask: *Where the error has occurred? Explain what he/she has done wrong?*

Fractions and decimals: tenths and hundredths

Expected prior learning

Children should be able to:

- understand simple fractions, such as ½ and ¼, as equal parts of a whole
- understand fractions as parts of a shape as well as part of a number.

Topic	Curriculum objectives	Expected outcomes
Fractions (including decimals and percentages)	**Lesson 1**	
	To compare and order fractions whose denominators are all multiples of the same number.	Find equivalent fractions [for example, $\frac{7}{10} = \frac{14}{20}$ or $\frac{19}{10} = 1\frac{9}{10}$].
	Lesson 2	
	To compare and order fractions whose denominators are all multiples of the same number.	Find equivalent fractions [for example, $\frac{7}{10} = \frac{14}{20}$ or $\frac{19}{10} = 1\frac{9}{10}$].
	Lesson 3	
	To compare and order fractions whose denominators are all multiples of the same number. To read and write decimal numbers as fractions [for example, $0.71 = \frac{71}{100}$].	Find equivalent fractions [for example, $\frac{7}{10} = \frac{14}{20}$ or $\frac{19}{10} = 1\frac{9}{10}$]. Relate fractions to their decimal representations.
	Lesson 4	
	To compare and order fractions whose denominators are all multiples of the same number. To read and write decimal numbers as fractions [for example, $0.71 = \frac{71}{100}$].	Find equivalent fractions [for example, $\frac{7}{10} = \frac{14}{20}$ or $\frac{19}{10} = 1\frac{9}{10}$]. Relate fractions to their decimal representations.
	Lesson 5	
	To compare and order fractions whose denominators are all multiples of the same number. To read and write decimal numbers as fractions [for example, $0.71 = \frac{71}{100}$].	Find equivalent fractions [for example, $\frac{7}{10} = \frac{14}{20}$ or $\frac{19}{10} = 1\frac{9}{10}$]. Relate fractions to their decimal representations.

Preparation

Lesson 1: make up to 4 cakes to demonstrate fractions (real if you like or cardboard replicas) and/or use commercially available plastic fraction sets; write the list of fractions for the individual activity on the board

Lesson 2: copy 'Fractions to order', one per child

Lesson 3: make the 'Fractions, decimals and percentages' cards, one set per pair but remove the percentages

Lesson 4: copy 'Decimal/ fraction families', one per child; make copies of 'Blank 100 square', one per pair if needed

Lesson 5: the children will need sets of blank cards to represent dominoes, approximately 20 cards per pair

You will need

Photocopiable sheets
'Fractions to order'; 'Decimal/ fraction families'

General resources
'Blank 100 square'; 'Fractions, decimals and percentages'

Equipment
Centimetre-squared paper; up to 4 cakes and/or commercially available plastic fraction sets; commercially available plastic fraction sets or home-made card equivalent; blank cards

Further practice

Check children's understanding of equivalent fraction by asking them to identify more equivalent fractions on the 'Decimal/ fraction families' sheet.

Oral and mental starters suggested for week 3

See bank of starters on pages 85 to 86. Oral and mental starters are also on the CD-ROM.

19 Double and halve

23 What's the question × 10

26 Pairs to make 1

Overview of progression

These lessons introduce fractions and the equivalent decimals in a fairly simple way, with some practical applications to help children understand the basic principles such as simple equivalents and ways in which fractions are related in 'multiple families'. Also the relationship of improper and mixed number fractions is explored, relating this to practical contexts. This knowledge is then used to order and compare fractions and then to develop the relationship further into an understanding of the way fractions can be expressed as equivalent decimals.

Watch out for

Some children may equate a decimal such as 0.2 with the fraction with the same digit as the denominator, ½, instead of equating it to $\frac{2}{10}$ or ⅕. Clarity about decimals being only powers of 10 which then may have fraction equivalents is important. The danger is to rush on too quickly.

Creative context

This work carries on neatly from division since sometimes when dividing a fraction or decimal fraction may be the result. Relating fractions of amounts to real-life experiences make fractions less daunting. For example, 10/20 for a spelling test would be understood by most children if you said *You got half of them correct!*

Vocabulary

cancel, decimal, decimal fraction, decimal place, decimal point, **denominator**, equivalent, fraction, hundredth, improper fraction, mixed number, **numerator**, proper fraction, tenth

Curriculum objectives

- To compare and order fractions whose denominators are all multiples of the same number.

Success criteria

- I can multiply and divide the numerator and denominator to make equivalent fractions.

You will need

Equipment

Centimetre-squared paper; up to 4 cakes and/or commercially available plastic fraction sets

Differentiation

Less confident learners

Ask the children to colour simple fractions up to one whole, for example: ¼; ½; ¾; 4/4; ⅕; ⅖; ⅗; ⅘; 5/5.

More confident learners

These children should be able to demonstrate multiple equivalent fractions such as:
3/2 = 1½ = 6/4 or
¾ = 6/8 = 12/16 or
1⅗ = 8/5 = 16/10.

Lesson 1

Oral and mental starter 19

Main teaching activities

Whole-class work: Write up the fraction ½. Explain that the top number is called the numerator (the number of pieces you have) and the bottom number is called the denominator (the total number of pieces there are). Hold up ⅔, ¾, ⅚ and so on, repeating the same language.

Ask what fraction has a numerator of 3 and a denominator of 5. Now ask how much you would be holding if you had 5/4. Show this using the cakes. Explain that this is called an improper fraction, because it is more than a whole. Demonstrate wholes such as 2/2 and 4/4. Explain that 5/4 is one whole cake and one quarter, so it can be written as 1¼ . This is called a mixed number, since it combines a whole number and a fraction.

Demonstrate several more examples of this such as 1⅔ , 1⅝, and 2¾. Ask the children to express these in terms of their denominators only and to explain how they determined the numerator. Repeat this in reverse changing 6/4, 7/3 and 9/2 into mixed number equivalents. Ask the children to create examples for others to find their equivalents, explaining their method each time.

Independent and paired work: Give each child a sheet of centimetre-squared paper. Write up the following fractions, which include improper fractions.

⅗; ½ ; ¼; ¾; 1/10; 3/10; ⅘; 6/5; 4/4; 9/4

Explain to the children that they need to draw shapes and shade and label the fractions you have written on the board on squared paper. When they have completed their fraction diagrams, they check them with their partner and then challenge each other to draw different fractions, including both improper fractions and mixed numbers.

Progress check: Ask a volunteer to come and demonstrate what 4/3 looks like by shading squares on the board. Ask the others to tell you another way to express this. Repeat with 7/5, 3/2 and 7/3. What about 8/4?

Review

Hold up 2/4 and ½ of a cake. Ask: *What do you notice?* (They are equivalent.) Ask them which fraction they would prefer. Now ask: *Would you rather have ½ or ⅓? 1/10 or ⅕? What helps you decide? If I cut one cake into ten pieces, what fraction would each piece be? If I cut it into five pieces, what fraction would each piece be? How do you know which fraction is bigger?* Invite the observation that the bigger the denominator, the smaller the fraction (if the numerator is the same). *If I divided this cake up so that everybody can have a piece, what fraction would each person get?* Share the cakes.

Curriculum objectives

- To compare and order fractions whose denominators are all multiples of the same number.

Success criteria

- I can recognise and order fractions whose denominators are all multiples of the same number.

You will need

Photocopiable sheets

'Fractions to order'

Equipment

Commercially available plastic fraction sets, or home-made card equivalent

Differentiation

Less confident learners

These children may benefit from using fraction sets to build the fractions given on photocopiable page 'Fractions to order' in order to compare them.

More confident learners

Once they have completed photocopiable page 'Fractions to order', challenge these children to suggest some other fractions that will fall between the fractions that they have already ordered.

Main teaching activities

Whole-class work: Demonstrate how the fractions have multiples of the original numbers, for example, $\frac{1}{3}$, $\frac{2}{6}$, $\frac{3}{9}$, and so on and so the numbers can be multiplied up or divided down but still equal the same amount.

For example, $\frac{2}{3}$ when multiplied by 2 becomes $\frac{4}{6}$. Demonstrate, using the fraction shapes, how this is actually the same amount expressed in a different fraction form. Repeat with several more examples such as: $\frac{3}{4}$ is the same amount as $\frac{6}{8}$ and $\frac{9}{12}$; $\frac{3}{5} = \frac{6}{10}$ or $\frac{21}{35}$; $\frac{80}{100} = \frac{40}{50} = \frac{8}{10} = \frac{4}{5}$.

Explain that when ordering fractions they need to be made into the same denominator so that they may be compared, for example 3/30; 5/10; 80/100; 3/5 can all be made into tenths by either multiplying or dividing. Remind the children that when multiplying they must apply the same rule to the denominator and the numerator, for example $\frac{3}{30} = \frac{1}{10}$ (divided by 3); 5/10; $\frac{80}{100} = \frac{8}{10}$ (divided by 10); $\frac{3}{5} = \frac{6}{10}$ (multiplied by 2). Then they may be ordered by size, $\frac{3}{30}$, $\frac{5}{10}$, $\frac{3}{5}$, $\frac{80}{100}$.

Paired work: Distribute photocopiable page 'Fractions to order' from the CD-ROM. Ask the children to work in pairs to reason about how to order the given sets of fractions, smallest first. The children should continue to order the sets. By listening to their reasoning you should be able to make observations about their understanding.

Progress check: Ask for one pair to tell you the order that they have placed the first set and why. Ask: *What information do I need to decide on the relative size of each fraction? Do I only compare the denominator or must I also look at the numerator? Are there any that are equivalents, that are exactly the same size?*

Review

Go through the answers with the children ensuring that they are clear about how to multiply and divide both top and bottom numbers in order to make common denominators. Ask the children to recap on what they have learnt about fractions so far. Make a list for displaying as a classroom reminder, for example:

- *The numerator at the top indicates the number of pieces; the denominator at the bottom indicates the number that a shape/cake/number is divided into.*
- *Fractions with a numerator of one with larger denominators are smaller amounts.*
- *Fractions with denominators that are multiples of each other may be multiplied up or divided down in order to compare their size.*

Curriculum objectives

- To compare and order fractions whose denominators are all multiples of the same number.
- To read and write decimal numbers as fractions [for example, 0.71 = $^{71}/_{100}$].

Success criteria

- I can relate fractions with denominators of tenths or hundredths to decimal fractions.

You will need

General resources

'Blank 100 square'; 'Fractions, decimals and percentages'

Differentiation

Less confident learners

Ask these children to match up only the 'tenths' fractions and decimals.

More confident learners

Ask the children to generate further fractions and their decimal equivalents, for example $^{1}/_{5}$, $^{2}/_{5}$, $^{4}/_{5}$, $^{20}/_{100}$.

Lesson 3

Oral and mental starter 23

Main teaching activities

Whole-class work: Talk about the word *equivalent*, meaning the 'same value as' just as they demonstrated last lesson. Give an example, such as ¾ and ½. Look at $^{70}/_{100}$. Explain that this number could be simplified by dividing both the numerator and the denominator by 10 to make them smaller. The total amount stays the same. So $^{70}/_{100}$ is equivalent to $^{7}/_{10}$. Use the 'Blank 100 square' to demonstrate: colour in 70 squares, then overshade seven lots of ten. You use the same number of squares.

Write $^{30}/_{100}$ and $^{90}/_{100}$ on the board and invite simplification to equivalent fractions ($^{3}/_{10}$ and $^{9}/_{10}$) demonstrating their equivalence. Tell them that there is yet another way of writing this and it is as a decimal fraction.

Explain that in a decimal everything has to be written as tenths or hundredths, though fractions can have any numbers. Relate decimal fractions to money, for example £0.50 is 50p or 5 lots of 10p (10p = $^{1}/_{10}$th of £1) and £0.05 is 5p or 5 lots of 1p (1p = $^{1}/_{100}$th of £1).

Paired work: Remove the percentage cards from the 'Fractions, decimals and percentages' cards and give a set to each pair. Ask the children to look at each fraction, use multiplication and division skills to convert them to either tenths or hundredths if necessary to discover the equivalent decimal, then arrange their cards in pairs on the table. When they have finished, they could check their answers using a calculator, for example, for ¼, key in 1 divided by 4 to get the answer 0.25.

Progress check: Ask the children to tell you the fraction equivalent of 0.2. Is there more than one answer? Can they simplify $^{2}/_{10}$ to a fraction with a smaller denominator?

Review

Compare the children's sets of paired cards. Ask each pair of children to hold up the fraction and decimal cards representing one half. Ask: *We know ½ = 0.5 and ¼ = 0.25. What do you think ¾ is? How can we work it out? How many lots of 0.25 do we need? Count together in 0.25s: 0.25, 0.50, 0.75, … What comes next? What fraction is 1 equivalent to?* Play 'Fraction Snap': call out a fraction or decimal and the children hold up the equivalent card. Alternatively, split the class into two teams: one team holds up fraction cards, the other team holds up decimal cards. Call out fractions and decimals alternately.

Curriculum objectives

● To compare and order fractions whose denominators are all multiples of the same number.
● To read and write decimal numbers as fractions.

Success criteria

● I can use my knowledge of equivalent fractions to work out decimal fraction equivalents.

You will need

Photocopiable sheets

'Decimal/fraction families'

General resources

'Blank 100 square'

Differentiation

Less confident learners

Children should complete only the tenths and hundredths to begin with; a blank 100 square will help children visualise these.

More confident learners

Once they have completed the chart ask these children how they would write an equivalent for 0.31 or 0.78.

Lesson 4 — Oral and mental starter 19

Main teaching activities

Whole-class work: Distribute photocopiable page 'Decimal/fraction families' from the CD-ROM. Tell the children you want them to complete the chart with the tenth and hundredth equivalents and to write at least three more equivalent fractions. Ask them how they think they will do this. Will they always be multiplying? What must they remember when they are multiplying up or dividing down fractions? (They must apply the multiple to both numerator and denominator.)

Paired work: The children work in pairs to complete the chart.

Progress check: Ask the children what fractions they have used for the family for 0.2. Check that their multiplying is correct.

Review

After ensuring that the children have completed the chart correctly ask them to consider 0.02. Ask: *How would you write this? Why is there no tenth equivalent? What is the common fraction that is the equivalent? How do you know? What did you have to do?*

Curriculum objectives

● To compare and order fractions whose denominators are all multiples of the same number.
● To read and write decimal numbers as fractions.

Success criteria

● I can match a decimal with equivalent fractions.

You will need

Equipment

Blank cards in the shape of dominoes

Differentiation

Less confident learners

These children will need to work with supervision and should use only tenth and hundredth equivalents.

More confident learners

These children should be encouraged to use more unusual equivalent fractions from their fraction families.

Lesson 5 — Oral and mental starter 26

Main teaching activities

Whole-class work: Explain to the children that they are going to use their knowledge of fraction and decimal equivalents to make and play a dominoes matching game. Demonstrate how dominoes have two numbers on them, one at either end of the card. These form a long trail or line with each number matching or being equivalent to the number on the next domino. To make this successfully they should start with their cards laid end to end across the table. Encourage them to use their chart from yesterday to make a domino trail of cards with a fraction at one end and a decimal at the other. The equivalent will be on the next touching domino.

Paired work: The children work in pairs to create the domino equivalents chain. After testing, they swap their game with another pair and attempt to play it. Shuffle the cards first and share them out equally. Look at them all. Take it in turns to place a domino in the chain. The ends of touching dominoes must be equivalent. In the event of not having a match the player misses a go. The winner is the person who lays down all their cards first.

Progress check: The danger here is that they put the decimal and its equivalent fraction on the same domino and so none of the dominoes will match when they play! Ensure that they test their game.

Review

Hold up a domino which has an unusual multiple fraction on it. Ask the children if they can work out its decimal pair. Ask: *How did you know? Can anyone tell me the fraction for 0.25 or 0.75? What knowledge did you have to use?*

Decimals: tenths, hundredths, thousandths

Expected prior learning

Children should be able to:

- understand simple fractions and their decimal equivalent to one or two decimal places
- understand place value.

Topic	Curriculum objectives	Expected outcomes
Fractions (including decimals and percentages)	**Lesson 1**	
	To read and write decimal numbers as fractions [for example, $0.71 = ^{71}/_{100}$].	Relate fractions to their decimal representations, including thousandths.
	Lesson 2	
	To read, write, order and compare numbers with up to three decimal places.	Explain what each digit represents in decimals with up to three places, and partition, round and order these numbers.
	Lesson 3	
	To round decimals with two decimal places to the nearest whole numbers and to one decimal place.	Round and order decimals with two decimal places.
	Lesson 4	
	To recognise and use thousandths and relate them to tenths, hundredths and decimals equivalents.	Use knowledge of place value and addition and subtraction of two-digit numbers to derive sums and differences and doubles and halves of decimals (for example, 6.5 ± 2.7, half of 5.6, double 0.34).
	Lesson 5	
	To solve problems involving number up to three decimal places.	Use knowledge of place value and addition and subtraction of two-digit numbers to derive sums and differences and doubles and halves of decimals (for example, 6.5 ± 2.7, half of 5.6, double 0.34).

Preparation

Lesson 1: laminate copies of 'Number lines', one per pair, so the children can write on and wipe off markings

Lesson 2: copy 'The rounding table', one per child

Lesson 3: write the egg problem on the board; copy 'Ordering problems', one per child

Lesson 5: copy 'Round up and calculate', one per child

You will need

Photocopiable sheets

'The rounding table'; 'Ordering problems'; 'Round up and calculate'

General resources

'Number lines'; 'Place value table'; '0–30 number cards'; 'Symbol cards'

Equipment

Blank playing cards, a set of at least 36 per group of four

Further practice

Use the interactive activity 'Decimal ordering' to practice ordering numbers with up to two decimal places.

Oral and mental starters suggested for week 4

See bank of starters on pages 85 to 86. Oral and mental starters are also on the CD-ROM.

18 Multiplication sort

20 Counting round the room

24 What's the question – decimals?

30 Round it up!

Overview of progression

During these lessons the children extend their knowledge of decimal fractions to include thousandths. They have opportunities to relate these to real-life problems where they need to round decimals to estimate and to solve problems.

> ### Watch out for
> Some children may still be insecure in their place value knowledge.

Creative context

Some children struggle to comprehend the size and value of decimal numbers, particularly when using thousandths. It is helpful to relate the work on decimals to that which puts these numbers into context, for example, measures. In this way links may be made across the curriculum to geography (distances) and art and design (quantities).

Vocabulary

decimal fraction, decimal place, decimal point, hundredth, tenth, thousandth

Curriculum objectives
- To read and write decimal numbers as fractions [for example, $0.71 = \frac{71}{100}$].

Success criteria
- I can relate fractions to their decimal equivalents up to three decimal places.

You will need

General resources
'Number lines'

Equipment
Blank playing cards, a set of at least 36 per group of four; pens

Differentiation

Less confident learners
These children might need adult support to work through the pairs more slowly, simply looking for matching pairs and explaining why each one is an equivalent.

More confident learners
These children should aim for speed and accuracy.

Lesson 1
Oral and mental starter 18

Main teaching activities

Whole-class work: Write $\frac{7}{10}$ on the board. Ask the children: *What does this mean? Is it more or less than 1? How would I write it as a decimal?* (0.7) Now write $\frac{7}{100}$. *How would I write this as a decimal?* (0.70 or 0.7) Point out that $\frac{7}{10}$ and $\frac{70}{100}$ are equivalent. Explain this by saying: *I have two identical cakes. I cut one into 10 pieces and the other into 100 pieces. Which would you rather have: 7 of the 10 pieces or 70 of the 100 pieces?* (They are the same amount.) Demonstrate that the fraction with the larger numbers can be divided by 10 to simplify it: $\frac{70}{100} = 7/10 = 0.7$.

Now ask: *How would you write $\frac{7}{1000}$ as a decimal?* (0.007) That is, one whole divided into 1000 pieces and you have 7 of them. Explain the place value notation of this, for example, 1000s 100s 10s 1s . 0.1s 0.01 0.001s.

Recap by reminding the children that the size of a fraction is determined by two things:
- how many pieces a whole (number, cake, and so on) is divided into (the denominator);
- how many of the pieces you are given (the numerator).

Paired work: Distribute a set of at least 36 blank playing cards to each group of four children. Ask them to work in pairs to produce a set of equivalent decimal and fraction playing cards, for example if one person writes $\frac{31}{100}$ on one card then their partner writes the equivalent decimal, 0.31, on another. They should use numbers with up to three decimal places. When they have completed and checked their cards, ask the children to stay in their groups of four, but to shuffle their cards well and to pass them to another group. The children should then play a game of 'Snap' aiming to find the equivalent pairs. The winner is the person who spots the most pairs.

Progress check: Ensure that the children have accurately paired up their fraction and decimal equivalents and that the place value is correct. Ask for children to hold up one of a pair of cards and the others should tell them the equivalent. Make sure they hold up a variety of fraction cards as well as decimal cards in order to check that the children are fluent in converting from one to another.

Review

Ask the children to use their knowledge of hundredths and thousandths to write the fraction equivalents of the following decimals on their whiteboards:

0.7,   0.4,   0.6,   0.65,   0.25,   0.006,   0.056,   0.156.

Then ask: *Which of those decimals cannot be represented as tenths?* (The ones not divisible by 10.) Demonstrate this on the board, for example, $\frac{70}{100} = 7/10$ but $\frac{65}{100}$ or $\frac{156}{1000}$ do not have a tenths equivalent, but do have a hundredths or thousandths equivalent of:

Curriculum objectives
● To read, write, order and compare numbers with up to three decimal places.

Success criteria
● I can explain what each digit represents in decimals and round these numbers.

You will need
Photocopiable sheets
'The rounding table'

Differentiation

Less confident learners
Some children may need to gain confidence with rounding only hundredths to tenths, with additional support using a number line. Provide numbers with only two decimal places.

More confident learners
On accurate completion of the table, ask these children to find three numbers with three decimal places which will round to 4. Challenge them to find the largest possible number and the smallest possible number with three decimal places that will do this.

Lesson 2

Oral and mental starter 20

Main teaching activities

Whole-class work: Write the number 1.836 on the board. Ask the children to tell you what each digit represents. (1 whole, 8 tenths, 3 hundredths and 6 thousandths or 1 and $^{836}/_{1000}$) Ask them to think of an occasion when they might see such a number written and what might it represent (for example, 1.836kg or 1 kg and 836g or litres or kilometres). Explain that thinking of real-life applications helps to see how they might be used.

Draw a number line from 1 to 2 and mark the centre 1.5. Tell the children that you want to place 1.836 on the number line. Ask: *Is 1.836 bigger or smaller than 1.5?* (Bigger) *How can you tell?* (Because 8 tenths is bigger than 5 tenths) *So should I put 1.836 closer to 1 or closer to 2?* Place 1.836 on the number line and say: *So 1.836 is closer to 2 on the number line so 1.836 rounded to the nearest whole number is 2.*

Erase 1.836. Divide and label the number line into tenths. Ask: *Which two numbers does 1.836 come between?* (1.8 and 1.9) *What number is halfway between 1.8 and 1.9?* (1.85) Continue asking questions to establish that 1.836 rounded to the nearest tenth is 1.8.

Erase 1.836. Divide and label the number line between 1.8 and 1.9 into hundredths. Indicate this section of the line and ask questions to establish that 1.836 rounded to the nearest hundredth is 1.84.

Paired work: Distribute photocopiable page 'The rounding table' from the CD-ROM. Ask the children to work in pairs to round these and write them in the table. When they have rounded the numbers given, ask them to generate some numbers to round themselves.

Progress check: Check the children understand that they should only be looking at the next most significant digit. Ask: *How would I round 1.836 to the nearest tenth in one step?* (Look at the digit in the hundredths place to see if it is bigger or smaller than 5 hundredths.) Ensure accurate rounding and place value especially where some digits are zero. Ask: *How would I round 3.002 to the nearest hundredth or tenth?*

Review

Ask the children to share their answers with you, each time explaining what decisions they made in order to round. Correct misconceptions. Ask: *Tell me a decimal number that will round to 3.7 or 1. Do all numbers round up?*

Curriculum objectives

● To round decimals with two decimal places to the nearest whole number and to one decimal place.

Success criteria

● I can round decimal numbers with two decimal places.

You will need

Photocopiable sheets

'Ordering problems'

General resources

'Number lines'

Differentiation

Less confident learners

These children may need support to read and interpret the instructions and to round and order. They could use photocopiable page 'Number lines' to help them round correctly.

More confident learners

Challenge these children to make up a similar problem of their own for a partner to solve.

Lesson 3   Oral and mental starter 24

Main teaching activities

Whole-class work: Explain to the children that they are now to apply their rounding of decimal numbers to real-life examples to order decimals to solve problems. Ask the children to look at the problem on the board.

Anna is making a cake. She has six eggs but they are all of varying size. She knows that she needs to use two eggs that together weigh the closest to 50g for her cake to be successful. Which two eggs should she use?

Egg A: 0.028kg   Egg B: 0.027kg   Egg C: 0.024kg
Egg D: 0.025kg   Egg E: 0.026kg   Egg F: 0.03kg

Talk through the process that children must go through to solve this problem. They might order by size first and then look for combinations to make 50g or 0.05kg.

Independent and paired work: Distribute photocopiable page 'Ordering problems' from the CD-ROM and ask the children to work through solving the problems using their skills of rounding, estimating and ordering. You may decide that it would be beneficial for some children to work in pairs so that you can listen to their reasoning. Continue to complete the work and compare answers, checking for accuracy and correcting errors.

Progress check: Ask some children to explain to you their ways of working in order to solve the problems to ensure that they are interpreting the questions correctly. Remind them that many of the questions have two parts to them in order to find an answer.

Review

Ask the children to order these numbers, from smallest to largest:

0.93; $\frac{1}{1000}$; $\frac{1}{10}$;   0.002; 0.09;   0.01

As each number is placed ask the children to explain their reasoning. Ask: *How will you decide which is the smallest number? What must you do first? Are there any numbers that stand out as easy to place? Why?*

Curriculum objectives
● To recognise and use thousandths and relate them to tenths, hundredths and decimals equivalents.
Success criteria
● I can calculate using decimals and my known number facts.

You will need
General resources
'Place value table'; '0–30 number cards'; decimal point from 'Symbol cards'

Differentiation
Less confident learners
These children should use numbers with one or two decimal places to build their confidence. Use the 'Place value table' and its associated digits to scaffold accurate place value.

More confident learners
These children could extend their thinking by using four-digits to create numbers to add and subtract as well as double and halve, using many different place values for each digit.

Curriculum objectives
● To solve problems involving number up to three decimal places.
Success criteria
● I can use rounding, estimating and calculating to solve problems involving number up to three decimal places.

You will need
Photocopiable sheets
'Round up and calculate'

Differentiation
Less confident learners
This group may need extra support to access and manage the information.

More confident learners
An extension task could be to research other sources of comparisons that use numbers with three or more decimal places.

Lesson 4 — Oral and mental starter 30

Main teaching activities

Whole-class work: Ask some quick-fire doubling and halving facts using two- and three-digit numbers, for example: *double 35; halve 72*. Differentiate for different groups. Explain that you are going to repeat with the same digits but in decimal numbers so the digits although the same, will have a different place value. Ask: *double 3.5; double 0.35, halve 7.2; halve 0.72*, and so on. Ask the children to suggest a strategy for ensuring the correct place value. Demonstrate using the 'Place value table' from the CD-ROM that the process is the same as with whole numbers. Aligning the decimal point will assist them to keep the place value accurate. Rounding and estimating first will also help. Take, for example, double 2.3. Rounding gives 2 + 2 so an estimate gives an answer in the region of 4.

Paired work: Distribute number cards 0–9 and decimal point cards from the 'Symbol cards' set. Ask the children to generate numbers with up to three decimal places to double and halve. They should round and estimate the approximate answer first and then go on to calculate. They should be able to do these mentally or with informal jottings.

Progress check: Ensure that children are rounding and estimating first and that their answer compares favourably in size with their estimate. Then ask: *What is double 3.6? Why is 6.12 incorrect? Is 0.12 bigger or smaller than 0.6? Would you expect a smaller number when you double? What about double 0.36 or double 0.036.*

Review

Ask: *What is half of 7.1? (3.55) How did you do this? Who partitioned the number? What about half of 0.71? (0.355)* Remind them that rounding and estimating will give them a guide to the size of number that they are looking for. Repeat with half of 9.5 or 3.7. Encourage the children to take you through their thinking step by step.

Lesson 5 — Oral and mental starter

Main teaching activities

Whole-class work: Explain that this lesson is an opportunity to bring together all the work done over the week. Revisit and revise equivalent fractions and decimals including thousandths; rounding and ordering decimal numbers; estimating and calculating using decimals.

Independent and paired work: Distribute photocopiable page 'Round up and calculate' from the CD-ROM. Decide whether children should work individually or in pairs as a 'talk partner'. Children should complete the table and use information in the table to answer the questions.

Progress check: Use this activity to check the understanding of groups and individuals and correct misconceptions.

Review

Share the results of the activity. Correct errors as they occur.

2D and 3D shapes

Expected prior learning

Children should be able to:

- tell you some of the properties of triangles
- use some of the vocabulary of shape, for example, sides, vertices, angles, and so on
- use a ruler accurately to draw straight lines.

Topic	Curriculum objectives	Expected outcomes
Geometry: properties of shapes	**Lesson 1**	
	To distinguish between regular and irregular polygons based on reasoning about equal sides and angles.	Identify, visualise and describe properties of rectangles, triangles, regular polygons. Draw and measure lines to the nearest millimetre.
	Lesson 2	
	To use the properties of rectangles (including squares) to deduce related facts and find missing lengths and angles.	Identify, visualise and describe properties of rectangles, triangles, regular polygons. Draw and measure lines to the nearest millimetre.
	Lesson 3	
	To distinguish between regular and irregular polygons based on reasoning about equal sides and angles.	Use knowledge of properties to draw 2D shapes. Use a ruler to draw shapes with perpendicular or parallel sides.
	Lesson 4	
	To distinguish between regular and irregular polygons based on reasoning about equal sides and angles.	Use knowledge of properties to draw 2D shapes. Use a ruler to draw shapes with perpendicular or parallel sides.
	Lesson 5	
	To identify 3D shapes, including cubes and other cuboids, from 2D representations.	Use knowledge of properties to identify and draw nets of 3D shapes.

Preparation

Lesson 1: draw an equilateral triangle, an isosceles triangle, a scalene triangle and a right-angled triangle on the board or use triangles from 'Shapes'; copy the triangles from 'Shapes' onto card, to demonstrate and one per child if needed; make copies of 'Isometric dotty paper', several per child

Lesson 2: copy the rectangles from 'Shapes' onto card, to demonstrate and one per child if needed

Lesson 3: copy the equilateral triangle, a square and the other regular polygons from 'Shapes' onto card, to demonstrate and one per child

Lesson 4: copy 'Shapes' onto card, to demonstrate and one per child

Lesson 5: copy of one of the squares from 'Shapes' onto card six per child if needed

You will need

General resources

'Isometric dotty paper'; 'Shapes'

Equipment

Rulers; protractors; scissors; glue; mirrors; Clixi or Polydron; squared paper; square templates

Further practice

Give children further experience of drawing shapes using given dimensions and angles. Provide 'Isometric dotty paper' for this purpose if necessary.

Oral and mental starters suggested for week 5

See bank of starters on page 86. Oral and mental starters are also on the CD-ROM.

25 Factor pairs

28 Fractions of numbers

29 Decimals and fractions

Overview of progression

This week the lessons briefly revisit the work on triangles and extend to the investigation of rectangles, squares (as special rectangles) and regular and irregular polygons, ending with a first look at 2D representations of nets of cubes. There is a particular emphasis on vocabulary of shape and symmetry (for example: acute, obtuse, isosceles, parallel, lines of symmetry, and so on) as children are encouraged to explore patterns and relationships between shapes and to make generalisations and predictions.

Watch out for

It is easy to accept incorrect descriptions which then become embedded and are hard to correct. Insist on correct use of the vocabulary. Accuracy of measurement both of lengths and angles is important for the drawing of shapes.

Creative context

The mathematical understanding of shape has many applications across the curriculum in areas such as art (mosaics and art styles such as Cubism), religious education (significant patterns and decorations in world faiths) and design and technology.

Vocabulary

2D, acute, angle, **bisect**, degrees (°), diagonals, equilateral triangle, **intersect**, irregular, isosceles triangle, kite, names of shapes, obtuse, parallel, parallelogram, perpendicular, polygon, protractor, quadrilateral, rectangle, regular, rhombus, right-angled triangle, scalene triangle, side, square, symmetry, two-dimensional

Curriculum objectives
● To distinguish between regular and irregular polygons based on reasoning about equal sides and angles.

Success criteria
● I can describe, accurately draw and sort triangles by definition.

You will need

General resources
'Isometric dotty paper'; the triangles from 'Shapes'

Equipment
Rulers; protractors; scissors; glue

Differentiation

Less confident learners
These children may need support with reading the scales on rulers and protractors. Alternatively, they could measure the sides and angles of the triangles from photocopiable page 'Shapes'.

More confident learners
These children should be able to produce more triangles of a higher quality of accuracy and drawing.

Lesson 1   Oral and mental starter 25

Main teaching activities

Whole-class work: Explain to the children that this lesson is for them to revise their knowledge of triangles. Display the triangles from photocopiable page 'Shapes'. Tell the children that you want them to think of definitions that will separate the triangles. They will have to consider the angles (acute, obtuse or right angle), length of sides (equal or not) and lines of symmetry (whether the halves would match exactly if we folded the triangle in half). Ask for observations and record appropriate ones on the board:

- Equilateral triangle: three sides of equal length; three equal angles, always acute; three lines of symmetry
- Isosceles triangle: two sides of equal length, one of a different length; two equal angles (acute) and one different (can be acute or obtuse); 1 line of symmetry
- Scalene triangle: three sides of different lengths; three different angles (one may be obtuse), no lines of symmetry
- Right-angled triangle: can be either isosceles or scalene; one right angle; can have one line of symmetry.

Paired work: Ask the children to copy the definitions they have just created onto a sheet of paper under the headings: 'Equilateral triangle'; 'Isosceles triangle', 'Scalene triangle' and 'Right-angled triangle'. Then, on a separate piece of paper, they should draw two examples of each triangle. They should exchange these with someone else and cut them out. They then measure the triangles carefully with a ruler and a protractor (you may need to revise the use of the protractor) and stick them under the correct heading. They create an accurate record of the different types of triangle for future reference.

Progress check: Listen for accurate use of the correct vocabulary and correct as needed. Also use this session to model accurate use of a ruler and a protractor.

Review

Ask: *Why can't a right-angled triangle also be an equilateral triangle?* (Three equal angles of 90° wouldn't make a triangle.) *An equilateral triangle is a regular shape, the rest are not. Give a definition for a regular shape?* Ask the children, in groups, to look around the room for right angles and angles that are greater than or less than a right angle. They should note these on their whiteboards. Invite feedback. Ask: *What do you notice about the angles in buildings? Which angle did you observe most frequently? Why was that?*

Curriculum objectives
● To state and use the properties of rectangles to deduce related facts.

Success criteria
● I can describe, accurately draw and classify rectangles.

You will need

General resources
'Shapes'

Equipment
Rulers; protractors

Differentiation

Less confident learners
These children can draw around rectangles and label them.

More confident learners
These children can explain why a square is a special type of rectangle. (Equal sides/four lines of symmetry.)

Lesson 2 — Oral and mental starter 28

Main teaching activities

Whole-class work: Show the children the selection of rectangles from photocopiable page 'Shapes' from the CD-ROM, excluding the squares to begin with. Ask them to define a rectangle in terms of sides, angles, diagonals and symmetry. Take suggestions from the class and write up a class definition. This should state that a rectangle must have: two pairs of parallel sides with each parallel pair the same length; four right angles; diagonals that bisect each other; two lines of symmetry.

Independent work: Ask the children to copy the definition of a rectangle, then draw examples of different rectangles and label their features.

Progress check: Ensure that the children are familiar with the vocabulary. Model how to indicate parallel lines.

Review

Explain that any four-sided shape is a quadrilateral. However not all of the same rules apply as they do to a rectangle. Draw a square. Ask the children to apply the rules for rectangles to this and identify the difference (more lines of symmetry since it is a regular shape). Draw other quadrilaterals such as a kite.

Curriculum objectives
● To distinguish between regular and irregular polygons based on reasoning about equal sides and angles.

Success criteria
● I can identify regular polygons and make observations and generalisations about their properties.

You will need

General resources
'Shapes'

Equipment
Mirrors

Differentiation

Less confident learners
These children could fold regular card shapes to find the lines of symmetry. These could be stuck down for recording purposes.

More confident learners
These children should investigate patterns in lines of symmetry of regular polygons. Is there a relationship they could spot and predict for other many-sided polygons? They might also investigate non-regular polygons.

Lesson 3 — Oral and mental starter 29

Main teaching activities

Whole-class work: Establish what is meant by 'reflective symmetry'. Using card or paper cut-outs of shapes from photocopiable page 'Shapes' from the CD-ROM, demonstrate by folding the shapes along the lines of symmetry. Ask: *How many lines of symmetry has an equilateral triangle?* (3) *What about a square?* (4) *Why does a square have diagonal lines of symmetry when a rectangle does not?* (A square is a regular shape. A rectangle has two longer sides so is not a regular shape.) Demonstrate how lines of symmetry can be checked using a mirror or tracing paper. Remind the children that a reflected shape 'flips' over on the opposite side of a mirror line.

Independent work: Ask the children to investigate the lines of reflective symmetry of a variety of polygons. They could draw around the shapes and then find the lines of symmetry using a mirror. As they continue the investigation, ask if they can see a pattern emerging.

Progress check: Hold up shapes that are not rectangles. Ask the children to tell you if they have lines of symmetry to test their understanding.

Review

Regular shape	Number of sides	Lines of symmetry
Equilateral triangle	3	3

Begin a results table on the board or on a large sheet of paper for display purposes. Ask: *Who can spot a pattern? Who can predict how many lines of symmetry a 20-sided regular polygon might have? Is the same true for irregular polygons? Do irregular polygons have lines of reflective symmetry?*

Curriculum objectives
● To distinguish between regular and irregular polygons based on reasoning about equal sides and angles.

Success criteria
● I can investigate properties of 2D shapes and make observations and generalisations.

You will need
Equipment
Mirrors

Differentiation
Less confident learners
These children should continue the investigation from yesterday.

More confident learners
These children should begin the new investigation about irregular polygons.

Lesson 4

Oral and mental starter 29

Main teaching activities

Whole-class work: Continuing from lesson 3, explain to the children that we suspect that there may be a relationship between the number of sides and the number of lines of symmetry but it is unlikely that enough samples were tested in one lesson. Divide the class into two groups. Ask one group to continue the investigation, encouraging them to 'fill the gaps' in the recording table from lesson 3. Ask questions such as: *Do all triangles or shapes with one right angle have the same number of lines of symmetry?* The second group should answer the question: *What about irregular polygons?* Can the children create a separate table to record their observations about irregular polygons? What sort of information will they record (number of sides, type of angles, number of right angles, lines of symmetry, and so on).

Paired work: Group one continue the investigation from the previous lesson. Group two create a recording grid for irregular polygons. Tell the groups to be prepared to report back to the other half of the class.

Progress check: Ask: *Have any patterns emerged? What observations have you made?*

Review

Groups report back to the class, explaining their thinking. Ask: *Did you notice any other patterns – for example, in triangles or in all shapes with one right angle?* Distribute strips of paper to the groups of children and ask them to write a statement about their observations. Display these statements with the recording chart.

Curriculum objectives
● To identify 3D shapes, including cubes and other cuboids, from 2D representations.

Success criteria
● I can visualise, draw and make nets of a closed cube.

You will need
Equipment
Clixi or Polydron; squared paper; rulers; square templates

Differentiation
Less confident learners
Support these children's drawing and decision making. Discuss how rotated or inverted shapes are still the same shapes. Provide square templates to assist drawing.

More confident learners
Ask these children to record the nets of successful open cubes and 'failed' nets that do not form a closed cube. Ask them to explain, in the latter cases, why the shape would be incomplete.

Lesson 5

Oral and mental starter 25

Main teaching activities

Whole-class work: Demonstrate what a cube looks like using Clixi or Polydron. Revise how many faces (6), vertices (8) and edges (12) it has. Open up the net of the cube. Explain that a net is the flat 2D shape made when a 3D shape is opened up. Ask: *Is this the only possible net? Visualise what another net of this cube might look like. Try to draw it.* Ask a volunteer to draw his or her visualisation on the board. Ask another child to build the net and fold it into a 3D shape to check whether it creates a cube. Discuss possible rotations of this net. Repeat with other nets suggested by children.

Paired work: Ask the children to investigate and draw a variety of different nets to make a closed cube, using Clixi to help. How many different ones can they find? (There are 11, surprisingly.) Warn the children that some nets are just rotations of others. Most children should be able to find and draw eight to ten different nets.

Progress check: Display some suggested nets. Explore the possible rotations or reflections that are repeats of the same net. Ask: *Has anyone a systematic strategy for finding these nets?*

Review

Use Clixi or Polydron to create and display the nets of a cuboid, a triangular prism and a square-based pyramid. Ask the children to identify the solid shapes from their nets. Ask: *Are there any other ways of making nets for these shapes? Visualise and draw what the other nets might look like?*

Statistics: tables and bar charts

Expected prior learning

Children should be able to:

- create pictograms and simple block and bar charts
- gather information to represent pictorially.

Topic	Curriculum objectives	Expected outcomes
Statistics	**Lesson 1**	
	To complete, read and interpret information in tables, including timetables.	Plan and pursue an enquiry; present evidence by collecting, organising and interpreting information; suggest extensions to the enquiry.
		Extend mental methods for whole-number calculations, for example subtract one near-multiple of 1000 from another.
	Lesson 2	
	To complete, read and interpret information in tables, including timetables.	Plan and pursue an enquiry; present evidence by collecting, organising and interpreting information; suggest extensions to the enquiry.
		Extend mental methods for whole-number calculations, for example subtract one near-multiple of 1000 from another.
	Lesson 3	
	To complete, read and interpret information in tables, including timetables.	Plan and pursue an enquiry; present evidence by collecting, organising and interpreting information; suggest extensions to the enquiry.
		Extend mental methods for whole-number calculations, for example subtract one near-multiple of 1000 from another.
	Lesson 4	
	To complete, read and interpret information in tables, including timetables.	Plan and pursue an enquiry; present evidence by collecting, organising and interpreting information; suggest extensions to the enquiry.
		Extend mental methods for whole-number calculations, for example subtract one near-multiple of 1000 from another.
	Lesson 5	
	To complete, read and interpret information in tables, including timetables.	Plan and pursue an enquiry; present evidence by collecting, organising and interpreting information; suggest extensions to the enquiry.
		Extend mental methods for whole-number calculations, for example subtract one near-multiple of 1000 from another.

Preparation

Lesson 1: copy 'Doubles in a minute (1) and (2)', one per child

Lesson 3: copy 'Lazy Larry's ice creams (1)', one per child

You will need

Photocopiable sheets

'Doubles in a minute (1) and (2)'; 'Lazy Larry's ice creams (1) and (2)'

General resources

'0–30 number cards'; interactive teaching resource 'Graphing tool'

Equipment

Interlocking cubes; individual whiteboards; Microsoft Excel® or 'Numberbox 2' (Black Cat software); squared paper

Further practice

Encourage the children to look for and collect examples of bar charts used in newspapers, magazines and leaflets. Encourage them to read and interpret the information given and to pose questions to interrogate the data.

Oral and mental starters suggested for week 6

See bank of starters on pages 85 to 86. Oral and mental starters are also on the CD-ROM.

19 Double and halve

23 What's the question ×10?

30 Round it up!

Overview of progression

As well as being a quick visual reference, children are taught that the 'picture' can be manipulated by changing scales. Once they are secure in representing their own data accurately they can go on to critically question the actual data from the "first impression" visual picture and then manipulate their own scales to represent a very different image to persuade the reader.

Watch out for

Some children may find setting and using values on a scale difficult since their charts will be inaccurate. Also be aware that sometimes commercially produced charts sometimes count the space in between the lines as a value (as in a block graph) but bar charts should place values on the line for the y-axis. Bar line graphs (also known as stick graphs or vertical line graphs) simply use a line with or without a cross or dot at the top instead of solid 'bars'.

Creative context

Graphs and charts are used for all manner of information representations and in projects for history or geography or even for children to chart their own progress (see lesson 1).

Vocabulary

axes, bar chart, bar line chart, calculate, calculation, chart, data, explain, graph, horizontal axis, interpret, label, pictogram, range, represent, scale, table, tally, title, vertical axis

Curriculum objectives

● To complete, read and interpret information in tables, including timetables.

Success criteria

● I can gather information and place the data on a bar chart.

You will need

Photocopiable sheets

'Doubles in a minute (1) and (2)'

General resources

'0–30 number cards'; interactive teaching resource 'Graphing tool'

Equipment

Interlocking cubes; individual whiteboards; Microsoft Excel® or 'Numberbox 2' (Black Cat software)

Differentiation

Less confident learners

Support the children with their bar charts (especially to check that they are representing odd-numbered values correctly as coming halfway up a square on the y-axis if using one square to represent two people).

More confident learners

When these children have completed their chart, ask: *What would the graph have looked like if we had used five squares per person. Why is getting the scale right important?* (Too much space for each unit means the chart will not fit on the page, too little space means the difference in the height of the bars is too difficult to see.) *Would we have used two people per square if we had collected this data from the whole school? Why? What would have been a better scale?*

Lesson 1

Main teaching activities

Whole-class work: Distribute photocopiable page 'Doubles in a minute (1)' from the CD-ROM. Look at the set of numbers in Part A. Ask the children to double as many of these as they can in one minute. Explain that you want to know how many numbers most of the children can double in one minute. To find this out, the children are going to represent their results as a bar chart. Emphasise that drawing a chart helps other people to interpret your data.

Revise frequency tables as opposed to tally charts. Tally charts are where individual children are asked and the data collected by putting a mark in sets of 5. Frequency tables simply canvass opinion, count the number of hands or votes and record the frequency, as in the table below. Draw up a blank table on the board, fill in the possible scores from zero to the highest number of correct doubles. By a show of hands, fill in the table which might show:

Score	0	1	2	3	4	5
Frequency	0	1	2	1	4	3

While this table is quite helpful for examining data, a graph gives a clearer visual impression of the data.

Display the interactive teaching resource 'Graphing tool' on the CD-ROM on an interactive whiteboard. Say that the class is now going to represent the information from the frequency table on a bar chart. Emphasise that a graph without labels has no meaning. Give the graph a title, such as: 'A graph to show the scores of Year 5's Doubles in a minute competition'. Agree on what the axes represent and label them. (The x-axis, the horizontal axis, is 'Number of correct doubles', the y-axis, the vertical axis, is 'Number of children'.) Complete the data table and then click 'Create Chart' and discuss the chart.

Independent and paired work: Show the children the blank axes on 'Doubles in a minute (2)'. Ask the children to complete the graph using the frequency table data but each partner should use a different y-axis scale, e.g. one person for every 1, 2 or 5 squares. You will have to decide. Ask: *What happens when we want to record three people?* (The level on the y-axis will be halfway between 2 and 4.) Note: you may have to alter the scale on the y-axis if there is an even distribution of children for each score. Alternatively they could use a spreadsheet program to draw the graph. On completion of their own bar charts the children should compare their results with their partner and discuss the differences when they have used a different scale for the y-axis.

Progress check: Ask the children to show you their charts so far. If they are very small and all populated in small bars at the bottom of the graph, suggest they try again and represent one child as two squares to make the bars clear.

Review

Look at and compare the children's graphs. Are they consistent? Complete the graph on the board and use it to extract information by asking, for example: *Which score did the most people get? Did a greater number of people score more or less than 7? How many people scored above 10? What can we say about Year 5's doubling ability? Did more people score above 10 than scored below 10?*

Now ask: *Why are graphs used to represent and compare data? Where might you see graphs? Are they all the same kind as ours?*

Curriculum objectives

- To complete, read and interpret information in tables, including timetables.

Success criteria

- I can interpret the information given on a bar chart and pose questions to interrogate the data.

Differentiation

Less confident learners

These children can concentrate on reading from straightforward facts such as 'eight people scored five doubles'.

More confident learners

These children should be able to make comparisons and create questions that require a calculation, such as: How many more people scored more than the most popular value? How many people scored more than 6 but less than 15?

Lesson 2
Oral and mental starter 23

Main teaching activities

Whole-class work: Build on the review session from lesson 1. Explain that a graph or chart provides information visually and so makes it easy to extract information. Discuss the sort of information you might want to know from our chart. Encourage the children to investigate questions such as: *Did more people score higher than 7 or lower?* They should use their mental calculation skills to check, adding all of the bars above the 7 and all of those below. They can also calculate the range: the difference between the highest and lowest scores.

Paired work: Ask the children to work in pairs to write six questions to elicit information from the chart. Ask the pairs to swap questions and answer them.

Progress check: Ensure the questions that the children pose are based on the data given in the bar chart and that they can provide the correct answer.

Review

Ask the children to evaluate the quality of the questions. Ask: *Which were the most challenging questions?* Ask some children to read out one of their questions; the other children answer them by interpreting their graph. Discuss the importance of carefully drawn, accurate graphs. Emphasise the importance of adding labels and a title. Ask: *What is the x-axis showing? What about the y-axis? Why would this graph be unhelpful if it did not have titles and labels? Pretend that the titles and labels are missing – what could this graph be about?* (For example, shoe sizes, age, pets.) *What is the range?*

Curriculum objectives

- As lesson 2 above.

Success criteria

- I can understand how a change of scale can alter the visual impact of a graph and what it appears to be representing.
- I can understand that graphs can be used to persuade as well as inform.

You will need

Photocopiable sheets

'Lazy Larry's ice creams (1) and (2)'

Equipment

Microsoft Excel® or 'Numberbox 2' (Black Cat software)

Differentiation

Less confident learners

Provide the children with 'Lazy Larry's ice creams (1)' they can concentrate on answering the one question.

More confident learners

Provide the children with 'Lazy Larry's ice creams (2)', which asks the children more questions about the two graphs.

Lesson 3
Oral and mental starter 23

Main teaching activities

Whole-class work: Explain that the scale used on the y-axis of a graph is very important. Firstly, it has to fit on the page. Secondly, changing the scale can produce graphs that look very different, and this can be misleading. Distribute photocopiable page 'Lazy Larry's ice creams (1)' from the CD-ROM. Explain that the chart of figures shows the number of ice creams a van driver has sold over an eight-month period. He is hoping for a bonus, so he wants the graph that he presents to his boss to look as impressive as possible. On the first graph, the y-axis (representing the number of ice creams sold) is marked in 2s; on the second, it is marked in 20s. Ask the children to put the data onto both graphs in the form of a bar chart or time series graph, if you feel it is appropriate.

Paired work: The children complete both graphs using the information given in the chart and then answer the question. Alternatively they could use a spreadsheet program to draw the graphs. The children complete the graphs and discuss your questions between them.

Progress check: Ensure that the children understand about the way the two scales are numbered and are able to complete them accurately. Ask: *Why do the bars look different? Have you changed the information? Why do you think one graph shows bigger variation than the other?*

Review

Discuss the visual impact of each graph, emphasising that both versions display the same data. Ask: *Which graph makes the salesman look more hardworking and successful?* (Graph 1, because the upward trend of the graph is steeper.) *How many more ice creams did Larry sell in June than in January? Is this what you would expect? Why? Do you think he may have taken some secret days off during the summer? What excuses might he have for not increasing his sales more during the summer? Do you think his boss will be impressed? How can you explain the difference between the two graphs*

Curriculum objectives
● To complete, read and interpret information in tables, including timetables.

Success criteria
● I can decide on an investigation, collect the information and record it on a tally chart.

You will need
Equipment
A bar chart

Differentiation
Less confident learners
A simple investigation collecting comparative numbers will be easier to manage, with some help constructing tally charts.

More confident learners
Children could start with a hypothesis, such as: Boys are generally taller/have longer arms/can throw further than girls. The graph would then have an x-axis showing a range and touching bars. Encourage them to choose something manageable within the time available.

Lesson 4
Oral and mental starter 30

Main teaching activities
Whole-class work: Explain to the children that different types of graph are appropriate for different kinds of data. All are to display information in one place, some can even compare different sets of data on the same graph. Ask: *If I wanted to compare the number of visitors to a shopping centre on different days of the week, what sort of graph would be most appropriate?* (Bar chart or time series graph) *How would my graph look different if I wanted to compare the numbers of males and females who visited the centre on each day?*

Tell the children that sometimes bar charts can be used to compare two sets of data. In this example, we could draw two bars in different colours for each day, comparing the numbers of male and female visitors. This is called a comparative bar chart and it extends the number of different factors that can be presented. Display a bar graph, without a title or any labels. Remind the children how graphs need titles and labels to tell the reader what was being measured or compared. Ask the children to guess what your unlabelled graph might be showing and suggest a title and suitable labels for the axes.

Paired work: Tell the children that they are going to produce a simple comparative bar chart. They are to collect information about two different groups (suggest boys and girls but it could be Year 5 and Year 2...). Today they have to decide on their investigation and collect their information on a tally chart. Tomorrow they will construct the graph. The children should construct the question and a recording tally chart before collecting the information. They decide who might find this information useful and what the data will show.

Progress check: Check that children choose closed question, for example 'Choose your favourite ice cream flavour from the following six options' as opposed to 'What is your favourite ice cream flavour?' The information collected can then be used to compare the choices of boys and girls or younger and older children.

Review
Ask: *Why do people represent information on a graph instead of writing it? Who would be interested in your data? How will you construct your graph to persuade them?* Remind the children that graphs tell people things, and often more useful information can be presented in a single graph than could be explained in several pages of writing.

Curriculum objectives
● As lesson 4 above.

Success criteria
● I can represent data on a comparative bar chart to provide information or to persuade.

You will need
Equipment
Squared paper

Differentiation
Less confident learners
These children may need support choosing the scale.

More confident learners
They should look for further implications of their findings.

Lesson 5
Oral and mental starter 30

Main teaching activities
Whole-class work: Remind the children that the graph must fit on one page, that they have to show the comparison (boys/girls or age groups) in different colours and that changing the scale can make the data look very different.

Paired work: The children create a graph to represent their data. Once complete, the children should think about the information they would want to highlight and what that means. Encourage them to draw conclusions since the graph is only a recording system, the interpretation of the data is the most important outcome.

Progress check: Remind the children that graphs tell people things, and often more useful information can be presented in a single graph than could be explained in several pages of writing.

Review
Ask: *How would your graph be different if you had asked the whole school about their food choices? How would you have changed the scale of the graph? What have you learned about data representation? How is it useful in the wider world?*

  ■SCHOLASTIC

Written multiplication with numbers up to four digits by one- or two digit-numbers

Most children should be able to use a written method to multiply numbers with up to four digits by a single digit and some will extend this to low two-digit numbers or multiples of 10.

Some children will not have made such progress and will require extra practice of multiplying two- and three-digit numbers by a single digit.

1. Check

21 Quick-fire multiplication and division facts

Confident learners will have instant recall of their times tables. Others may still be calculating by repeated addition or 'working through' their tables. They may need extra practice to learn them.

- *If we know 6 × 2 how can this help with 6 × 20 or 60 × 20? How would you multiply by 14? At what point do you think you need a written calculation? Give me an example.*

2. Assess

Ask the children to work through photocopiable page 87 'Trying Times (3)' demonstrating their preferred methods. Observe the children carefully watching for confident use of columnar multiplication and for those who still need to use an expanded method such as the grid method. Some children may understand their chosen method but make errors due to insecure times table knowledge. Record the outcomes.

3. Further practice

Use a blank multiplication grid to give children further practice at the times tables they find most difficult. This can be a timed activity. Use the interactive activity 'Trying times' to practice multiplication of three-digit numbers.

Written methods for short division

Most children should be able to use the formal written method of short division.

Some children will not have made such progress and will require the support of a Multiplication square to aid their division skills and may still use an expanded method such as 'chunking'.

1. Check

25 Factor pairs

Use the oral and mental starter to establish the children's understanding of factors for division. Note those who have a good understanding and those who still need to refer to a Multiplication square to check for factors.

- *Tell me the factors of 32. Are there any others? How can this knowledge help you when you are dividing?*

2. Assess

As the children work through photocopiable page 88 'Share it out', watch how they calculate and ask them to describe each step to you. Ask questions about the context and whether it is appropriate to always have remainders. Some children will confidently calculate but will not understand the contextual relevance. Others will need a 'Multiplication square' from the CD-ROM to support their division. Record the outcomes.

3. Further practice

Use the oral and mental starters to build confidence with multiplication and division. By having to create a question, children will build their understanding of the concepts of division and the meaning of the numbers.

Curriculum objectives
● To compare and order fractions whose denominators are all multiples of the same number.

You will need
1. Check
Oral and mental starter
28 Fractions of numbers

2. Assess
'Fair shares for all'

3. Further practice
Oral and mental starter
29 Decimals and fractions
General resources
'Blank 100 square'

Compare fractions where the denominator is a multiple

Most children should be able to understand the idea of equivalent fractions and be able to multiply and divide to prove equivalence.

Some children will not have made such progress and will require more practice with fractions of shapes and practical activities to demonstrate equivalence.

1. Check

28 Fractions of numbers

Observe the children making the link between fractions of a number and division. Confident learners will be able to find both ½ and ⅛ of a number by converting to the equivalent. Some children will need more practice making this link.

● *Which would you prefer, ¾ of a cake or ⁶⁄₁₂? Why? If I eat ⅜ of a bar of chocolate and you eat ²⁄₁₂ how much of the bar is left. Explain how you worked this out?*

2. Assess

As the children answer the questions on photocopiable page 89 'Fair shares for all', observe the connections that they make between equivalent fractions. Less confident learners may only be able to understand equivalence with shapes that they can compare; others will compare by calculating. Record the outcomes.

3. Further practice

The oral and mental starters will consolidate knowledge of instant recall of known fractions and decimal equivalents. Children should use a blank 100 square to cut out and compare equivalents for tenths to begin to understand how different fractions can be equivalent.

Curriculum objectives
● To read and write decimal numbers as fractions (for example 0.71 = 71/100).

You will need
1. Check
Oral and mental starter
29 Decimals and fractions

2. Assess
The decimals and fractions from 'Fractions, decimals and percentages', one per pair

3. Further practice
Oral and mental starters
28 Fractions of numbers
26 Pairs to make 1
General resources
'Blank 100 square'

Decimal and fraction equivalents

Most children should be able to express any two-digit decimal as its fraction equivalent.

Some children will not have made such progress and will require further practice with practical equipment to help them understand two-digit decimals as fractions of 100 or 10.

1. Check

29 Decimals and fractions

Use the questions in the oral and mental starter to assess individuals' ability to express a decimal as a fraction out of 100. Some children will confidently go further and simplify fractions to their lowest form. Others may need a 'Blank 100 square' to understand this concept.

● *Tell me two equivalent fractions of 0.7. Explain how you know. Why can we not simplify 0.71 to tenths? Do some decimals have more equivalent fractions than others? Give some examples.*

2. Assess

Use the fraction and decimal cards to play a game. Players turn over a decimal card and name as many equivalent fractions as they can, scoring a point for each. Listen to their explanations demonstrating an understanding of both equivalent fractions and that decimals are fractions of 100. Record the outcomes.

3. Further practice

For children who still need evidence that decimals are fractions of 100, use a 'Blank 100 square' to show this by shading. The oral and mental starter will also give practice in understanding decimals as fractions of a whole.

Oral and mental starters

Multiplication and division

18 Multiplication sort

Using selected times tables, for example, 3-, 4-, 5- and 6-times or 6-, 7-, 8- and 9-times, write up ten multiples, randomly distributed on the board. Assign each multiple a different colour and distribute board pens accordingly to four children. Ask them to circle the multiples of their given multiplication table. Ask the other children to assist and check their decisions. Ask the class why some numbers are circled in more than one colour. (They are common multiples. Ask the children to explain why this is the case and can they suggest any more for these multiplication tables.)

19 Double and halve

Write up a list of ten two-digit numbers to double and ten two-digit numbers to halve. Explain to the children that they have 1 minute to double or halve as appropriate and write their answers. Talk about speed strategies, for example, not spending a long time on a tricky number. Remind them that this is a mental task so they should not try to do too many written jottings. When the minute is up go through the answers discussing how they recorded answers such as half of 29 (14½ or 14.5). Discuss the strategies used, for example, did they partition tens and ones to double and halve and then recombine or did they round to the nearest known double and adjust? A quick show of hands and assessment of how many the children managed to complete the task correctly in the time will give you a good idea of their known number facts proficiency.

20 Counting round the room

This activity can encompass any number pattern such as, counting on and back in 2s from 5, counting in jumps of 5 from 3, counting on and back in 10s from 1, all the square numbers to 100, and so on. You start the pattern and the children chant with you until you indicate that they should stop or begin to count backwards.

Alternatively, an extension to this is to choose a pattern to chant but when children come to an 'unusual' number such as a prime or a square number they should say instead 'Goose' or 'Duck', to demonstrate to you their understanding.

21 Quick-fire multiplication and division facts

Call out a range of multiplication or division facts using a variety of vocabulary, for example, 8 lots of 45; What is 12 times bigger than 6?; 4 times 3; 32 shared by 4; half of 48; 108 divided 9, and so on. The children write their answers on their whiteboards and show you when you say: *Show me*.

22 What's the question?

Write up a selection of multiples, for example, 25, 12, 48, 6, 30. Ask the children to give multiplication and division questions that make each answer. This can include word problems too.

23 What's the question × 10?

As oral and mental starter 22 but replace the numbers on the board with higher multiples of 10 and 100, for example, 250, 1200, 480, 600 and 3000.

Fractions

24 What's the question – decimals?

As oral and mental starter 22 but replace the numbers on the board with decimal numbers, for example, 0.2, 1.2, 0.75, 0.05 and 0.01.

25 Factor pairs

Ask the children to identify the factor pairs to make the numbers that you give them. They should write these on to their individual white boards and hold them up when you say: *Show me.*

The numbers could include: 10, 18, 24, 16, 30, 45, 49, 121, 72, 15 and 56.

26 Pairs to make 1

Write up the number sentence 0.4 + ______ = 1. Ask the children to identify the missing number and explain the position of the decimal point. Ask them about the number knowledge that they use to help them solve this. Repeat with other number sentences. For example, 0.6 + ______ = 1; 0.55 + ______ = 1; 0.32 + ______ = 1; 0.78 + ______ = 1, and so on or, alternatively, 1 – ______ = 0.7.

27 Pairs to make 10

As oral and mental starter 26 but this time making 10. For example 1.2 + ______ = 10; 4.8 + ______ = 10.

28 Fractions of numbers

Use individual whiteboards to display the answers to fraction questions. Discuss the links between known multiplication and division facts.

Ask questions such as: $\frac{1}{4}$ of 24; $\frac{1}{2}$ of 17; $\frac{1}{3}$ of 27; $\frac{1}{5}$ of 35; $\frac{1}{3}$ of 36.

This activity can be repeated using more challenging fractions of numbers when you feel the children are ready. For example, $\frac{2}{3}$ of 27; $\frac{3}{5}$ of 45; $\frac{3}{4}$ of 12; $\frac{3}{5}$ of 40; $\frac{2}{9}$ of 81; and so on.

29 Decimals and fractions

Ask the children to match fractions to their decimal equivalents. Write up a mixed selection of fractions and known decimal equivalents randomly.

For example: $\frac{1}{2}$; $\frac{27}{100}$; $\frac{1}{4}$; $\frac{89}{100}$; $\frac{3}{10}$; $\frac{9}{10}$; 0.9; 0.25; 0.89; 0.5; 0.27; 0.3

The children match them. Each time ask them to explain the decimal place value, for example, 0.4 is no whole numbers but 4 tenths or the fraction knowledge that they used, for example, 0.5 equals $\frac{1}{2}$ because $\frac{1}{2}$ is equal to $\frac{5}{10}$ so making 0.5.

This activity can be repeated with other fraction/decimal equivalents.

30 Round it up!

Explain to the children that they are going to practise rounding decimal numbers. Write up the number 9.38. Ask the children to identify the whole number, tenths and hundredths. Demonstrate the position of this number on a number line marked with whole numbers and tenths. Ask the children to identify whether it is nearer 9.4 or 9.3. Explain that 8 hundredths is nearer to the next tenth up therefore to round this number to one decimal place would mean 9.4. Repeat with a range of other numbers with two decimal places.

This activity can be extended to round numbers to the nearest whole number.

Trying times (3)

■ Answer these questions using your preferred method for multiplication.

1. 136 × 4

2. 214 × 6

3. 45 × 21

4. 185 × 9

5. Cara scored 1428 on her computer game. After a week she has scored 7 times as many points. What is her total now?

6. There are 128 rows of 40 chairs in a theatre. How many chairs is that?

> I can multiply numbers up to four digits by one-
> or two-digit numbers.
>
> How did you do?

Share it out

- Answer these questions using formal written method of short division.

1. 186 ÷ 3

2. 432 ÷ 8

3. a) Coloured pencils are sold in packs of ten. Mrs Jones needs 488 pencils for the school. How many packs does she need to buy?

b) There are six classes. She share the pencils equally. How many pencils does each class receive?

4. Joe says: 'There are 824 wheels in a car park. There are only cars parked there today. How many cars are there?'

5. Classes 4, 5 and 6 are all entering a seven-a-side tournament. There are 91 children altogether. How many teams will be taking part?

I can divide numbers using the formal written method of short division.

How did you do?

Fair shares for all

1. Shade the grids to show an equivalent fraction for each of these. Label the fraction.

$\frac{1}{4}$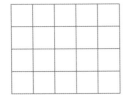

$\frac{3}{5}$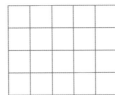

$\frac{1}{2}$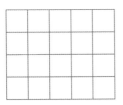

$\frac{2}{10}$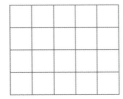

2. Write three equivalent fractions for each of these.

$\frac{3}{4}$ _____ _____ _____

$\frac{2}{5}$ _____ _____ _____

3. Write these fractions in order, smallest first.

$\frac{1}{3}$ $\frac{3}{6}$ $\frac{1}{12}$ _____ _____ _____

$\frac{4}{8}$ $\frac{11}{16}$ $\frac{3}{4}$ _____ _____ _____

$\frac{3}{10}$ $\frac{1}{20}$ $\frac{40}{100}$ _____ _____ _____

4. Explain which you would prefer: $\frac{2}{5}$ of a cake or $\frac{4}{10}$?

I can compare and order fractions.

How did you do?

Negative numbers and solving problems involving numbers

Expected prior learning

Children should be able to:

- identify place value for comparing and ordering from the previous term
- round in order to estimate
- identify number patterns in steps of 10, 100 and 1000.

Topic	Curriculum objectives	Expected outcomes
Number and place value	**Lesson 1**	
	To read, write, order and compare numbers to at least to 1,000,000 and determine the value of each digit. To count forwards or backwards in steps of powers of 10 for any given number up to 1,000,000.	Explain what each digit represents in whole numbers and decimals up to two decimal places, and partition, round and order these numbers.
	Lesson 2	
	To interpret negative numbers in context, count forwards and backwards with positive and negative whole numbers, including through zero.	Count from any given number in whole-number and decimal steps, extending beyond zero when counting backwards; relate the numbers to their position on a number line.
	Lesson 3	
	To interpret negative numbers in context, count forwards and backwards with positive and negative whole numbers, including through zero.	Count from any given number in whole-number and decimal steps, extending beyond zero when counting backwards; relate the numbers to their position on a number line.
	Lesson 4	
	To solve number problems and practical problems that involve all of the above.	Solve problems involving place values, rounding and number sequences.
	Lesson 5	
	To solve number problems and practical problems that involve all of the above.	Solve problems involving place values, rounding and number sequences.

■SCHOLASTIC

Preparation

Lesson 1: copy 'Multiple jumps', one per child

Lesson 2: make the 'Negative number cards', one set per child

Lesson 3: copy 'Weather around the world', one per child

Lesson 4: copy 'Rise and fall', one per child

Lesson 5: copy 'One two buckle my shoe... (2)', one per child; copy '100 square' onto card, one per child, if needed

You will need

Photocopiable sheets

'Multiple jumps'; 'Weather around the world'; 'Weather around the world template'; 'Rise and fall'; 'One two buckle my shoe... (1) and (2)'

General resources

'Place value cards'; '0–30 number cards'; 'Negative number cards'; '100 square'; 'Symbol cards'; interactive teaching resource 'Thermometer'

Further practice

Use the interactive teaching resource 'Number line' to practice counting and ordering negative numbers. Ask the children to identify the position of numbers on the line. Use the slider to check if they are correct.

Oral and mental starters suggested for week 1

See bank of starters on page 126. Oral and mental starters are also on the CD-ROM.

31 Counting round the room

32 Order, order!

33 Target number

Overview of progression

During this week the children will have opportunities to reinforce reading, writing and ordering numbers to 1,000,000 and will round numbers to the nearest 1000. They will begin to understand the value of negative numbers when counting back beyond zero in real-life contexts. They solve problems involving place value, rounding and number sequences in order to apply their knowledge.

Watch out for

Some children may believe that a number smaller than zero has no value or that a number sentence such as 8 − 17 'can't be done'. They need help to understand that the value is measured as the 'distance from zero' and the digits get larger as the value becomes smaller. It may assist their understanding for you to demonstrate this concept as paces away from a given point labelled 'zero', explaining that they haven't 'disappeared' but have simply travelled away from zero. Most children accept this when applied to temperature so using thermometers is helpful.

Creative context

There are plenty of opportunities to relate negative numbers to real-life contexts such as the temperature of places and of substances. This gives relevance to numbers used in geography and science.

Vocabulary

above/below zero, approximately, ascending, compare, decimal place, decimal point, descending, digit, estimate, greater than (>), hundred thousands, hundredths, **integer**, less than (<), million, minus, **negative number**, **numeral**, order, pattern, place value, place value, positive number, round, sequence, size, ten thousands, tenths, thousands

Curriculum objectives
● To read, write, order and compare numbers at least to 1,000,000 and determine the value of each digit.
● To count forwards or backwards in steps of powers of 10 for any given number up to 1,000,000.

Success criteria
● I can order numbers and accurately create comparative number sentences using symbol cards.

You will need
Photocopiable sheets
'Multiple jumps'
General resources
'Place value chart'; '0–30 number cards'

Differentiation
Less confident learners
These children should use the 'Place value chart' and '0–9 number cards' to help them to increase the numbers in sequence correctly and to create their own patterns.
More confident learners
Challenge these children to extend their own number patterns beyond zero and using decimal numbers.

Lesson 1

Main teaching activities

Whole-class work: Remind the children about the way they decided on ordering numbers by looking at each digit and comparing the place value. Explain to the children that they are going to create sequences or number patterns by counting in steps of powers of 10 (that is 10, 100, 1000, and so on) from given, but less usual starting points. Demonstrate on the board.

+100 starting from 3: 3; 103; 203; 303; and so on

+10 starting from 3.2: 3.2; 13.2; 23.2; 33.2; and so on

−10 starting from 114,210: 114,210; 114,200; 114,190; 114,180; and so on

−100 starting from 305: 305; 205; 105; 5; and so on

Discuss what happens to this sequence next. (Subtract 100 therefore the next numbers in the sequence are −95; −195; and so on)

Paired work: Distribute photocopiable page 'Multiple jumps' from the CD-ROM explaining that the children should complete the given patterns and then generate sequences of their own.

Progress check: Ask the children to explain to you which part of the number is changing as they create their sequences. Say: *Tell me the value of this digit in the number.*

Review

Write some pairs of numbers on the board. Invite children to write symbols between them. Include some decimal numbers, negative numbers and some numbers that are equal. For example: 25.6 < 45.6; 0.05 < 0.1; 3809 > 3807; 12,084 > 12,083; 0.3 > 0.03; 3.4 = 3.40; 1.77 < 1.78; −6 < 6; 8 > −2; −1 < 1; 112 = 112.0. Ask the child as he or she completes each example: *What part of the number are you using to help you decide which number is larger? Is it the same digit in every example? What must we consider when we are looking at negative numbers?* Discuss the fact that the minus sign in front of a negative number tells us that we are counting back from zero – the bigger the number size, the further below zero it is.

■SCHOLASTIC

Curriculum objectives

- To interpret negative numbers in context, count forwards and backwards with positive and negative whole numbers, including through zero.

Success criteria

- I can order and compare positive and negative numbers.

You will need

General resources

'0–30 number cards'; 'Negative number cards'; the greater than (>) and less than (<) cards from 'Symbol cards'

Differentiation

Less confident learners

These children may need a number line with zero marked on it for them to place and order the numbers.

More confident learners

Having ordered their numbers they could begin to discuss how they would find the difference between a positive and a negative number.

Lesson 2 — Oral and mental starter 31

Main teaching activities

Whole-class work: Draw a number line from −10 to +10. Display the positive and negative number cards, including zero. Ask the children to estimate each card's place on the line. Discuss the minus sign as meaning an amount less than zero or a distance from zero. The larger the number, the further from zero. Link this to temperatures below zero. Ask: *Which is colder, −1°C or −10°C?* (−10°C.) Use the number line to count on and back, crossing zero, in intervals of ones and twos to familiarise the children with negative numbers.

Write on the board a list of 12 random positive and negative integers within the range −20 to +20. Ask the children to say the coldest temperature (the lowest number), the next coldest and so on. Now ask the children to choose two numbers and create a number sentence using the symbol cards, for example, −10 < 1; 4 > −2.

Paired work: Distribute 0–9 number and symbol cards (three per pair) and explain to the children that they are to make two positive two digit numbers and two negative ones. They should then create number string sentences using the < and > symbol cards, discussing the value of the numbers. They write their number strip sentence, and repeat another nine times, making different numbers each time.

Progress check: Check that the children have understood that a negative number does have a value that is determined by how much smaller than zero it is. Hence the larger the digits the smaller the value, for example, −32 < −12 < 14 < 34.

Review

Discuss the fact that the minus sign in front of a negative number tells us that we are counting back from zero – the bigger the number size, the further away from zero it is.

Say: *Tell me two numbers that fall between 0 and −6, −8 and −15, −4 and −11.* For each answer, ask: *Which temperature is warmer?* Ask the children how they might calculate the difference between a positive and a negative temperature.

Curriculum objectives

● To interpret negative numbers in context, count forwards and backwards with positive and negative whole numbers, including through zero.

Success criteria

● I can calculate differences between positive and negative numbers.

You will need

Photocopiable sheets

'Weather around the world'; 'Weather around the world template'

General resources

Interactive teaching resource 'Thermometer'

Differentiation

Less confident learners

Work with the children using the interactive teaching resource 'Thermometer' on the CD-ROM. Check they understand differences between positive and negative temperatures on the scale.

More confident learners

Adapt the 'Weather around the world template' to add more challenge to this activity.

Lesson 3 Oral and mental starter 32

Main teaching activities

Whole-class work: Continuing from the last lesson, explain to the children that they are going to calculate differences in temperature. It may not be as simple as subtracting one number from another. For example, What is the difference between −6°C and 2°C? You cannot take the 2 from the −6 because 2 is the bigger number. It is better to count on from −6°C to zero and then on to 2°C (making a difference of 8°C). Repeat with some more examples. Alternatively, display the interactive teaching resource 'Thermometer' on the CD-ROM. Set the thermometer to a negative temperature (click on the mercury) and ask children to calculate changes in temperature, for example: *The thermometer is on −9°C. The temperature rises by 11°C. What is the temperature now?* Check using the thermometer and highlight the temperature changes.

Independent and paired work: Distribute photocopiable page 'Weather around the world' from the CD-ROM. The children have to place temperatures on the number line and calculate some differences. As the children calculate, ask them to explain their thinking to a partner. An extension to this work might be to link this work to geography and find out where in the world these places are to be found.

Progress check: Ensure that the children are counting on from the smaller number up to zero before adding on the positive number.

Review

Remind the children that counting on from the 'coldest' to the 'warmest' is the best method. Draw a vertical number line and mark on zero to help the children with counting through zero. Ask: *What is the difference between −3.5 and −8.5? 4.5 and −3.5? 8 and −15?* Pose word problems such as: *If the temperature is −5°C at 02:00 and rises by 8 degrees by midday, what is the temperature then?* Invite children to pose similar questions to the class.

Curriculum objectives

- To solve number problems and practical problems that involve counting forwards and backwards with positive and negative whole numbers, including through zero.

Success criteria

- I can use the language associated with positive and negative numbers in the context of temperatures.

You will need

Photocopiable sheets
'Rise and fall'

General resources
Interactive teaching resource 'Thermometer'

Differentiation

Less confident learners
Work with children to help them to understand the distance to zero and then count on.

More confident learners
Challenge them to create their own set of problems or statements about temperature changes.

Lesson 4
Oral and mental starter 33

Main teaching activities

Whole-class work: Display the interactive teaching resource 'Thermometer' on the CD-ROM. Explore the real-life context of calculating temperatures and the language associated with it. Pose questions such as:

- *The temperature was −2°C at 7am, but had risen by 4 degrees by 11 o'clock. What was the new temperature?*
- *The temperature fell from 7°C to −1°C. By how many degrees did it fall?*
- *The temperature rose from −4°C by 10 degrees. What was the new temperature?*

Remind the children to count from the start temperature through zero to the new temperature. Some children will add 10 degrees to −4°C and say the result is 14°C. Discuss why this is wrong. (It does not take account of the negative number.) Demonstrate how to enter a negative number into a calculator, and use it to check the temperature calculations. Emphasise that a negative number is less than zero.

Independent and paired work: Distribute photocopiable page 'Rise and fall' from the CD-ROM. Ask the children to calculate the temperature differences. When completed, challenge them to make up their own questions to ask their partner.

Progress check: Insist on the appropriate language (rise and fall, increase and decrease) as this helps support calculating and contextualises the answers.

Review

Share feedback of the children's work to assess their confidence in calculating with negative numbers. Ask: *If it is −8°C in Helsinki and 2°C in London, what is the temperature difference?* (10°C) *Cairo is 33°C hotter than Oslo. In Oslo it is −3°C. What is the temperature in Cairo?* (30°C) *Can anyone suggest a rule for calculating temperature differences across 0°C?* (Count up or down to zero and on from there.)

Curriculum objectives

- As Lesson 4 above.

Success criteria

- I can recognise sequences and spot patterns in numbers.

You will need

Photocopiable sheets
'One two buckle my shoe... (1) and (2)'

General resources
'100 square'

Differentiation

Less confident learners
Provide photocopiable page 'One, two, buckle my shoe (1)'. They can use a '100 square' to support their work.

More confident learners
Challenge the children to create their own sequences including the use of negative numbers and the use of two or even three steps in the sequence.

Lesson 5
Oral and mental starter 33

Main teaching activities

Whole-class work: Ask: *What is the pattern? 1, 0, −1, −2, −3?* (Counting back in ones, past zero into the negative numbers.) Ask: *What is the pattern? 1, 4, 9, 16, 25, 36, 49, 64, 81, 100.* Establish that this is the sequence of square numbers. Remind the children that a number multiplied by itself gives a square number. Ask the children to consider 0.2, 0.4, 0.6, 0.8, 1.0, 1.2 ... (Jumps of 0.2). Explain that a number pattern rule can have more than one step, as long as the pattern follows the rule faithfully. Look at the rule 'Double it and add 1': start at 1, double it is 2 and add 1 is 3. So the pattern begins 1, 3 ... Apply the rule again: double 3 is 6 and add 1 is 7. So the pattern is 1, 3, 7 ... Ask the children to think of the next three numbers in the pattern. Ask whether anyone can invent a new rule for the class to try. Apply it on the board together.

Independent and paired work: Distribute photocopiable page 'One, two, buckle my shoe (2)'. When completed, they should compare their ideas with a friend. They should then make up their own patterns to challenge their friends.

Progress check: Encourage the children to look for sequential patterns but also two-step ones. When making their own patterns, they should try to use other number knowledge and use negative numbers, decimals and squared numbers.

Review

Go through some of the trickier patterns from the sheets. Ask the children to explain the pattern or rule. Ask: *What do you look for when continuing a pattern? Do the rules always involve finding a difference?* Explain that a number sequence can follow any mathematical rule that gives a pattern.

Addition and subtraction of large numbers and money

Expected prior learning

Children should be able to:

- perform written calculations using either formal or informal methods
- recall number bonds to 100
- double and halve whole numbers.

Topic	Curriculum objectives	Expected outcomes
Addition and subtraction	**Lesson 1**	
	To add and subtract numbers mentally with increasingly large numbers. To use rounding to check answers to calculations and determine, in the context of a problem, levels of accuracy.	Use knowledge of place value and addition and subtraction of two-digit numbers to derive sums and differences and doubles and halves of decimals (6.5 + 2.7, half of 5.6, double 0.34). Extend mental methods for whole-number calculations, for example to multiply a two-digit number by a one-digit number (12 × 9), to multiply by 25 (16 × 25), to subtract one near-multiple of 1000 from another (6070 − 4097). Explain what each digit represents in whole numbers and decimals with up to two decimal places, and partition, round and order these numbers.
	Lesson 2	
	To add and subtract numbers mentally with increasingly large numbers. To use rounding to check answers to calculations and determine, in the context of a problem, levels of accuracy.	Use knowledge of place value and addition and subtraction of two-digit numbers to derive sums and differences and doubles and halves of decimals (6.5 + 2.7, half of 5.6, double 0.34). Extend mental methods for whole-number calculations, for example to multiply a two-digit number by a one-digit number (12 × 9), to multiply by 25 (16 × 25), to subtract one near-multiple of 1000 from another (6070 − 4097). Explain what each digit represents in whole numbers and decimals with up to two decimal places, and partition, round and order these numbers.
	Lessons 3, 4 and 5	
	To add and subtract whole numbers with more than four-digits, including using formal written methods (columnar addition and subtraction). To use rounding to check answers to calculations and determine, in the context of a problem, levels of accuracy. To solve addition and subtraction multi-step problems in contexts, deciding which operations and methods to use and why. To solve problems involving number up to three decimal places.	Use formal written methods to add and subtract whole numbers and decimals with up to decimal two places. Solve one-step and two-step problems involving whole numbers and decimals and all four operations, choosing and using appropriate calculation strategies, including calculator use.

Preparation

Lesson 1: copy 'Predict and estimate', one per child; make copies of 'Number lines' or use the write on wipe off versions you made earlier in the year

Lesson 2: copy 'Close to ten', one per child

Lesson 3: copy 'Written methods for addition', one per child

Lesson 4: copy 'Emma's Emporium', one per child

Lesson 5: copy 'Written methods for subtraction', one per child

You will need

Photocopiable sheets

'Predict and estimate'; 'Close to ten'; 'Written methods for addition'; 'Emma's Emporium'; 'My Emporium'; 'Written methods for subtraction'

General resources

'Number lines'

Equipment

Calculation aids such as Base Ten apparatus

Further practice

Screen 2 of 'Written addition and subtraction' offers further opportunities to practice at solving number problems with up to three decimal places.

Oral and mental starters suggested for week 2

See bank of starters on pages 126 to 127. Oral and mental starters are also on the CD-ROM.

35 Decimal doubling

36 Decimal halving

Overview of progression

This week revisits addition and subtraction, extending mental calculations to larger numbers including near multiples of 10, 100 and 1000. Throughout the week there is an emphasis on choosing an formal, reliable and accurate method, moving towards secure use of columnar calculations. There is a greater emphasis on decimal numbers through the context of money.

> ## Watch out for
>
> Some children may still have an insecure knowledge of place value or use haphazard written notation for calculations which contain numbers with different numbers of decimal places. Provide practical equipment to support children with their visualisation of the relative size of numbers and also to calculate. Squared paper could be provided and a model of how to set out written calculations accurately in order to avoid place value miscalculations.

Creative context

Real-life contexts using money supports the understanding of these processes.

Vocabulary

add, decimal place, decimal point, difference, digit, estimate, hundred thousand, hundreds, hundredths, million, minus, **numeral**, partition, place value, plus, round, subtract, sum, ten thousand, tens, tenths, thousands, total, ones

Curriculum objectives
● To add and subtract numbers mentally with increasingly large numbers.
● To use rounding to check answers to calculations and determine, in the context of a problem, levels of accuracy.

Success criteria
● I can use my knowledge of number patterns and estimation to calculate a wider range of numbers mentally.

You will need
Photocopiable sheets
'Predict and estimate'
General resources
'Number lines'

Differentiation
Less confident learners
Photocopiable page 'Number lines' would also support their calculating.

More confident learners
Insist that these children are specific about the clues that they are using, not just quick at calculating. They must be able to explain the process too. They may wish to find out if this is a formal method for increasingly large numbers, for example 10,077 − 5981.

Lesson 1

Main teaching activities

Whole-class work: Explain to the children that they have a number of strategies, including estimation and knowledge of odd and even numbers, which will assist with accuracy in calculation. The children should ask themselves: Odd or even? Estimation will then give them an approximate answer, so they should have a good idea if they have the correct answer when they calculate.

Demonstrate with 470 + 380.

Odd or even?	even + even = even
Estimate:	500 + 400 = 900
Calculate:	400 + 300 = 700
	70 + 80 = 150 (near double)
Then:	700 + 150 = 850, which is even and close to the estimate.

Repeat with differences, for example 810 − 380.

Odd or even?	even − even = even
Estimate:	800 − 400 = 400
Calculate:	380 + 20 = 400
	400 + 400 = 800
	800 + 10 = 810

So the difference is 20 + 400 + 10 = 430.

Ask: *Who can suggest an alternative method?* Ask them to explain why they find this more logical. *Does it work with decimal numbers? How efficient are these strategies?*

Repeat the strategies with decimal numbers: 81 − 38 and 8.1 − 3.8; 7.4 + 9.8.

Repeat with four-digit near multiples of 1000, for example 8119 − 4997, and so on.

Independent work: Distribute photocopiable page 'Predict and estimate' from the CD-ROM to the children and explain that they should use their knowledge of odd and even numbers and estimation to aid calculation with the numbers given. As they continue to calculate, remind the children that they can check their work using an inverse operation.

Progress check: Ask the children to talk you through the way they might solve a question such as 4001 − 1284. Discuss the estimated size of the answer. Ask: *How did you know? What did you do? What steps will you now take to calculate?* Ensure security with number fact knowledge.

Review

Write 3.52 + 3.58 on the board. Ask: *How would you calculate this?*

 3.52 + 3.58 = 6.00 + 1.00 + 0.1 = 7.1

Ask: *Who can suggest a strategy for helping someone to calculate using decimals? Should it be any different from 3-digits if you have a good grasp of place value? Explain why.*

Now calculate 0.01 + 0.02 + 0.14. Take alternative suggestions for strategies. (For example, add the hundredths first: 0.03 + 0.14 = 0.17) Ask the children to explain why it works for them. Discuss with the children the method that is the most efficient and leads to the least number of possibilities for error. Encourage children to make informal jottings to avoid errors.

Curriculum objectives

• To add and subtract numbers mentally with increasingly large numbers.
• To use rounding to check answers to calculations and determine, in the context of a problem, levels of accuracy.

Success criteria

• I can round and adjust numbers to help me estimate and calculate.

You will need

Photocopiable sheets

'Close to ten'

Equipment

Calculation aids such as Base Ten apparatus

Differentiation

Less confident learners

Adult support to assist with rounding and adjusting may be necessary. Practical equipment such as Base Ten (generic) apparatus would also support their calculating.

More confident learners

Offer some further number sentences including three-m and four-digit numbers, e.g. 1098 + 115; 2334 – 179 etc. Ask the children to explain how they answered each question.

Lesson 2

Oral and mental starter 35

Main teaching activities

Whole-class work: Explain that today's activity is about using familiar number facts and adjusting them in order to calculate with more difficult numbers. They are going to add and subtract near multiples of 10, 100 or 1000. Say: *Round 49 to the nearest 10.* (50) Explain that as 50 is easier to add than 49, we can add 49 quickly by rounding and adjusting. For example: 49 + 114 is 1 less than 50 + 114 = 164. So the answer is 164 − 1 = 163.

Demonstrate how this can also help with subtracting: 204 − 57 is 4 more than 200 − 57 = 143. So the answer is 143 + 4 = 147. Repeat with several examples of addition and subtraction to make sure the children know which way to adjust the answer after rounding up or down. For example: 39 + 46; 156 + 206; 49 − 23; 2031 − 1897. Remind the children that informal jottings can help us to keep track, especially when rounding and adjusting.

Independent and paired work: Distribute photocopiable page 'Close to ten' from the CD-ROM. The children can use this to practise addition and subtraction by rounding and adjusting near multiples of 10 or 100. On completion of the sheet ask the children to work in pairs to discuss their thinking, step by step.

Progress check: Ask the children: *Who can tell me what I could do to calculate 303 − 89.* Check that children are clear about how much they need to adjust after rounding and calculating.

Review

Write 1003 − 69 on the board. Ask for a volunteer to come and work it out.

For example: 1003 − 69 rounded to 1000 − 70 = 930

So the answer is 930 + 4 = 934.

Ask: *How can this method help us to calculate money?* (We can round to the nearest £1 or £10). Ask the children to solve this problem: *I have £29.58 and my aunt has sent me £15. How much do I have now?* (£29.58 is 42p less than £30 and £30 + £15 = £45, so answer is £45 − £0.42 = £44.58).

Curriculum objectives

● To add and subtract whole numbers with more than four-digits, including using efficient written methods (columnar addition).
● To solve problems involving number up to three decimal places.

Success criteria

● I can use a written method to calculate addition problems.

You will need

Photocopiable sheets

'Written methods for addition'

Differentiation

Less confident learners

These children may not be confident enough to use columnar addition and may need to count on using a number line.

More confident learners

These children should be able to use standard columnar methods with accuracy. Challenge them to turn simple calculations into word problems to put them into context for others.

Lesson 3
Oral and mental starter 36

Main teaching activities

Whole-class work: Revise columnar addition. It is probable that some children will be using the expanded method, adding the most significant digit first, and some will be using the standard compact method and 'carrying' digits. (You will need to refer to your school calculation policy to plan the development of the various methods.) The most important thing is that each child should have a reliable and accurate written method of addition that they can use with confidence.

Ask for volunteers to solve this problem using their chosen method to demonstrate the alternatives.

```
      2   1   6
  +   1   4   8
```

Each time, also demonstrate the standard written method, emphasising the 'carried' digit. Remind the children of the value of rounding and estimating their answer first.

Independent and paired work: Distribute photocopiable page 'Written methods for addition' from the CD-ROM for the children to work through using their chosen method. You may wish to use this time to focus on a group who are ready to move from the expanded method to a more compact one. When they have completed the task, the children check their calculations with a partner.

Progress check: Write up an incorrectly calculated addition. Ask the children to check it for you and help you to put it right. The most common errors will be poor number bonds and forgetting the 'carried' digit.

Review

It may be useful to go through some of the problems from the sheet, asking individuals to demonstrate and talk through their method on the board.
Ask: *Can a written calculation be used for adding more than two numbers?* (Both methods will work for adding multiple numbers, though the standard compact method can accommodate larger 'carried' digits more easily.) Ask for a confident volunteer to demonstrate how they would add three 3-digit numbers, for example: 123 + 456 − 388 (= 967).

Curriculum objectives

● To add and subtract whole numbers with more than 4-digits, including using efficient written methods.
● To solve problems involving numbers up to three decimal places.

Success criteria

● I can accurately add more than two amounts using columnar addition.

You will need

Photocopiable sheets

'Emma's Emporium'; 'My Emporium'

Differentiation

Less confident learners

In mixed-ability pairs, encourage confident partners to explain the calculations.

More confident learners

Give children 'My Emporium'. In pairs ask them first to build their own price list, then swap the price lists with a partner to then build shopping lists.

Curriculum objectives

● As for Lesson 4, and:
● To solve addition and subtraction multi-step problems in contexts.
● To use rounding to check answers.

Success criteria

● I can use a written method of calculation to solve subtraction problems.

You will need

Photocopiable sheets

'Written methods for subtraction'

Equipment

Calculation aids such as Diennes apparatus or straws

Differentiation

Less confident learners

Provide practical apparatus.

More confident learners

Provide more challenging subtractions to complete.

Lesson 4 — Oral and mental starter 36

Main teaching activities

Whole-class work: Explain to the children that they are continuing their work on addition by adding more than two numbers. Write the shopping list below on the board and demonstrate the calculation, using the compact method. Encourage the children to look for numbers to 'make 10' when adding a large column of figures. Emphasise that the ones add up to 22, that is, 2 ones and 2 tens (to be added to the tens column). Repeat for decimal numbers.

crisps	64p	apples	£1.54
sweets	26p	squash	£1.29
carrots	39p	chicken	£3.99
banana	+ 43p	biscuits	+ £0.90
	172p = £1.72		£7.72
	2		2 2

Highlight the fact that the decimal points must always stay aligned, one under the other, in all the numbers, including the answer.

Paired work: Ask the children to use photocopiable page 'Emma's Emporium' from the CD-ROM to create a shopping list. They record the items and calculate the total, then discuss their calculating process together.

Progress check: The most common mistakes result from misalignment of digits and movement of the decimal point. Write an incorrect calculation on the board and ask the children to correct the errors with you.

Review

Ask the children to devise a class rule for helping someone add a long list of prices: line up the decimal points; keep the place value correct; 'carry over' any extra digits to the next place value and record them beneath the sum; remember to add any 'extras' to the next column.

Lesson 5 — Oral and mental starter 36

Main teaching activities

Whole-class work: Revise column subtraction, using both the expanded method and the standard compact method with decomposition. Ask for two volunteers to come and calculate the following using their preferred method (one child using each method) for 239 − 146:

Independent and paired work: Distribute photocopiable page 'Written methods for subtraction' from the CD-ROM. Explain that these are all subtraction questions to be solved using a written method. On completion of the task children could check their work with a partner, spotting errors. Their conversations could inform your assessments.

Progress check: Decomposition or the accurate redistribution of the larger number is the most common problem. Ask for the children to explain to you how they have done this where the digits are smaller on the top than the bottom. Check for children who simply find the difference between the two digits, for example incorrectly saying 3 − 7 is 4.

Review

Write an incorrect calculation on the board.

Ask the children to look at the calculation carefully. Can they spot the error? Ask them to decide where the person has made a mistake. Then say: *Tell me how to correct this calculation. What tips would you give someone to help them with column subtraction?*

Long multiplication, square numbers and cube numbers

Expected prior learning

Children should be able to:

- recall quickly multiplication facts up to 12 × 12
- use informal written methods for multiplication
- understand the process of multiplication, based on arrays and 'lots or groups of'.

Topic	Curriculum objectives	Expected outcomes
Multiplication and division	**Lesson I** To recognise and use square numbers and cube numbers, and the notation for squared (^{2}) and cubed (^{3}). To calculate and compare the area of rectangles (including squares) and including using standard units, square centimetres (cm^2) and square metres (m^2) and estimate the area of irregular shapes.	Use multiplication knowledge to find squared numbers and square roots. Use the formula for the area of a rectangle to calculate the rectangle's area.
	Lesson 2 To multiply and divide whole numbers and those involving decimals by 10, 100 and 1000. To multiply numbers up to four-digits by a one- or two-digit number using a formal written method, including long multiplication for two-digit numbers.	Recall quickly multiplication facts up to 10 × 10 and use them to multiply pairs of multiples of 10 and 100; derive quickly corresponding division facts. Refine and use efficient written methods to multiply and divide 3-digits × 1-digit, 2-digits × 2-digits, 1-digit.1s × 1-digit, and 3-digits ÷ 1-digit.
	Lesson 3 To multiply and divide whole numbers and those involving decimals by 10, 100 and 1000. To multiply numbers up to four-digits by a one- or two-digit number using a formal written method, including long multiplication for two-digit numbers.	Recall quickly multiplication facts up to 10 × 10 and use them to multiply pairs of multiples of 10 and 100; derive quickly corresponding division facts. Refine and use efficient written methods to multiply and divide 3-digits × 1-digit, 2-digits × 2-digits, 1-digit.1s × 1-digit, and 3-digits ÷ 1-digit.
	Lessons 4 and 5 To solve problems involving multiplication and division, including scaling by simple fractions and problems involving simple rates. To multiply numbers up to four-digits by a one- or two-digit number using a formal written method, including long multiplication for two-digit numbers.	Recall quickly multiplication facts up to 10 × 10 and use them to multiply pairs of multiples of 10 and 100; derive quickly corresponding division facts. Refine and use efficient written methods to multiply and divide 3-digits × 1-digit, 2-digits × 2-digits, 1-digit.1s × 1-digit, and 3-digits ÷ 1-digit.

Preparation

Lesson 1: copy 'Making square numbers', one per child

Lesson 2: write up some differentiated 3-digits × 1-digit and 2-digits × 1-digit multiplication questions for the children to solve

Lesson 3: copy 'Multiple mixed bag', one per child

Lesson 4: copy 'The cake bake', one per child

You will need

Photocopiable sheets
'Making square numbers'; 'Multiple mixed bag'; 'The cake bake'

General resources
'Multiplication square'

Equipment
Blocks or centimetre cubes; cake baking ingredients and equipment, if desired

Further practice

Interactive activity 'The school barbeque'

Oral and mental starters suggested for week 3

See bank of starters on pages 126 to 127. Oral and mental starters are also on the CD-ROM.

33 Target number

34 What's the question?

37 Fast times

Overview of progression

This week focuses on multiplication and its application in puzzles and real-life problems. The first lesson explores square numbers by providing a visual prompt in the form of a puzzle which should aid understanding of these special numbers. There are some lessons spent on moving children towards formal columnar methods of multiplication and finally some scaling problems using multiplication such as they might encounter in daily life.

Watch out for

Some children may not be sufficiently secure in their multiplication facts and understanding of place value for them to move onto columnar methods. They must be clear about expanded multiplication and what is happening to numbers before moving on. Teachers should be explicit about the relative size of the numbers being multiplied, for example when multiplying 14 × 23 children must be very clear that they are multiplying 10 × 20 and 4 × 20 as well as 10 × 3 and 4 × 4. Unless this place value is clear, children will either miss out stages or misunderstand the place value of the resulting answer.

Creative context

Ideally, the scaling problems using recipes should fit into an event or activity that the class are actually planning, simply because errors in multiplying are very clear when trying to use the figures for an actual recipe.

Vocabulary

answer, approximately, **area,** calculate, calculation, decimal place, divide, estimate, method, multiply, operation, place value, place, problem, product, **quotient,** solution, square number, square root, strategy

Curriculum objectives

● To recognise and use square numbers and cube numbers, and the notation for squared (^{2}) and cubed (^{3}).
● To calculate and compare the area of squares including using standard units, square centimetres (cm^2).

Success criteria

● I can understand and use the notation for square numbers.

You will need

Photocopiable sheets
'Making square numbers'

General resources
'Multiplication square'

Equipment
Blocks or centimetre cubes

Differentiation

Less confident learners

These children may only find the squares of 2, 3, 4 and 5. They can count the squares on the jigsaw pieces to calculate the square numbers and areas.

More confident learners

These children should be able to complete the squares quickly. They can go on to calculate the squares of 13, 14 and 15 and, using squared paper, create the jigsaws for a friend.

Lesson 1 — Oral and mental starter 34

Main teaching activities

Whole-class work: Display the photocopiable page 'Multiplication square' from the CD-ROM. Explain to the children that today they are going to look at special multiples: numbers that are multiplied by themselves, or square numbers.

Ask volunteers to highlight on the 'Multiplication square' the numbers that are obtained by multiplying a number by itself, for example, 4 or 49. After the first few, ask: *Can you see the pattern on the grid?* (The square numbers form a diagonal line.) Explain that they are called square numbers because when one of these numbers is arranged as squares or dots, it makes a square. Demonstrate with squared paper squares showing 2 × 2 and 4 × 4. Explain that this is recorded as 2^2 or 4^2. Ask the children to count the individual squares: 2 × 2 = 4 and 4 × 4 = 16. The inverse or opposite of a square is known as a square root, for example, 4 is the square root of 16. Explain that if they need to find the side length of a square, given the area, they would need to find the square root, for example: *What is the side length of a square with an area of 25cm^2?* (5cm since 5 is the square root of 25.) *What is 12^2?*

Paired work: Distribute photocopiable page 'Making square numbers' from the CD-ROM. The children make and solve the jigsaws of square numbers, count or calculate each square number and write the relevant multiplication fact and area in cm^2 beneath each jigsaw square. They can use the displayed Multiplication square to check their answers.

Progress check: Hold up a 5 × 5 square. Ask: *How would we write this? Why?*

Review

Check the results of the jigsaw puzzles and the square numbers calculated. Ask questions such as: *What is the square of 4? What is the square root of 25?* Invite the children to demonstrate the square numbers by using themselves to form a square 'grid' of bodies: 4 × 4, 5 × 5, and so on.

Ask for a volunteer to make a 3 × 3 square grid using centimetre cubes and ask them to record it as 3^2, explaining the notation. Now ask them to add another two layers to make a 3 × 3 × 3 shape (a cube). Explain that this is recorded as 3^3 because of the three dimensions or directions in which this shape is constructed.

Curriculum objectives
● To multiply and divide whole numbers and those involving decimals by 10, 100 and 1000.
● To multiply numbers up to four-digits by a one- or two-digit number using a formal written method, including long multiplication for two-digit numbers.

Success criteria
● I can use a written method to solve 3-digit × 1-digit problems.

You will need
Equipment
Individual whiteboards

Differentiation
Less confident learners
Use the grid method only. They may only manage 2-digit × 1-digit problems, such as 45 × 5; 23 × 5; 52 × 2; 43 × 2.
More confident learners
These children could work through the compact standard method, with more difficult multiples such as 319 × 8; 243 × 7; 745 × 9; 246 × 8.

Lesson 2   Oral and mental starter 37

Main teaching activities

Whole-class work: Explain to the children that you are going to revise the grid method for multiplying large numbers and also show them two other, more compact, methods. Emphasise that no method is 'better': the children must choose the method with which they feel most comfortable and which gives the most accurate results. Provide opportunities for the children to attempt each method on their whiteboards and hold them up to show you their calculations. Discuss the following methods of doing the calculation 134 × 5, approximating first. Then try some further examples.

The grid method
134 × 5

×	5
100	500
30	150
4	20
	670

The expanded vertical method

	1	3	4
×			5
	5	0	0
	1	5	0
		2	0
	6	7	0

Repeat using the expanded method above, but starting with the least significant digit (ones) and thus inverting the recording. This prepares the children for:

The compact standard method

	1	3	4
×			5
	6	7	0
	1	2	

Independent and paired work: Write three or four examples for children to attempt using their (or your) chosen method. For example: 146 × 2; 231 × 5; 315 × 3; 336 × 4. The children should complete each calculation individually, but then share their answers with their partner. They can discuss any differences in method or answer.

Progress check: Watch out for children who try to replicate a method which they do not understand. Ask questions such as: *What is the value of the 3 in 134? How will you record that 3 multiplied by 5? What is its value? How do you make sure that it keeps that value in your answer? Did you round and estimate first?*

Review

Discuss the methods used and problems encountered. Make this more fun by dividing the class into three groups, each representing a different calculating method. The children have five minutes to jot down reasons why they believe their chosen method to be the best and most accurate one. They then present their reasons to the class, with opportunities for questioning and debate.

Curriculum objectives
● To multiply and divide whole numbers and those involving decimals by 10, 100 and 1000.
● To multiply numbers up to four-digits by a one- or two-digit number using a formal written method, including long multiplication for two-digit numbers.

Success criteria
● I can extend written methods for multiplication to include 2-digit × 2-digit problems.

You will need
Photocopiable sheets
'Multiple mixed bag'

Differentiation
Less confident learners
Remind the children that they can multiply by 10 and that this should help them to estimate the size of their final answers.

More confident learners
These children should be able to multiply increasingly large numbers and decimals using long multiplication. Further challenge them to explore how this would work for other decimal numbers such as £2.10 × 14. Encourage estimating first.

Lesson 3
Oral and mental starter 37

Main teaching activities

Whole-class work: Explain that this lesson is to consolidate written multiplication and to extend it to include 2-digit × 2-digit questions, as appropriate. Demonstrate the three methods from yesterday and include multiplying by two-digit numbers. When you demonstrate the columnar version, explain that is called long multiplication and involves using a zero as a place value holder.

		6	3
×		1	4
	2	5	2
+	6	3	0
	8	8	2

Multiply by the 4 first, as yesterday, remembering to 'carry' 1 ten.
Use zero to hold the place value so that you are multiplying by 10 not 1.
Add the two parts together.

Independent and paired work: Distribute photocopiable page 'Multiple mixed bag'. The children attempt them individually first and then explain their calculating to a partner.

Progress check: The most common error with multiplying by a two-digit number is the confusion about the place value whether using the grid method or long multiplication. Ask: *What is the value of the 1 in this question?* If children are finding it difficult, use the expanded vertical method to demonstrate that they are multiplying by 10 not 1.

Review

Ask a volunteer to demonstrate their chosen method using one of the problems from the lesson. Ask a more confident learner to explain what they found about multiplying decimal numbers. (Align the decimal point and use place holding zero as before.) Some children may return to partitioning the £2 and 10p and multiplying them separately.

■ SCHOLASTIC

Curriculum objectives
● To solve problems involving multiplication and division, including scaling by simple fractions and problems involving simple rates.
● To multiply numbers up to four-digits by a 1- or 2-digit number using a formal written method, including long multiplication for 1- and 2-digit numbers.

Success criteria
● I can solve problems using my multiplication skills.

You will need
Photocopiable sheets
'The cake bake'

Differentiation
Less confident learners
Children may need adult help to interpret the context and define the calculations.
More confident learners
After completing the questions, these children should discuss additional questions that they would like to answer in order to plan for their cake bake.

Lesson 4
Oral and mental starter 33

Main teaching activities
Whole-class work: Explain to the children that, over the next two days, they are going to solve a real-life problem using multiplication. Distribute photocopiable page 'The cake bake' from the CD-ROM. Explain that the recipe given is to make six plain cakes. Their task is to decide on decorations, work out the costs and how much they intend to sell their cakes for. Talk the children through how to interpret the problem and model how to multiply to scale up. For example: *If six cakes cost £0.80 to make, how much would 12 cakes cost to make? How much flour is required for 48 cakes? How many eggs are required for 18 cakes?* Demonstrate how to calculate how much one cake costs to make, known as a unit cost. Show how to calculate the profit they would make if they sell 12 cakes for £2.50. Explain that the information and questions given on the sheet are only the start and they are going to investigate the best way to make the maximum profit for their chosen charity (real or imaginary).

Paired work: Work in pairs to answer the questions given on the photocopiable page, reasoning about their choices and checking their calculations. They continue to use their multiplication and other calculating skills to answer the questions on the sheet. Encourage the children to record their calculations in order to demonstrate their thinking.

Progress check: Some children will find the interpretation of the information difficult. Check that they have specific tasks and know what calculations they need to do to solve them.

Review
Go through the children's calculations so far checking for any common mistakes or misconceptions which need to be addressed. Pose further questions about the process of investigation, such as: *If you have a maximum of £20.00 to spend on ingredients, what choices would you have to make to maximise your profit?* For example, they might choose only to make the cheapest cakes.

Curriculum objectives
● As per lesson 4 above.
Success criteria
● I can make decisions and solve problems using my multiplication skills.

You will need
Photocopiable sheets
'The cake bake'
Equipment
Cake baking ingredients and equipment

Differentiation
Less confident learners
Scaling in action can be seen by using a recipe multiplied up to make the product.
More confident learners
These children could be asked to budget the maximum profit they could make for their charity, giving reasons for their choices.

Lesson 5
Oral and mental starter 33

Main teaching activities
Whole-class work: During this lesson the children should continue to investigate further questions based on photocopiable page 'The cake bake' from the CD-ROM. It may be appropriate to actually bake some cakes to test the scaling multiplications of groups of children. Explain that the children will need to use calculations to present a plan of how they would organise their charity event and how much profit they expect to make. They prepare to present their plan for the cake bake to the class.

Paired work: Children should pose additional questions and produce a plan for their cake bake which includes an estimate of how much profit they would make.

Progress check: Ensure accurate multiplying and that questions pose sufficient challenge for different groups of children.

Review
During the review the children should present their calculations and explain their reasoning. The rest of the class should ask questions. After everyone has made their presentation, the class should vote on the best plan.

Adding and subtracting fractions

Expected prior learning

Children should be able to:

- recall quickly multiplication facts up to 12 × 12 and derive the corresponding division facts
- understand simple fractions of shapes
- understand that fractions relate to whole numbers and shapes divided into equal parts.

Topic	Curriculum objectives	Expected outcomes
Fractions (including decimals and percentages)	**Lesson 1** To recognise mixed numbers and improper fractions and convert from one form to the other and write mathematical statements > 1 as a mixed number.	Find equivalent fractions (for example, $\frac{7}{10} = 1\frac{4}{20}$ or $\frac{19}{10} = 1\frac{9}{10}$).
	Lesson 2 To recognise mixed numbers and improper fractions and convert from one form to the other and write mathematical statements > 1 as a mixed number.	Find equivalent fractions (for example, $\frac{7}{10} = 1\frac{4}{20}$ or $\frac{19}{10} = 1\frac{9}{10}$).
	Lesson 3 To recognise mixed numbers and improper fractions and convert from one form to the other and write mathematical statements > 1 as a mixed number.	Find equivalent fractions (for example, $\frac{7}{10} = 1\frac{4}{20}$ or $\frac{19}{10} = 1\frac{9}{10}$).
	Lesson 4 To multiply proper fractions and mixed numbers by whole numbers, supported by material and diagrams.	Express a smaller whole number as a fraction of a larger one (for example, recognise that 5 out of 8 is $\frac{5}{8}$); find equivalent fractions (for example, $\frac{7}{10} = 1\frac{4}{20}$ or $\frac{19}{10} = 1\frac{9}{10}$); relate fractions to their decimal representations. Find fractions using division (for example, $\frac{1}{100}$ of 5kg), and percentages of numbers and quantities (for example, 10%, 5% and 15% of £80).
	Lesson 5 To multiply proper fractions and mixed numbers by whole numbers, supported by material and diagrams.	Express a smaller whole number as a fraction of a larger one (for example, recognise that 5 out of 8 is $\frac{5}{8}$); find equivalent fractions (for example, $\frac{7}{10} = 1\frac{4}{20}$ or $\frac{19}{10} = 1\frac{9}{10}$); relate fractions to their decimal representations. Find fractions using division (for example, $\frac{1}{100}$ of 5kg), and percentages of numbers and quantities (for example, 10%, 5% and 15% of £80).

Preparation

Lesson 1: copy 'Bits and pieces (1)', one per child

Lesson 2: draw a number line from 0 to 2 divided into fifths on the board; copy 'Improper fractions and mixed numbers (1)', one per child

Lesson 3: make copies of 'Number lines', one per child

Lesson 4: prepare some simple fraction of numbers questions and write them on the board

Lesson 5: copy 'A fraction of your number', one per child

You will need

Photocopiable sheets

'Bits and pieces (1), (2) and (3)'; 'Improper fractions and mixed numbers (1) and (2)'; 'A fraction of your number (1), (2) and (3)'

General resources

'Number lines'

Equipment

Interlocking cubes or similar; counters; card strip; marker pen; blank cards; pens; card or commercially available fraction pieces; calculators; Blu-Tack®

Further practice

Give children further practice of ordering mixed fractions on a number line.

Oral and mental starters suggested for week 4

See bank of starters on pages 126 to 127. Oral and mental starters are also on the CD-ROM.

32 Order, order!

38 Growing number chains

40 Units of measure

Overview of progression

The lessons this week use the many links between fractions, the times tables and division. The children will need to draw on this knowledge to find fractions of numbers and quantities and also to convert fractions into decimals. The lessons this week capitalise on the links between division and fractions for example $\frac{1}{4}$ of 28 is found by dividing 28 by 4. Equally fractions can be multiplied up to find equivalent fractions. For example, $\frac{3}{4} = \frac{6}{8} = \frac{50}{100}$, $\frac{15}{4} = 3\frac{3}{4}$, and so on.

Watch out for

Some children may not understand the difference between the numerator and the denominator. These children will need practical activities in order to clarify that the denominator is the number of pieces a whole item is divided up into and the numerator is how many of those pieces we are counting. The best analogy is cutting up cake. If I cut a cake into 8 equal pieces, then the denominator or fraction piece is an eighth. The numerator shows how many of those pieces I am going to eat. For example, $\frac{3}{8}$ or 3 out of a possible 8 pieces.

Also watch out for the child that thinks every fraction is a half, which is a very common mistake. This indicates that the child is replacing the word fraction for the word half, without understanding of the physical representation indicated above. This understanding is fundamental to any fraction work.

Creative context

We use the language of fractions often in daily life, especially when sharing things or telling the time. Look for opportunities to be explicit when using these, linking them to this week's lessons.

Vocabulary

cancel, **denominator**, equivalent, fraction, **improper fraction**, mixed number, **numerator**, proper fraction, unit fraction

Curriculum objectives

● To recognise mixed numbers and improper fractions and convert from one form to the other and write >1 statements as a mixed number.

Success criteria

● I can recognise mixed number and improper fractions and convert from one form to the other and write > 1 statements as a mixed number.

You will need

Photocopiable sheets

'Bits and pieces (1), (2), (3)'

Equipment

Interlocking cubes or similar; counters; calculators; card strip; marker; Blu-Tack®

Differentiation

Less confident learners

Use the photocopiable page 'Bits and pieces (2)', which provides diagrams for the children to shade before they write the answers.

More confident learners

Use the photocopiable page 'Bits and pieces (3)', which has larger numerators to provide multiple whole numbers and more challenging calculations.

Lesson 1 — Oral and mental starter 40

Main teaching activities

Whole-class work: Revise how many fractions there are in a whole: two halves, three thirds, and so on. Discuss how $\frac{6}{5}$ must be more than a whole. Demonstrate this using interlocking cubes. Make a tower of five red cubes and say this is a whole chocolate bar. Now make a tower of six red cubes, compare it to the original and record it as $\frac{6}{5}$ or $1\frac{1}{5}$.

Write $\frac{11}{10}$ on the board. Count out 11 counters and stick them to the board with Blu-Tack®. Explain that each counter is $\frac{1}{10}$ of a packet of sweets, so we must have more than one whole packet. Draw a circle around 10 counters, then write $1\frac{1}{10}$. Ask the children to enter $11 \div 10$ into a calculator. The display will show 1.1. Explain that the first decimal place represents tenths, so the calculator shows that $\frac{11}{10}$ is greater than 1 whole.

Now write $\frac{15}{6}$. Use the counters to illustrate that this improper fraction contains 2 wholes or lots of six sixths. Demonstrate that this can be calculated by dividing the numerator by the denominator: $15 \div 6 = 2.5 = 2\frac{1}{2}$. Repeat using $\frac{13}{4}$.

Independent work: Distribute photocopiable page 'Bits and pieces (1)' from the CD-ROM. Explain that this sheet gives practice in changing improper fractions to mixed numbers and vice versa.

Progress check: Ensure that the children have understood that a mixed number fraction shows whole numbers and fractions and that they can represent this pictorially as well as with numbers.

Review

Ask the children to convert $3\frac{3}{4}$ to an improper fraction ($\frac{15}{4}$). Ask: *How did you do that? What about $5\frac{2}{3}$? What do you have to multiply? What must you remember to add? Can anyone come and write a rule saying how to do this, so we can display the rule to remind us what to do?* (Provide a card strip and marker pen for this.) Ask: *Which is bigger, $\frac{10}{3}$ or $\frac{12}{4}$?* ($\frac{10}{3} = 3\frac{1}{3}$ and $\frac{12}{4} = 3$, so $\frac{10}{3}$ is bigger). *Explain how you worked it out. Convert $\frac{82}{10}$ to a mixed number. Who can draw this on the board?*

Curriculum objectives
- To recognise mixed numbers and improper fractions and convert from one form to the other and write > 1 statements as a mixed number.

Success criteria
- I can convert mixed numbers to improper fractions and vice versa.
- I can recognise equivalent fractions.

You will need
Photocopiable sheets

'Improper fractions and mixed numbers (1) and (2)'

Equipment

Interlocking cubes

Differentiation
Less confident learners

These children could use interlocking cubes to model the number lines shown on photocopiable page 'Improper fractions and mixed numbers (1)'.

More confident learners

These children could complete photocopiable page 'Improper fractions and mixed numbers (2)', which involves converting written improper fractions to mixed numbers and vice versa, and suggesting a rule for the conversion. (For example: $\frac{33}{5} = 33 \div 5 = 6\frac{3}{5}$.)

Lesson 2

Oral and mental starter 32

Main teaching activities

Whole-class work: Ask the children to identify some simple fractions, using folded paper circles and cubes, for example: *Two cubes are green and three are blue. What fraction is blue?* ($\frac{3}{5}$) Then show them shapes or cube towers that are all one colour: *Six cubes are blue. What fraction is that?* (6 or 1 whole.) Now hold up $\frac{7}{6}$ using circles. Ask: *How many sixths is that?* (7) Write it on the board and explain that $\frac{7}{6}$ is called an improper fraction. *How else could we say this fraction?* (1 whole and $\frac{1}{6}$) Repeat using $\frac{5}{3}$ and $\frac{13}{5}$.

Display a number line divided into fifths. Count the fifths out loud together: *one fifth, two fifths, ... , five fifths or 1 whole.* Demonstrate that we can then count on in fifths (*six fifths, seven fifths, ...*) or in whole numbers and fifths (*one and one fifth, one and two fifths, ...*). Use the number line to find more equivalent fractions, such as: *What is the same as $\frac{7}{5}$?* (1 and $\frac{2}{5}$)

Paired work: Distribute photocopiable page 'Improper fractions and mixed numbers (1)' from the CD-ROM. Explain that it presents shapes and number lines for the children to identify as improper fractions and mixed numbers. (For an ICT link, look at the similar examples on www.visualfractions.com.) When they have completed the work, ask them to explain their thinking to you.

Progress check: By listening to the children discussing the placing of the fractions you will be able to assess their understanding of mixed number and improper fractions. Encourage the children to look carefully at the marked divisions on the number lines and to work out the placing accordingly.

Review

Ask the children to convert some improper fractions (such as $\frac{15}{6}$) to mixed numbers ($2\frac{3}{6}$). Ask: *Do you notice anything about that fraction?* Remind them that sometimes fractions can be further simplified because they are equivalent: $\frac{3}{6} = \frac{1}{2}$, so $\frac{15}{6} = 2\frac{3}{6} = 2\frac{1}{2}$.

Divide the class into groups of four to six children and play 'Speedy equivalents'. Call out a mixed number, such as $2\frac{4}{8}$, and ask the groups to write down as many equivalent fractions as they can in two minutes. Compare their answers, which may include $2\frac{1}{2}$, $\frac{20}{8}$, $\frac{10}{4}$, $\frac{15}{6}$, $2\frac{3}{6}$, and so on. Ask the children to explain how they decided on some of the more unusual fractions. Repeat with $1\frac{3}{4}$.

Curriculum objectives
● To recognise mixed numbers and improper fractions and convert from one form to the other.

Success criteria
● I can make decisions about ordering and comparing mixed numbers.

You will need

General resources
'Number lines'

Differentiation

Less confident learners
These children could write in all the halves first (½, 1½, 2½, ...) and then the quarters and three quarters (¼, ¾, 1¼, 1¾, 2¼, ...) halfway between these to encourage logical division of the lines.

More confident learners
Include more challenging fractions that require different divisions of the line, such as 1⅓, 3⅔, 4⅛ and 4⅜, to test the children's understanding of these divisions.

Lesson 3

Main teaching activities

Whole-class work: Explain that this lesson is about ordering mixed numbers. Draw a number line and label the ends zero and 5. Ask: *How can we mark different numbers and fractions on this line? Where on this number line would we place 2½? What about 3½? How would I know where to place 1¼ or 1¾?* Explain that we need some 'markers' to help us place numbers correctly on a line. In this instance, it would be helpful to mark the whole numbers 1 to 5 first. These in turn will enable us to find the 'half' numbers. Finally, we can mark in the quarters by halving each half. Demonstrate this on the number line, asking individuals to mark the numbers and fractions. Repeat with a number line from 10 to 20, asking the children to mark mixed numbers such as 13½, 15¼ and 17¾.

Paired work: Ask the children to draw a number line 10cm long on squared paper and label it from zero to five, marking in the integers (whole numbers) every 2cm. Now ask them to label the line with the following: 1½, 3¼, 3¾, 2¼, 4½, 4¾, ½, ¼, 2½, 3⅛, 4⅛.

Progress check: Ensure that the children are clear about the comparative size of ½, ¼ and ⅛ and how a whole number is divided by the denominator. Ask: *Which is smaller, ¼ or ⅛? How do you know?*

Paired work: If the children are ready to move on, ask them to repeat the exercise but using other fractions that are multiples of each other, for example ⅓ and ⅙.

Review

Discuss how the children have placed the mixed numbers on the number line by dividing the line between the two successive integers into the appropriate fraction of a whole. Ask questions such as: *On a number line from zero to one, where would you place ⅓? How would you divide up the line? What about finding ⅛? Or 1/16?*

Discuss how repeated halving of the line can give quarters, eighths and sixteenths. In theory you could use this method to find 1/64, but in practice it would be difficult to do that on paper. Now discuss how it is possible to mark multiples of a fraction (such as ¾) on a number line. Ask: *Where should we place ⅜ or 2³/₁₆?* Invite volunteers to demonstrate this on the board using a number line from zero to five.

Curriculum objectives
• To add and subtract fractions with the same denominator and related fractions, write mathematical statements > 1 as a mixed number.

Success criteria
• I can add and subtract fractions with the same denominator.

You will need

Equipment
Blank cards; card or plastic fraction pieces

Differentiation

Less confident learners
These children should have the support of fraction pieces to help them see how fractions can be added together to make a whole or more than one whole.

More confident learners
These children should be encouraged to use more adventurous fractions, such as twelfths, and consider what other equivalent fractions they could use to make number sentences that can be added.

Lesson 4 — Oral and mental starter 40

Main teaching activities

Whole-class work: Explain to the children that fractions represent numbers and amounts and can be added and subtracted just as with whole numbers. It is important that you add the same things together so the fractions must have the same denominator. Demonstrate some examples, such as $\frac{1}{5} + \frac{3}{5} = \frac{4}{5}$ and $\frac{3}{8} + \frac{4}{8} = \frac{7}{8}$. Liken this to fractions of a cake cut up into eighths; first you serve out three eighths and then you serve out another four eighths, so in total you have served seven of eight pieces.

Now demonstrate that it is possible to exceed one whole when adding fractions. For example, $\frac{3}{5} + \frac{2}{5} + \frac{4}{5} = \frac{9}{5}$ or 1 and $\frac{4}{5}$. Repeat with other fractions.

Paired work: Give each pair a set of blank cards and they choose a set of fractions, for example fifths or eighths, and to write the complete set out, one per card, for example $\frac{1}{5}, \frac{2}{5}, \frac{3}{5}, \frac{4}{5}, \frac{5}{5}$. They shuffle the cards and turn these face down. Ask the children to draw two cards and write them as a number sentence, adding the fractions together. They should then try adding three fractions and, if they create an improper fraction, convert it to a mixed number. Ask the children to attempt some subtraction number sentences. Then swap card sets with another pair and repeat with a different fraction set.

Progress check: Write $\frac{2}{7} + \frac{5}{7}$ on the board. Ask the children what this makes and its equivalent. Now write $1 - \frac{2}{7}$. Ask for a volunteer to tell you how you might solve this. (Convert 1 into $\frac{7}{7}$ and then subtract.)

Review
Explain that equivalent fractions can be used to allow you to add fractions if the denominators are multiples of the same number. For example: $\frac{1}{4} + \frac{1}{2}$ **does not** make $\frac{2}{6}$. They can tell this because a sixth is much smaller than either of the original fractions. Emphasise that the denominator has to be the same if we want to add fractions, change $\frac{1}{2}$ to $\frac{2}{4}$: $\frac{1}{4} + \frac{2}{4} = \frac{3}{4}$.

Curriculum objectives
• To multiply proper fractions and mixed numbers by whole numbers, supported by material and diagrams.

Success criteria
• I can calculate fractions of numbers by using division and multiplication.

You will need

Photocopiable sheets
'A fraction of your number (1), (2), (3)'

Differentiation

Less confident learners
Provide photocopiable page 'A fraction of your number (1)' which asks for simple fractions and multiple fractions using tenths only.

More confident learners
Provide photocopiable page 'A fraction of your number (3)' which asks for more complex fractions.

Lesson 5 — Oral and mental starter 32

Main teaching activities

Whole-class work: Say: a simple fraction of a number is linked to division. For example, we can find a half by dividing by 2, a quarter by dividing by 4, and so on. Ask the children to find a half of 18, 22, 24, 32. Ask: *What is a half of 7, 17, 23?* (3.5 or 3½, and so on) Extend this process by asking the children to find a third of numbers such as 12, 9, 18, 30. Ask: *If we can find ⅓ of a number, can anyone explain how we might find ⅔?* (Find ⅓ and double it.) *What is ⅔ of 15? 24? 36?* Repeat, finding ¼ and then ¾ of 32, 24, 40.

Independent and paired work: Distribute photocopiable page 'A fraction of your number (2)' from the CD-ROM. When finished, ask the children to work with a partner to find a rule to help others to know what to do.

Progress check: Ask: *If I wanted to find ⅙ of a number, what must I do? What part of a fraction determines what we divide by?* (the denominator)

Review
Write the number 5 on the board and ask the children to tell you some division facts that give this answer. Write these up around the number. Repeat for 2, 10 and 12. Encourage the children to use a wide range of times-table facts. Ask: *How did you work this out?*

Now ask the children to tell you some fractions of numbers that give the answers above. Add these to the facts already recorded on the board. Discuss how fractions are closely related to division: the denominator is the divisor and the numerator is the multiple. Ask: *What is ¾ of 24? ⅔ of 9?* and so on.

Reflections and translations

Expected prior learning

Children should be able to:

- mark a square and identify a point on a grid using alphanumeric coordinates
- name and recall the basic properties of 2D shapes.

Topic	Curriculum objectives	Expected outcomes
Geometry: position and direction	**Lesson 1**	
	To identify, describe and represent the position of a shape following a reflection or translation, using the appropriate language, and know that the shape has not changed.	Read and plot coordinates in the first quadrant. Draw the position of a shape after a reflection or translation.
	Lesson 2	
	To identify, describe and represent the position of a shape following a reflection or translation, using the appropriate language, and know that the shape has not changed.	Read and plot coordinates in the first quadrant. Draw the position of a shape after a reflection or translation.
	Lesson 3	
	To identify, describe and represent the position of a shape following a reflection or translation, using the appropriate language, and know that the shape has not changed.	Read and plot coordinates in the first quadrant. Draw the position of a shape after a reflection or translation.
	Lesson 4	
	To identify, describe and represent the position of a shape following a reflection or translation, using the appropriate language, and know that the shape has not changed.	Read and plot coordinates in the first quadrant. Draw the position of a shape after a reflection or translation.
	Lesson 5	
	To identify, describe and represent the position of a shape following a reflection or translation, using the appropriate language, and know that the shape has not changed.	Read and plot coordinates in the first quadrant. Draw the position of a shape after a reflection or translation.

■SCHOLASTIC

Preparation

Lesson 1: copy 'Drawing quadrilaterals (1)', one per child

Lesson 2: make copies of '20 × 20 grid', one per child

Lesson 3: make copies of '20 × 20 grid', one per child

Lesson 4: make copies of '20 × 20 grid', one per child

Lesson 5: copy 'Translations', one per child

You will need

Photocopiable sheets
'Drawing quadrilaterals (1) and (2)'; 'Translations'

General resources
'20 × 20 grid'; interactive teaching resource 'Squared paper'

Further practice

Encourage children to play the game 'Battleships'.

Oral and mental starters suggested for week 5

See bank of starters on pages 126 to 127. Oral and mental starters are also on the CD-ROM.

31 Counting round the room

35 Decimal doubling

36 Decimal halving

Overview of progression

These lessons explore the use of coordinates and how shapes can be reflected in a mirror line to create symmetrical patterns. There is also a focus on how the coordinates can be manipulated in order to move or translate a shape. Once the children have mastered how to use coordinates, their next challenge is to understand how adding and subtracting numbers to coordinates can have the effect of moving by sliding a shape across a grid. This can be effectively demonstrated either by creating a grid and using children to represent a point, sliding along the x or y coordinates. This is different to reflecting shapes where coordinates are used to identify the position of a point or shape and the corresponding place of the reflection. Mirrors demonstrate the need to 'flip' the shape over the mirror line.

Watch out for

Some children may confuse reflection, which requires the shape to flip over as it crosses the mirror line, and translation, which is the sliding of a shape. The latter can be done by applying a formula or 'signpost instruction'. Accurate drawing is essential and do ensure that children use coordinates that are the crossing of two lines at a point not the space between the lines.

Creative context

A good way of practising the use of coordinates is by playing the game 'Battleships'. Symmetrical patterns as created by the reflection of shapes has an application in art and design as does repeated patterns created by translations.

Vocabulary

coordinates, direction, line of symmetry, mirror line, origin, position, reflection, reflective symmetry, **translation**, x-axis, x-coordinate, y-axis, y-coordinate,

Curriculum objectives
- To represent the position of a shape.

Success criteria
- I can use coordinates to mark points on a grid and join them to draw shapes.

You will need

Photocopiable sheets
'Drawing quadrilaterals (1) and (2)'

General resources
'20 × 20 grid'; interactive teaching resource 'Squared paper'

Differentiation

Less confident learners
These children will need support from an adult to transfer from using alphanumeric coordinates to using numeric coordinates only.

More confident learners
These children can use photocopiable page 'Drawing quadrilaterals (2)', which has coordinates across two quadrants, using negative numbers on the x-axis.

Lesson 1

Main teaching activities

Whole-class work: Display photocopiable page '20 × 20 grid' from the CD-ROM and demonstrate the use of coordinates. Alternatively, draw the grid using the annotation tools on interactive teaching resource 'Squared paper' on the CD-ROM and the annotation tools. Remind the children that the x-coordinate is given first, then the y-coordinate and that they are written in brackets with a comma between them, for example: (2, 3). Write some coordinates and then mark them on the grid using small crosses and join them up with a ruler. (Do not use the coordinates given on the activity sheet.)

Independent and paired work: Distribute photocopiable page 'Drawing quadrilaterals (1)' from the CD-ROM for the children to complete individually. Make sure they understand what to do. Once the children have completed the activity, they should check their diagrams and coordinates with a partner and correct any errors.

Progress check: Accuracy when plotting the coordinates and drawing the lines to join the points is essential for these diagrams to be correct. Do not accept drawings that are a near approximation of the coordinates.

Review

Call out these coordinates for children to mark with a small cross on the second grid on the photocopiable page: (8, 10), (6, 10), (5, 9), (5, 7), (6, 6), (8, 6). Reinforce the importance of putting the x-coordinate first. Ask the children to join up these points. Ask: *What shape have you made?* (A hexagon) Discuss what would happen if the coordinates were the wrong way round. (The shape would be turned on its side.) Check the children's shapes to inform your assessment.

Curriculum objectives

● To identify, describe and represent the position of a shape following a reflection, using the appropriate language.

Success criteria

● I can reflect a pattern or shape in a mirror line to create a symmetrical pattern.

You will need

General resources

'20 × 20 grid', interactive teaching resource 'Reflection grid'

Differentiation

Less confident learners

These children may need adult support.

More confident learners

Encourage these children to use unusual shapes in their patterns such as diagonal lines, where each corner needs to be counted for reflection.

Lesson 2

Oral and mental starter

Main teaching activities

Whole-class work: Display interactive teaching resource 'Reflection grid' on the CD-ROM. Explain that the dotted red line represents a mirror and that any shape on one side will need to be reflected vertically. Demonstrate this by clicking on a square and then click 'Done'. Reflect the shape by counting the squares to the mirror line and then by counting the same number away from the mirror line on the opposite side, check this by clicking 'Check'. Repeat with a horizontal mirror line (choose this from the 'Options' menu). Repeat as necessary using patterns with two or three squares. Alternatively, complete this activity using photocopiable page '20 × 20 grid'.

Independent work: Distribute the photocopiable page sheet '20 × 20 grid'. Give the children counters to practise reflecting from square to square using different mirror positions, both vertical and horizontal.

Progress check: Ensure that the children count the squares carefully and that the reflections are correctly placed. Encourage them to stand back and check the symmetry of their pattern from time to time.

Review

Display a pattern with an incorrect reflection. Ask the children what is wrong with the reflection shown. Ask for volunteers to check by counting the squares or corners to the mirror lines. Display photocopiable page '20 × 20 grid'. Ask a child to create a pattern using coloured counters or crosses. Then ask the children to reflect the pattern, using the axes as the mirror lines. Ask: *What rule would you write to help others to reflect shapes in a mirror line?*

Curriculum objectives

● To identify, describe and represent the position of a shape following a translation, using the appropriate language, and know that the shape has not changed.

Success criteria

● I can translate a shape.
● I can read the coordinates of the translated shape.

You will need

General resources

'20 × 20 grid'

Differentiation

Less confident learners

These children group may need help to ensure that points move only in one direction along a line.

More confident learners

These children should be able to draw and translate an additional shape of their own.

Lesson 3

Oral and mental starter 35

Main teaching activities

Whole-class work: Explain to the children that when we translate a shapes it slides up or down, or left or right. Contrast this with reflecting a shape, when the shape turns over when it crosses a mirror line. Demonstrate a translation using photocopiable page '20 × 20 grid' and a 2D shape. Slide the shape along from coordinate to coordinate. Name the new coordinate. Remind the children that the x-coordinate is always given first and that coordinates are written using brackets, for example (2, 6).

Independent work: Distribute the photocopiable page sheet '20 × 20 grid' from the CD-ROM. Write the following coordinates on the board, (2,4), (2,7), (5,5). Ask the children to mark and label these points (A, B, C) and join together with a ruler. Now ask them to translate the whole shape 3 spaces to the right, draw the shape and label the points A1, B1, C1. Repeat the process, this time translating the shape 4 spaces upwards, labelling it A2, B2 and C2. Emphasise that to move the shape to the left or right the x-coordinate will change and for up and down, the y-coordinate is affected.

Progress check: Remind the children that these shapes simply slide so they should look exactly the same but will be in a different position. Ask: *What do you notice about the x- and the y-coordinates?*

Review

Ask the children to look at the coordinates of the original and translated shapes. Ask: *What pattern can you see in these coordinates? How many squares did we move the shapes? What has happened to the coordinates?* (For the first translation each x-coordinate has had six subtracted from it; for the second translation, each the y-coordinate has had seven subtracted from it.)

Curriculum objectives
● To identify, describe and represent the position of a shape following a translation, using the appropriate language, and know that the shape has not changed.

Success criteria
● I can apply a simple formula to explain the direction in which a shape is translated.

You will need
General resources
'20 × 20 grid'

Differentiation
Less confident learners
These children will need adult support to ensure accuracy.

More confident learners
These children could draw an irregular 2D shape (see diagram) and translate each point.

Lesson 4 — Oral and mental starter 17

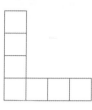

Main teaching activities

Whole-class work: Recap on how when a shape is translated, it slides. Draw a shape onto the '20 × 20 grid' resource and ask the children to name each coordinate and to identify which coordinate would change if the shape were to be translated 3 points to the right (x) Record the coordinates like this:

A (2, 15)	$\longrightarrow$	AI (3, 15)
B (5, 13)	$\longrightarrow$	BI (8, 13)
C (I, 13)	$\longrightarrow$	CI (4, 13)

Explain that this can be written as a formula $(x +3, y)$ indicating that the x coordinate has had 3 added to it but the y remains the same. Plot the new translated position of the shape and label the new coordinates. Ask the children to check the new position by counting the squares to verify the translation. Ask them to tell you the formula for moving the new shape 4 spaces downwards $(x, y − 4)$.

Independent work: Distribute '20 × 20 grid'. Ask them to draw a four sided shape in the bottom right hand corner of the grid and label the coordinates. Tell them that they are going to translate this shape into three different positions, to the top right of the grid, to the bottom left and finally to the top right of the grid. The first one may be achieved using the formula $(x, y + 8)$. Ask the children to create a recording table as shown, and to draw and mark the coordinates of the new shape on the grid. They should work out a formula and draw and record to translate the shape into the other new positions.

Progress check: Ask: *What formula have you used? If your shape has moved too far off the grid, how must you correct the formula? What is the maximum number you can use?*

Review

Ask: *Is there a single formula you could have used to move the shape diagonally in one move?* (Yes, add to the y axis and subtract from the x. For example $(x-8, y +9)$) *Did anyone do this?* Ask a child to demonstrate on the board.

Curriculum objectives
● As lesson 4 above

Success criteria
● I can understand and apply a simple formula for translating shapes.

You will need
Photocopiable sheets
'Translations'

Differentiation
Less confident learners
These children will need adult support to apply the formula correctly.

More confident learners
These children should draw more complicated shapes.

Lesson 5 — Oral and mental starter 31

Main teaching activities

Whole-class work: Consolidate the work done yesterday by asking: *If I want to translate a shape 5 spaces to the right, how does the formula change?* (add 5 to the x coordinate). *How could I move a shape diagonally 7 spaces down and left?* (Subtract 7 from both x and y coordinates).

Independent and paired work: Distribute the photocopiable page, 'Translations'. Explain that there are some shapes which need different formulas applying to them in order to translate them across the grid. Remind them that they must label each coordinate point and record the new points as AI, BI and so on to avoid confusion. When they have completed the work they should check the translated shapes with a partner and correct any errors.

Progress check: Ask: *Where do you estimate that shape 3 will move to? How do you know?*

Review

Ask: *Why is a formula used when translating points on shapes?* (A shortcut method to avoid counting squares). *How is translating a shape different to reflecting one? Describe the key differences.*

Mass

Expected prior learning

Children should be able to:

- weigh objects and read scale to determine mass
- understand that scales are made up of equal divisions that need reading.

Topic	Curriculum objectives	Expected outcomes
Measurement	**Lesson 1**	
	To convert between different units of measure [for example, kilometre and metre; centimetre and metre; centimetre and millimetre; gram and kilogram; litre and millilitre].	Solve one-step and two-step problems involving whole numbers and decimals and all four operations, choosing and using appropriate calculation strategies, including calculator use.
	To understand and use approximate equivalences between metric units and common imperial units such as inches, pounds and pints.	Represent a puzzle or problem by identifying and recording the information or calculations needed to solve it; find possible solutions and confirm them in the context of the problem.
	To use all four operations to solve problems involving measure [for example, length, mass, volume, money] using decimal notation, including scaling.	
	Lesson 2	
	To convert between different units of measure [for example, kilometre and metre; centimetre and metre; centimetre and millimetre; gram and kilogram; litre and millilitre].	Solve one-step and two-step problems involving whole numbers and decimals and all four operations, choosing and using appropriate calculation strategies, including calculator use.
	To understand and use approximate equivalences between metric units and common imperial units such as inches, pounds and pints.	Represent a puzzle or problem by identifying and recording the information or calculations needed to solve it; find possible solutions and confirm them in the context of the problem.
	To use all four operations to solve problems involving measure [for example, length, mass, volume, money] using decimal notation, including scaling.	
	Lessons 3, 4 and 5	
	To convert between different units of measure [for example, kilometre and metre; centimetre and metre; centimetre and millimetre; gram and kilogram; litre and millilitre].	Solve one-step and two-step problems involving whole numbers and decimals and all four operations, choosing and using appropriate calculation strategies, including calculator use.
	To understand and use approximate equivalences between metric units and common imperial units such as inches, pounds and pints.	Represent a puzzle or problem by identifying and recording the information or calculations needed to solve it; find possible solutions and confirm them in the context of the problem.
	To use all four operations to solve problems involving measure [for example, length, mass, volume, money] using decimal notation, including scaling.	

Preparation

Lesson I: assemble a variety of items (or pictures of items) and a variety of equipment for measuring mass using a variety of scales

Lesson 2: assemble a variety of equipment for measuring mass

Lesson 3: assemble a collection of items to measure, a variety of equipment for measuring mass and some known weights

Lesson 4: copy 'Imperial/metric mass conversion chart', one per child; assemble some recipe books, a variety of equipment for measuring mass and food packaging displaying weight labels

Lesson 5: assemble a suitcase and a variety of items that children might choose to pack for a winter holiday and a variety of equipment for measuring mass

You will need

Photocopiable sheets

'Imperial/metric mass conversion chart'

General resources

Interactive teaching resource 'Weighing scales'

Equipment

Variety of different weighing equipment, items to measure; known weights such as 50g, 500g and 1kg; recipe books; food packaging displaying weight labels, and items that children might choose to pack for a winter holiday, such as jumpers, shoes, book, toothbrush and so on

Further practice

Opportunities for practical applications of measuring mass and converting between units, for instance, an exploration of food sold by weight. Use the interactive teaching resource 'Weighing scales' for practice in reading scales.

Oral and mental starters suggested for week 6

See bank of starters on pages 126 to 127. Oral and mental starters are also on the CD-ROM.

33 Target number

38 Growing number chains

39 Shrinking number chains

Overview of progression

This week's lessons focus on mass and the common units, both metric and imperial, used to measure mass. An important part of accurate measuring is reading the scales effectively, which can be confusing when different pieces of measuring equipment use differently graduated scales. Children are given the opportunity to read and measure with a variety of different scales and to estimate and to understand the likely weight of common items.

Watch out for

Some children may confuse imperial and metric measures since ounces, pounds and stones are often commonly used alongside grams and kilograms on market stalls for example.

Creative context

There are many practical applications of this type of measure and good examples of where accuracy is very important, for example, in baking.

Vocabulary

grams (g), imperial measures (ounces, pounds, stones), kilograms (kg), scale

Curriculum objectives
● To convert between different units of measure (for example, gram and kilogram).

Success criteria
● I can understand that there are different instruments to measure mass and that they have different scale divisions.
● I can choose an appropriate measure for weighing different items.

You will need

Equipment
A variety of items (or pictures of items) for children to match to appropriate measuring equipment; A variety of equipment for measuring mass using a variety of scales: for example, a top pan balance, a set of bathroom scales, a spring balance; You may also wish to introduce electronic digital scales

Differentiation

Less confident learners
Provide a number of real items for these children to handle and experiment using the various measuring instruments.

More confident learners
These children should be able to estimate and categorise without actual items and to choose appropriate scales, for example, the weight of an elephant would be estimated in kilograms (although it probably wouldn't fit on their bathroom scales) whereas sweets are measured in grams.

Lesson 1 — Oral and mental starter 33

Main teaching activities

Whole-class work: Show the children the collection of equipment for measuring mass. Ask them to tell you what could be measured with each one, and in what units. Discuss the need for a range of units of measure. Explain that different types of measuring equipment use different units and that particular units are more suitable for some things than for others. For example, the spring balance scales would be useful for weighing flour, pencils or raspberries within the range of a few grams to 3 or 4 kilograms. However, standing scales are more appropriate for weighing people in kilograms or stones and pounds, as weighing a person in grams would result in a large and awkward number.

Remind the children that in the UK some people still use the imperial measures of stones, pounds and ounces and tell them that they will look at equivalents later in the week.

Paired work: Provide a variety of items (or pictures of items) for children to match to appropriate measuring equipment, based on the scale that each is divided into. Once they have done this they could begin to estimate the weight of the items. If you can provide real items, the children can check their ideas.

Progress check: It may prove difficult for some children to understand the different scales used by different pieces of weighing equipment. Hold up a small item such as a pencil or an apple and place it on the standing scales. Ask the children to explain why this is not a helpful choice of instrument. Demonstrate how it does not register on such a large scale. Ask the children to identify the scale divisions.

Review

Discuss the activity. Go through the different pieces of equipment that you have provided identifying the scale divisions, the maximum and minimum weight that could be measured and checking the children's estimates. Ask the children to sort the items (or pictures) by appropriate unit of measure.

Curriculum objectives
● To convert between different units of measure (such as gram and kilogram).
Success criteria
● I can work out what the divisions on a weighing scale represent.

You will need
General resources
Interactive teaching resource 'Weighing scales'
Equipment
A variety of equipment for measuring mass

Differentiation
Less confident learners
These children may need adult support.
More confident learners
Challenge these children to add an extra column to their table, suggesting items that could be suitably measured using each type of apparatus.

Lesson 2
Oral and mental starter 33

Main teaching activities

Whole-class work: Show the children the collection of measuring equipment. Explain that they have to decide what units of measure are being used by each piece of equipment and how big the divisions are. For example, a top pan balance may measure in divisions of 25g. Ask a child to write a label, for example 'Divisions of 25g', and place it on the balance. Do this with the other items of measuring equipment. Some may have two labels; for example, kitchen scales may measure in both kilograms and grams. Explain that the children will need to look for clues on the equipment, for instance, weighing scales often have the weight divisions written on the dial. Noticing the divisions is important for accurate measuring and reading from a scale.

Paired work: The children work in pairs to examine the equipment and complete a table to record the scale and unit that each piece of apparatus uses for measurement. For example:

Apparatus	Division of measure
Top pan balance	25g

They complete this for all the equipment that you have provided, including the interactive teaching resource 'Weighing scales' on the CD-ROM.

Progress check: Check that the children have understood how to read the scale and that they have taken account of the whole number divisions such as 100g, 25g or 1kg in order to 'count on' accurately.

Review

Discuss the information the children used when making their decisions about the steps in the scale. Ask: *Do all scales start from zero? Why would it not be helpful for all scales to count on in 'ones'?*

Curriculum objectives
● To convert between different units of measure.
Success criteria
● I can measure accurately using kilograms and grams.

You will need
General resources
Interactive teaching resource 'Weighing scales'
Equipment
Items to measure; a variety of equipment for measuring mass; weights such as 50g, 500g and 1kg

Differentiation
Less confident learners
Ask these children to compare the items that they are weighing with 50g, 500g and 1kg weights.
More confident learners
Ask children to group items which total 1kg when added together. Check by weighing.

Lesson 3
Oral and mental starter 38

Main teaching activities

Whole-class work: Explain that while it is important to choose the correct unit of measure, sometimes it is more convenient to use mixed units than just to use one unit. For example, if we want 1.5 kilograms of dried fruit for a cake, it is easier to measure 1kg and 500g than to measure using only grams or kilograms. In order to measure accurately, it is useful to know the equivalent amounts for each unit: 1000 grams = 1 kilogram. It may help the children to remember that 'kilo' means 1000 and 'milli' means $\frac{1}{1000}$.

Demonstrate using the interactive teaching resource 'Weighing scales' on the CD-ROM how to work out the divisions on various scales. Discuss how to estimate when the pointer falls midway between two divisions. Remind the children that they need to look for and count on from whole kilograms or 100g as well as reading the small divisions.

Paired work: Ask the children to use a variety of instruments to weigh accurately the items that you have provided. Ask them to estimate their approximate weight first. Record the results in both kilograms and grams and just kilograms.

Progress check: Ask individuals to describe how they are calculating the exact measures. Ensure that they have understood the divisions and are counting on accurately.

Review

Ask: *How can we write 550g as kilograms? Which is bigger: 5000g or 6kg? Which items could we add together to make the closest to 1kg?*

■SCHOLASTIC

Curriculum objectives
• To understand and use approximate equivalences between metric units and common imperial units such as inches, pounds and pints.

Success criteria
• I can recognise the common imperial measures for mass.
• I can estimate equivalence between imperial and metric measures.

You will need
Photocopiable sheets
'Imperial/metric mass conversion chart'

Equipment
Recipe books; a variety of equipment for measuring mass; food packaging displaying weight labels, such as bag of apples, flour, sugar

Differentiation
Less confident learners
These children may need adult support to convert the equivalent measures.

More confident learners
These children could go on to research other systems of measurement for mass.

Lesson 4
Oral and mental starter 39

Main teaching activities
Whole-class work: Remind the children that the UK has a dual system of units of measurement. While metric measures are standard in shops, education and commerce, many people still use the imperial units of measure that were in common usage until the 1970s. This is particularly noticeable with units of measure for mass since many people still use ounces, pounds and stones. Most adults will know their weight in stones rather than kilograms and, although by law food has to be sold in metric amounts, many people still use the imperial equivalents at home for quantities, particularly when cooking. Explain that it is worth knowing the approximate equivalents in order to make comparisons when presented with imperial measures.

Paired work: Distribute photocopiable page 'Imperial/metric mass conversion chart'. The children should work in pairs to search through recipe books to find which units of measure are used. (Sometimes both are given).They should then convert a recipe from one unit to the other, such as grams to ounces or vice versa. They look at the labels on food packaging. Convert the weights given to their approximate imperial equivalent and record it in the table on the photocopiable page. They continue finding equivalents to get a feel for the amounts. If children wish to volunteer, they could weigh themselves and convert their mass in kilograms to its approximate imperial equivalent.

Progress check: Ensure that children are using the approximations to estimate equivalents and that they are calculating accurately. Ask: *Which is smaller, one gram or one ounce?*

Review
Ask: *Why is it a bad idea to mix imperial and metric measures in a cake recipe?* (The approximations are not exact and so the quantities would not be an accurate balance.) *Why do you think people still use two systems of measures for mass?* (Common usage, habit, common understanding) *Why do you think the metric system was introduced in Britain?* (To be in step with the rest of Europe. It was confusing for trading with other countries.)

Curriculum objectives
• To solve problems involving measure (mass) using decimal notation.

Success criteria
• I can add measures together and convert between grams and kilograms.

You will need
Equipment
Items for a winter holiday (jumpers, book, toothbrush; equipment for measuring mass

Differentiation
Less confident learners
Children may need adult help with the organisation, measuring and calculations.

More confident learners
These children should be able to estimate by rounding and estimating first.

Lesson 5
Oral and mental starter 39

Main teaching activities
Whole-class work: Explain to the children that they are going to use their acquired knowledge of measuring mass in a practical situation. Tell them that they are going to pack a suitcase to go on a snowy winter holiday. Tell them that many airlines have a weight restriction on luggage. Tell them that their luggage must weigh less than 10kg and they must work out what they are going to pack. Demonstrate how they might keep a running total of the masses.

Paired work: In pairs they should make a list of desirable items, for example, how many numbers of jumpers they require, and so on. Then they should weigh their chosen items and add them together to keep a running total. Once they have completed their list they should pack their suitcase and weigh it. They will need to think about how to do this.

Progress check: Check the accuracy of the addition especially if the children are adding mixed measures – grams and kilograms. Check the place value.

Review
Ask: *How did you decide to weigh your suitcase. Which piece of apparatus was the most useful? Which couldn't you use?* (It is likely that the best way would be to weigh a person on bathroom scales and then weigh the person plus the suitcase.) Ask: *Did you take the mass of the suitcase into consideration?*

Curriculum objectives
● To interpret negative numbers in context, count forwards and backwards with positive and negative whole numbers, including through zero.

You will need
1. Check
Oral and mental starter
31 Counting round the room

2. Assess
Books; individual whiteboards

3. Further practice
General resources
'Number lines';
'Negative number cards'

Negative numbers

Most children should be able to understand negative numbers as the distance from zero in a real-life context.

Some children will not have made such progress and will require extra practice with a number line to visualise that a negative number is smaller than zero.

1. Check

31 Counting round the room

Use the oral and mental starter to count back in various even steps from 10 to beyond zero. Repeat this several times in order for you to observe children who confidently cross zero and those who are less confident.

- *What is 3 less than 1? How do you know? Which is smaller, minus 8 or minus 15? Explain why. Can you calculate the difference between minus 6 and 3? Explain how you do this? Where in life do we use negative numbers?*

2. Assess

Extend the oral and mental starter to include stopping at any point in the counting and asking the children to calculate the difference between a negative and a positive number. Watch out for children who still think that negative numbers are the same as fractions or do not have a real value. Record the outcomes.

3. Further practice

Use number cards to represent negative numbers and encourage less confident learners to place them accurately in order on a number line. Continue to use the oral and mental starter to practise counting when crossing zero.

Curriculum objectives
● To add and subtract whole numbers with more than four-digits, including using efficient written methods (columnar addition and subtraction).

You will need
1. Check
Oral and mental starter
38 Growing number chains

2. Assess
'Total score'

3. Further practice
Oral and mental starter
31 Counting round the room

General resources
'Number lines'

Efficient adding: using mental skills in written addition

Most children should be able to use a formal written calculation to add 4-digit numbers together.

Some children will not have made such progress and will require support with counting on using a number line to cross the 10 or 100 boundaries.

1. Check

38 Growing number chains

The oral and mental starter will demonstrate the children's skill in quick addition to support their written calculations. Look for the less confident learners who are not secure with number bonds or who do not have a variety of strategies to draw upon for adding on. Observe the confident learners who can mentally make 10 or 100 in a variety of ways so that they can add rapidly. Ask: *What pattern are you looking for when adding? How do you cross the tens or hundreds boundary? What strategy do you use? Explain what you do?*

2. Assess

As the children solve the addition questions on photocopiable page 128 'Total score', observe their ways of working and their confidence with addition. Confident learners will be able to use a version of columnar addition, either expanded or with carrying. Less confident learners may be insecure with their number bonds and still be counting on using fingers or be misunderstanding the place value of the digits they are adding. Record the outcomes.

3. Further practice

Use the oral and mental starter to build extra confidence when adding mentally in order to support written calculations. Some children may need to return to using number lines to count on efficiently.

Curriculum objectives
● To solve addition and subtraction multi-step problems in contexts, deciding which operations and methods to use and why.

You will need
1. Check
Oral and mental starter
39 Shrinking number chains

2. Assess
'Give and take'

3. Further practice
Oral and mental starter
38 Growing number chains

Written addition and subtraction to solve problems in context

Most children should be able to use efficient methods of addition and subtraction to solve problems.

Some children will not have made such progress and will require further practice to decode a problem and to calculate accurately.

1. Check

39 Shrinking number chains

Use the oral and mental starter to assess the speed and accuracy of mental subtraction methods. Watch for the children who are trying to 'count back' in ones using their fingers and provide extra practice with number bonds. *Which subtractions are easy? Which ones are trickier? How do you calculate when crossing a 10 or 100 boundary? Tell me your strategy.*

2. Assess

Distribute photocopiable page 129 'Give and take'. Observe the ways in which the children organise the information and interpret the context of a problem. Confident learners will be able to subtract using a formal method. Less confident learners may need the support of a number line. Record the outcomes.

3. Further practice

Use the oral and mental starter to practise more efficient methods of mental calculations.

Curriculum objectives
● To solve problems involving number up to three decimal places.

You will need
1. Check
Oral and mental starters
35 Decimal doubling
36 Decimal halving

2. Assess
'Measures mayhem'

3. Further practice
Oral and mental starter
15 Place value shuffle

General resources
'Place value chart'; '0–30 number cards'

Understand the value of decimal digits and use this to solve problems

Most children should be able to identify the value of digits up to three decimal places and use this knowledge to solve problems in context.

Some children will not have made such progress and will require extra practice with the place value of decimals.

1. Check

35 Decimal doubling

36 Decimal halving

Use these oral and mental starters to give practice in calculating with 2 and 3 place decimals, recording the accuracy of the place value. *Tell me the value of this digit. Explain your strategy you are using to double and halve decimals. If this number were a fraction of a litre, how many millilitres would it be? How do you know?*

2. Assess

As the children work through photocopiable page 130 'Measures mayhem', observe the ways in which they convert between decimals and whole numbers. Some children need extra practice first with one and 2-digit decimal numbers. Confident children will be able to use the equivalence to solve problems. Record the outcomes.

3. Further practice

Use the oral and mental starter to make numbers with two and three decimal places, encouraging the children to identify the value of the digits and to understand their value in contexts of money and measures. Support their understanding by placing number cards on a place value chart.

Oral and mental starters

Number and place value

31 Counting round the room

This activity can encompass any number patterns such as: counting on and back in 100s from 7, counting in jumps of 1000 from 3, counting on and back in 10s from 1, all the square numbers to 100, and so on. You start the pattern and the children chant with you until you indicate that they should stop or begin to count backwards.

Alternatively, an extension to this is to choose a pattern to chant but when children come to an 'unusual' number such as a prime number or a square number they should say instead 'Goose' or 'Duck', to demonstrate to you their understanding.

32 Order, order!

Write up a combination of fractions and decimal fractions. Ask the children to order them, smallest to largest explaining their reasons as they go. For example,

Order the following: 0.78; $\frac{1}{76}$; $\frac{1}{10}$; $\frac{1}{100}$; 0.2; 0.99; $\frac{1}{2}$

Repeat with different fraction equivalents as the children become more confident.

Multiplication and division

33 Target number

Select the following cards from the numbers cards 1–100: 2, 3, 4, 5, 6, 7, 8, 9, 10, 20, 25, 30, 50, 100.

Shuffle them and invite a child to select three or four cards. Challenge them to make the smallest or the largest number possible using all the numbers only once and any of the four operations.

Alternatively, you could choose a target number and then the children select three or four cards which they use to make it exactly or as near to it as possible. For example,

Target number: 205

Numbers selected: 4, 5, 10, 25

$(25 \times 10) - (5 \times 4) = 205$

This activity can be extended to use five or six number cards.

34 What's the question?

Explain to the children that they are going to use their knowledge of known times tables as well as multiples of 10 and 100 to make plausible and accurate suggestions to complete the following number sentences. Remind them that there may be more than one answer for each sentence. They should record their answers on a whiteboard and be prepared to explain their thinking.

On the board write blank number sentences such as:

___ ÷ ___ = 3;   ___ ÷ ___ = 25;   ___ ÷ ___ = 40;

___ ÷ ___ = 4;   ___ ÷ ___ = 9;   ___ ÷ ___ = 15

37 Fast times

Tell the children that they are going to see how many multiplication facts they can complete in 3 minutes. All they need to do is write down the answer on their whiteboard. If they do not recall an answer they should put a small cross or a dot, which will help them to identify the facts that they still find tricky to recall instantly.

Call out multiplication facts, for example, 4 × 6; 2 × 8; and so on, at a reasonably fast pace. It is helpful for you to jot them down as you call them out for ease of checking later.

This activity can be repeated often, to see if the children can improve the number that they can complete accurately in the time.

Addition and subtraction

35 Decimal doubling

In pairs, named A and B: A is given the starting decimal number, B doubles it and so on until one of them can say 'over 10' and wins a point. Play starts again with player B. The person with the most points at the end wins.

Starting numbers could be: 0.2; 1.1; 0.5; 1.3; 0.7; 1.3; 0.08

36 Decimal halving

In pairs, named A and B: A is given a starting decimal number over 10. B halves it and they take turns to continue halving until one of them can say 'less than 1' and wins a point. Play starts again with B. The person with the most points wins.

Starting points might be: 100; 250; 112.2; 128.6; 170.5

38 Growing number chains

Groups of children should be given a dice or pair of dice. Explain that they are going to roll the dice (or both dice) and add the numbers to their previous total until they reach or exceed an agreed total. (50 or 100 should be sufficient for a single dice.) They can do this altogether or round the group, with the other members of the group checking for accuracy as they go. This will give them practice at quick addition.

39 Shrinking number chains

Groups of children should be given a dice or pair of dice and a starting number such as 500. They throw the dice (or both dice) and subtract the number thrown from the previous total until they reach less than 10. They can do this altogether or round the group, with the other members of the group checking for accuracy as they go. This will give them practice at quick subtraction.

Measurement

40 Units of measure

Practising equivalent measures will give children the opportunity to learn the equivalents but also to practise multiplying and dividing by 100 and 1000 as well as increasing their familiarity with decimal fractions. Write on the board:

0.5 litres; 1.25kg; 300mm; 1625cm; 600g; 1.4kg; 7.2km; 300m

Ask the children to work in pairs to discuss ways in which these measures could be expressed differently using larger or smaller units of measure. It might help them to revise standard equivalents first. For example:
1 litre = 1000ml; 100cm = 1 m; 10 mm = 1cm; 1000mm = 1m; and so on.

Total score

■ Here are the scores of four friends who played a computer game together.

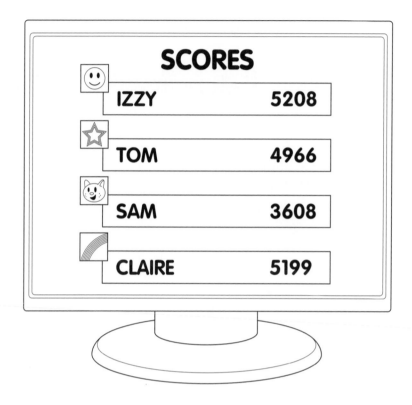

SCORES

☺	IZZY	5208
☆	TOM	4966
🐱	SAM	3608
🌈	CLAIRE	5199

1. Izzy and Tom were on one team and Sam and Claire on another. What were the team scores?

   Izzy and Tom's team: _____

   Sam and Claire's team: _____

2. What was the combined score for the girls? _____

3. What was the combined score for the boys? _____

4. What was the total score of all four players? _____

I can use formal addition methods to solve problems.

How did you do?

Name: _____   Date: _____

Give and take

■ Solve the following problems using your chosen methods.

I. 2014 − 938

2. Double 278

3.

  a) On Saturday 2964 people attended a football match and on the following week 1953 people attended a hockey match at the same ground. How many people went through the turnstile?

  b) In the week before the football match, 8202 people had crowded through the gate to watch a boy band. How many more people went to the concert than attended the sports matches?

4. Gran raised £3062 for charity in one year. Alfie raised half as much. How much did they raise for charity altogether?

5. A park keeper planted 8260 bulbs in the park. 1021 were tulips, 2884 were daffodils and the rest were bluebells. How many bluebells were there?

I can use formal addition and subtraction methods to solve everyday problems.

How did you do?

Measures mayhem

- Dougal the DIY store keeper has a problem. All of his items have been delivered with only decimal amounts on the label and he needs to convert them to millilitres, grams and metres. Help him to complete the labels.
- Remember: 1000ml = 1 litre   1000m = 1km   1000g = 1kg

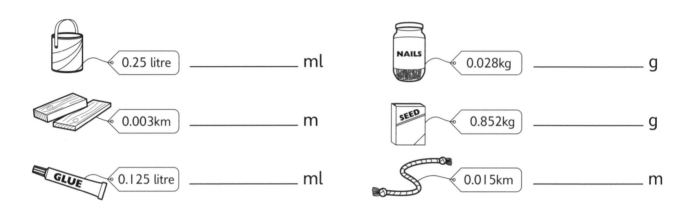

0.25 litre	_____ ml
0.003km	_____ m
0.125 litre	_____ ml
0.028kg	_____ g
0.852kg	_____ g
0.015km	_____ m

- Hamish came into the store with a shopping list. How many of each item does he need to buy?

3 litres of paint

18m of wood

0.5 litres of glue

500g of nails

4.5kg of seed

100m rope

I can understand the value of decimal digits and use this knowledge to solve problems.

How did you do?

PHOTOCOPIABLE

Addition and subtraction: mental and written methods for large numbers

Expected prior learning

Children should be able to:

- be secure in the understanding of the process for addition and subtraction
- use a range of strategies for adding and subtracting numbers, either formal or informal.

Topic	Curriculum objectives	Expected outcomes
Addition and subtraction	**Lesson 1**	
	To add and subtract whole numbers with more than four-digits, including using formal written methods (columnar addition and subtraction). To add and subtract numbers mentally with increasingly large numbers.	Use formal written methods to add and subtract whole numbers and decimals with up to two decimal places. Extend mental methods for whole-number calculations, for example to multiply a two-digit by a one-digit number (12 × 9), to multiply by 25 (16 × 25), subtract one near-multiple of 1000 from another (6070 − 4097).
	Lesson 2	
	To add and subtract whole numbers with more than four-digits, including using formal written methods (columnar addition and subtraction). To add and subtract numbers mentally with increasingly large numbers.	Use formal written methods to add and subtract whole numbers and decimals with up to two decimal places. Extend mental methods for whole-number calculations, for example to multiply a two-digit by a one-digit number (12 × 9), to multiply by 25 (16 × 25), subtract one near-multiple of 1000 from another (6070 − 4097).
	Lesson 3	
	To use rounding to check answers to calculations and determine, in the context of a problem, levels of accuracy. To solve addition and subtraction multi-step problems in contexts, deciding which operations and methods to use and why.	Solve one-step and two-step problems involving whole numbers and decimals and all four operations, choosing and using appropriate calculation strategies, including calculator use.
	Lessons 4 and 5	
	To use rounding to check answers to calculations and determine, in the context of a problem, levels of accuracy. To solve addition and subtraction multi-step problems in contexts, deciding which operations and methods to use and why.	Solve one-step and two-step problems involving whole numbers and decimals and all four operations, choosing and using appropriate calculation strategies, including calculator use.

Preparation

Lesson 1: copy 'Sid's snowy sports shop', one per child

Lesson 2: make copies of 'Number lines', one per child if needed

Lesson 3: copy 'Maths Theme Park', one per child

Lesson 5: copy 'Lots to think about', one per child

You will need

Photocopiable sheets

'Sid's snowy sports shop'; 'Maths Theme Park'; 'Lots to think about'

General resources

'Number lines'

Further practice

Give children squared paper to practise lining up digits using formal written methods of calculation. Interactive teaching resource 'Squared paper' on the CD-ROM can also be used for demonstration purposes.

Oral and mental starters suggested for week 1

See bank of starters on pages 167 to 168. Oral and mental starters are also on the CD-ROM.

41 Ordering measures

43 Hit the target number

46 It's all in a word

Overview of progression

This week addition and subtraction includes the use of larger numbers including decimals in the context of money. There are opportunities to solve problems in a 'real' context, adding more than two numbers accurately, using column addition. The totals can then be used to calculate the change in a formal way.

Watch out for

Some children may find presentation of their work difficult. It is important that they set out their digits in the correct place value columns and that they align the decimal point for accurate answers.

Creative context

The photocopiable sheets offer a context although there may be a similar 'real-life' scenario at school that offers the same opportunities for adding and subtracting money. This could be shopping with the family, prices at a school fair, choosing in a café or visiting a gift shop. Any links you can create with events at school would make the experiences more meaningful.

Vocabulary

add, answer, calculate, calculation, decimal place, decimal point, difference, explain, **inverse**, jotting, method, multiple, operation, problem, reasoning, significant digit, solution, strategy, subtract, sum, symbol, total

Curriculum objectives

- To add whole numbers with more than four-digits, including using formal written methods (columnar addition and subtraction).
- To add numbers mentally with increasingly large numbers.

Success criteria

- I can add more than two items using columnar addition.

You will need

Photocopiable sheets

'Sid's snowy sports shop'

Differentiation

Less confident learners

Children may still need to use informal methods of calculating.

More confident learners

Encourage the children to use the standard compact method for their calculations and to check their answers by adding in a different order.

Lesson 1 — Oral and mental starter 41

Main teaching activities

Whole-class work: Explain that today's activities will include adding more than two items. Revise how to do this, including 'carrying', for example: 84p + 98p involves 8p +4p making more than 10 so one 'ten' or 10p is 'carried' into the tens column= £1.82. Remind the children of familiar addition strategies, such as looking for opportunities to make 10 or using near doubles. Also demonstrate how we can check an addition by adding the numbers in a different order, perhaps adding the most significant digits first.

Independent work: Distribute photocopiable page 'Sid's snowy sports shop' from the CD-ROM. Ask the children to calculate the given shopping bills from the price list. The last question is relatively open. The children should complete the work and check their calculations by adding in a different order or by explaining their thinking to a partner.

Progress check: Choose three items from the price list and ask the children to round their value first before you write them on the board. Then ask the children to add them mentally. Remind them that rounding and estimating is a good way to ensure that the final answer that they calculate is the correct size. Encourage them to do this each time.

Review

Write a list of three of the items from Sid's snowy sports shop on the board. Ask: *Why is it not advisable to try to add more than two of these numbers mentally? What advice would you give to someone who is adding a list of numbers, especially decimal numbers such as amounts of money?* Listen to reasons for the choice of various methods. Make a class checklist of suggestions. This should include: line up the place values exactly; write the carried-over number below the calculation in the correct place value position; look for easy addition strategies; check with an alternative calculation. Share some of the children's answers to the photocopiable sheet. Ask the children to use the class checklist to find out where they have made errors and to correct some of the calculations together on the board. Use this to establish any problem areas.

Curriculum objectives

● To add and subtract whole numbers with more than four-digits, including using formal written methods (columnar addition and subtraction).
● To add and subtract numbers mentally with increasingly large numbers.

Success criteria

● I can decide how to formally calculate to find the amount of change due in money problems.

You will need

Photocopiable sheets

'Sid's snowy sports shop'

General resources

'Number lines'

Differentiation

Less confident learners

Children may find it helpful to count on using a number line.

More confident learners

Offer an additional challenge to these children, for example: *Imagine you have £200 to spend at Sid's snowy sports shop. You cannot go over this limit. Try to spend as much money as possible. What is the smallest amount of change you could receive?*

Lesson 2 Oral and mental starter 41

Main teaching activities

Whole-class work: Explain that today's activity continues with the theme of Sid's snowy sports shop, but involves problems with more than one step. For example: *If I buy my nephew a pair of skates, a pair of socks, a pair of gloves and a hat, how much change will I get from £100?* Work through this problem together, pointing out that the first step is to work out how much was spent and the second step is to subtract that from £100. Ask for volunteers to work through the steps on the board. Ask: *Do we need written subtraction to work out the change?* Help the children to see that it is easier to count on to £100, since this is a relatively small difference.

Independent and paired work: Set a budget and ask the children to calculate the change for five sets of two items, using the price list on photocopiable page 'Sid's snowy sports shop' from the CD-ROM. On completion of the activity, the children should check their answers with a partner. Ask the children to discuss in particular the steps taken to calculate the appropriate change. Did both children calculate this in the same way? Where are the 'tricky' parts, where errors can easily be made?

Progress check: Use this activity to assess the efficiency and accuracy of the children's written addition calculations and to correct any misconceptions. Remind the children that to round and estimate both the additions and the subtractions will help them recognise if they have made a mistake with their calculations.

Review

Ask the class: *What is an inverse operation? How can using the inverse operation help us to check this work?* Remind the children that the inverse is the opposite of a given operation, reversing the effect – for example, adding after subtracting or multiplying after dividing. Explain that this is helpful for checking an answer: for example, we can check a subtraction by adding the answer and the lower of the original numbers and should get the higher number of the original numbers. Demonstrate this using some of the sports shop examples. Ask one child to provide a back-up by checking these examples on the board, using the expanded method of addition with informal jottings.

Curriculum objectives

● To use rounding to check answers to calculations and determine, in the context of a problem, levels of accuracy.
● To solve addition and subtraction multi-step problems in contexts, deciding which operations and methods to use and why.

Success criteria

● I can add and subtract to solve 'real-life' problems in context.

You will need

Photocopiable sheets

'Maths Theme Park'

Differentiation

Less confident learners

You could prepare a supplementary planning sheet for these children to use as a framework for planning activities and calculating costs.

More confident learners

Differentiate the activity by outcome. Look for more adventurous choices.

Lesson 3   Oral and mental starter 43

Main teaching activities

Whole-class work: Explain to the children that during the next two days, they are going to use all of their problem-solving, addition and subtraction skills. They have to use the information on photocopiable page 'Maths Theme Park' from the CD-ROM to plan a seven-day holiday for two people. They will need to plan visits and activities over the seven days but they must keep to a budget. Their holiday spending money is €1000 for the week and this must pay for everything including drinks, lunch, snacks and so on. Model an example that might represent Day 1, such as:

Visit to the Maths Theme Park – Day 1

Entry fees	2 × €16.00	= €32.00
Tricky Tractors	2 × €1.50	= €3.00
Wacky Walrus	2 × €4.00	= €8.00
Skyrider	2 × €3.00	= €6.00
Ice cream	2 × €1.00	= €2.00
Sandwich and drink	2 × €7.00	= €14.00
Total for the day		= €65.00
Money left over	€1000 − €65	= €935.00

Paired work: Ask the children to use the price lists on the photocopiable sheet to plan holiday activities for two people for seven days, keeping within the €1000 overall budget. Allow the children to work in pairs at their own pace. Some may manage only a few days' planning; others may complete the week.

Progress check: Remind the children of the importance of aligning digits and decimal points to avoid errors with place value and incorrect addition. Ask: *How much have you spent so far? How much have you left? Don't forget that there are two people not just yourself.*

Review

Use this time to check the children's progress and troubleshoot difficulties. Remind the children that there are two people and everything has to be paid for per person, so some doubling will be needed.

Ask: *What method are you using to keep track of your running total?* Some children may prefer to draw a number line and count on each day's spending; others will be subtracting as they go, using the compact written method. Ask: *If I spend €379 in the first two days, how much will I have left for the rest of the week?* Ask for volunteers to demonstrate their methods of finding the answer, one of which is shown below.

$$
\begin{array}{r}
{}^{0}\!\!\not{1}\;\;{}^{9}\!\!\not{0}\;\;{}^{9}\!\!\not{0}\;\;{}^{1}0 \\
-\quad 3\;\;\;7\;\;\;9 \\
\hline
6\;\;\;2\;\;\;1
\end{array}
$$

Lesson 4

Main teaching activities

Paired work: Continue from the previous lesson. An extension challenge, for children who have finished the main task, might be to plan an alternative day out. Allow them to add to the lists of tariffs with their own ideas of holiday fun. Set a budget of €100 and tell them that all expenses must be fully accounted for. They can invent places to visit and think of likely costs.

Progress check: Encourage the children to talk through their choices with you, explaining their calculation strategies and checking answers against their estimates.

Review

Ask questions to assess the children's ability in computation, estimation and decision-making: *What skills have you employed to solve this problem?* (The children should be able to identify decision-making, doubling, adding, subtracting and so on.) *How did you decide which part to do first? Did you plan how much to spend each day? How did you calculate the cost of that excursion? Can you persuade us that this is the most suitable method to use? Are your strategies most suited to these particular numbers? Which operation did you use? Did anybody run out of money?*

Lesson 5

Main teaching activities

Whole-class work: Distribute photocopiable page 171 'Lots to think about'. Explain that some problems need more than one calculation or operation to solve them. The skill is understanding the problem and selecting the correct numbers and operations to use. Sometimes mathematical wording might be used in the question and at other times they will need to understand the sense of what is being asked.

Paired work: Ask the children to read each question one at a time and discuss with a partner the clue words. Each time they should identify the key words, decide on the operation, round and estimate to find the likely size of the answer and decide whether it is a mental calculation or one that requires jotting or a written calculation. When you are confident they have understood all the questions, they should solve the problems, being prepared to explain their choices of operation to you.

Progress check: Ask: *Do you expect the answer to be bigger or smaller than the original numbers? Which 'clue' words tell you which operation to use?* Share these by underlining the key words on the board.

Review

Go through the questions identifying with the children the operations they chose and what information they used to decide. Convert some of the questions into diagrams to clarify thinking. Identify any difficulties and share the questions that some of the children may have written.

Multiplication and division: written methods

Expected prior learning

Children should be able to:

- recall multiplication facts to 12 × 12
- understand how multiplication and division are linked
- use a written calculation for multiplication and division even if only an expanded version.

Topic	Curriculum objectives	Expected outcomes
Multiplication and division	**Lesson 1**	
	To multiply and divide whole numbers and those involving decimals by 10, 100 and 1000.	Use understanding of place value to multiply whole numbers by 10, 100 or 1000.
	Lesson 2	
	To multiply and divide whole numbers and those involving decimals by 10, 100 and 1000.	Use understanding of place value to multiply whole numbers by 10, 100 or 1000.
	To multiply numbers up to four-digits by a one- or two-digit number using a formal written method, including long multiplication for two-digit numbers.	Refine and use formal written methods to multiply 3-digits × 1-digit, 2-digits × 2-digits.
	Lesson 3	
	To divide numbers up to four-digits by a one-digit number using the formal written method of short division and interpret remainders appropriately for the context.	Use understanding of place value to multiply whole numbers by 10, 100 or 1000.
	Lesson 4	
	To divide numbers up to four-digits by a one-digit number using the formal written method of short division and interpret remainders appropriately for the context.	Use understanding of place value to multiply whole numbers by 10, 100 or 1000.
	Lesson 5	
	To solve problems involving addition, subtraction, multiplication and division and a combination of these, including understanding the meaning of the equals sign.	Solve one-step and two-step problems involving whole numbers and decimals and all four operations, choosing and using appropriate calculation strategies, including calculator use.

Preparation

Lesson 2: prepare some 2-digits × 1-digit, 2-digits × 2-digits and 3-digits × 2-digits questions and write them on the board

Lesson 3: select the cards 2–9 from '0–30 number cards', two sets for each pair

Lesson 4: write the questions on the board

Lesson 5: copy 'The electronic game championship', one per child

You will need

Photocopiable sheets
'The electronic game championship'

General resources
'0–30 number cards'; 'Multiplication square'

Equipment
Book; individual whiteboards; Diennes apparatus; Base Ten apparatus, straw bundles or bead strings

Further practice

Give children regular practice of using long multiplication and short division using squared paper to practise lining up digits in each calculation. Interactive teaching resource 'Squared paper' on the CD-ROM can also be used for demonstration purposes.

Oral and mental starters suggested for week 2

See bank of starters on page 168. Oral and mental starters are also on the CD-ROM.

46 It's all in a word

47 Kris-cross 100 square

49 Multiplication Snap

Overview of progression

This week children have the opportunity to extend their written multiplication and division strategies to solve problems involving larger numbers. As always, the children should progress through the different methods of calculating according to their own development and stage of progression and according to the school's calculation policy. The final lesson provides an opportunity to solve a problem in a real-life context and to apply all four operations to do so.

Watch out for

Some children may understand the underlying concepts of multiplication and division and have a good mental knowledge of their multiplication tables. These children should be able to progress to using long multiplication and short division without too much difficulty. However some children may not have such a good grasp of place value and multiplying and dividing multiples of 10, 100 and 1000. These children may need further practice using expanded methods such as grid multiplication and division using 'chunking' which has been covered earlier.

Creative context

Encourage the children to convert the given algorithms into word problems or stories to put them into context rather than simply working with abstract numbers.

Vocabulary

add, answer, calculate, calculation, difference, divide, divisor, **factor**, **inverse**, method, minus, multiple, multiply, operation, plus, problem, product, **quotient**, remainder, solution, subtract, sum, symbol, total

■ SCHOLASTIC

Curriculum objectives
● To multiply whole numbers and those involving decimals by 10, 100 and 1000.

Success criteria
● I can use my knowledge of place value to multiply by 10, 100 and 1000.

You will need

Equipment
Book or individual whiteboards

Differentiation

Less confident learners
These children can start with a simple table fact such as 2 × 3 or 4 × 2 and extend the diagram with adult support.

More confident learners
These children can extend their diagram to a third or fourth layer, exploring numbers into the thousands.

Lesson 1 — Oral and mental starter 49

Main teaching activities

Whole-class work: Revise the idea of an inverse (opposite) operation – for example, division is the inverse of multiplication. Remind the children that they can do many two-digit calculations mentally, using their known multiplication facts and place value. For example, ask: *What is 70 × 8? What about 70 × 80? How did you calculate that? What knowledge did you use? Are there any other calculations that knowing 7 × 8 might help you to solve?* (for example, 14 × 8 or 7 × 16)

Ask questions to elicit a variety of number facts related to 7 × 8, such as: *What number sentence could I make if I doubled each of the factors? What about if I multiplied each factor by 100? What about using the inverse operation to create division facts: how are they related?* Display the related facts as a diagram:

$$56 \div 7 = 8$$
$$56 \div 8 = 7$$
$$70 \times 8 = 560$$
$$700 \times 8 = 5600$$
$$7 \times 8 = 56$$
$$70 \times 80 = 5600$$
$$7 \times 16 = 112$$
$$14 \times 8 = 112$$
$$7 \times 80 = 560$$
$$7 \times 800 = 5600$$

Paired work: Ask the children to create their own 'related facts' diagram, based on a known multiplication fact such as 8 × 3, 6 × 7 or 5 × 6. They should use a calculator to check their facts when they have finished.

Progress check: Ask: *If you are multiplying a two-digit number by a one-digit number, what size of answer are you expecting? What about a two-digit number by two-digit number, for example 20 × 30?*

Review

Write 400 × 800 on the board. Ask: *Can you calculate 400 × 800 mentally? How?* (By using a known fact and increasing the place value by four places.) *How did you know the approximate size of the answer?* (By the number of zeros in the question.) *What other number facts can 4 × 8 help you to find?* (Multiples, such as 40 × 80, 40 × 800, 32,000 ÷ 80.)

Now write the number 250 in the middle of the board. Invite the children to use their knowledge of numbers and place value to find number facts with this answer (such as 25,000 ÷ 100, 25 × 10, 50 × 5, 2.5 × 100). Discuss how this will help when multiplying larger numbers using a written method.

Curriculum objectives
● To multiply and divide whole numbers and those involving decimals by 10, 100 and 1000.
● To multiply numbers up to four-digits by a one- or two-digit number using a formal written method, including long multiplication for two-digit numbers.

Success criteria
● I can use a written method to multiply 3-digits by 1-digit and 2-digits by 2-digits.

You will need

Equipment
Book or individual whiteboards

Differentiation

Less confident learners
These children may prefer to use the grid method since each part is clearly separated, although when working with an adult, they may be able to transfer their working onto the expanded column version, in preparation for moving on to long multiplication.

More confident learners
These children should be able to multiply 3-digits by 2-digits. A further challenge to them would be to introduce decimal numbers in the form of money into the calculations. Ensure that they keep the decimal point in the same position in order to maintain correct place value when multiplying.

Lesson 2
Oral and mental starter 49

Main teaching activities

Whole-class work: Recap with the class the various methods of multiplying they have learned and are confident to use. This will include the grid method, multiplying using multiples of known facts (from yesterday), using factors of numbers in a different order and columnar methods. Revise multiplying 2-digits by 1-digit using the column method and then extend this to 2-digits × 2-digits and 3-digits × 2-digits. Remind the children that it is the place where their digits are put which denotes their value therefore by putting in a place holding zero, they are already multiplying the answer by 10 and so they need only be concerned with multiplying single digits. However, it may help some children to make the transition from the grid method to long multiplication if you demonstrate the expanded column version alongside in order to clarify the place-holding zero, and to demonstrate each step. This helps children to understand the place value of the number they are multiplying.

$$
\begin{array}{r}
3\ 7 \\
\times\quad 4 \\
\hline
1\ 4\ 8
\end{array}
\qquad
\begin{array}{r}
3\ 7 \\
\times\quad 1\ 4 \\
\hline
1\ 4\ 8 \\
{}_2 \\
3\ 7\ 0 \\
\hline
5\ 1\ 8
\end{array}
\qquad
\begin{array}{rl}
3\ 7 & \\
\times\quad 1\ 4 & \\
\hline
2\ 8 & (4\ \times\ 7) \\
1\ 2\ 0 & (4\ \times\ 30) \\
7\ 0 & (10\ \times\ 7) \\
+\ 3\ 0\ 0 & (10\ \times\ 30) \\
\hline
5\ 1\ 8 &
\end{array}
\qquad
\begin{array}{r}
1\ 3\ 7 \\
\times\quad 2\ 4 \\
\hline
5\ 4\ 8 \\
{}_{1}{}_{2} \\
2\ 7\ 4\ 0 \\
{}_{1} \\
\hline
3\ 2\ 8\ 8 \\
{}_{1}
\end{array}
$$

Throughout this modelling explain each part that you are multiplying and be clear about the 'carried' digit, which needs to be added into the answer of each stage. Ask for children to vocalise what you are doing, for example, 4 times 7 is 28, write the 8 in the ones column and 'carry' the 2 across to be added in with the tens; 4 times 3 (tens) is 12 but I need to add in the 2 tens from the previous part of the calculation so the answer is 148.

Paired work: Write 46 × 5, 46 × 15 and 146 × 25 on the board for the children to attempt in pairs, talking through their work as they go. When you are confident the children are secure with the method, write up a further set of related calculations for them to attempt, such as: 38 × 9, 38 × 19, 138 × 29, and so on.

Progress check: As the children are working ask: *What is the value of this digit? How have you ensured that you have multiplied by ten not one? How does the place-holding zero ensure that the answer is of the correct size?*

Review

Write 129 × 34 on the board. Ask the children to talk you through the calculation, telling you each step you must take to work it out. Discuss where you should write any 'carried' digits to avoid adding them into your answer at the end. Make sure they tell you about the place-holding zero and its function. If the children are unsure about how long multiplication works, do an expanded version alongside and ask them to identify the equivalent steps in each method.

SCHOLASTIC

Curriculum objectives

● To divide numbers up to four-digits by a one-digit number using the formal written method of short division and interpret remainders appropriately for the context.

Success criteria

● I can use short division to divide numbers.
● I can express remainders as fractions.

You will need

General resources
'0–30 number cards'

Equipment
Diennes apparatus

Differentiation

Less confident learners

These children may need adult support to attempt short division, which depends on an understanding of place value in order to be successful. Diennes apparatus may be used to demonstrate 3-digits.

More confident learners

These children should to be able to divide four-digit numbers. Set the further challenge of using 12, 13 or 15 as divisors.

Lesson 3

Oral and mental starter 47

Main teaching activities

Whole-class work: Revise short division of a three-digit number by a one-digit number. You may choose to use this lesson to focus on children who need extra help in this area. Demonstrate a division such as $137 \div 3$:

$$3 \overline{\smash{)}\, 1 \; {}^13 \; {}^17} \quad \begin{array}{c} 4 \;\; 5 \; r\, 2 \end{array}$$

Relate this method to the times-table facts the children already know. Explain that the remainder can be expressed as a fraction. In this case, we have 2 left over out of the 3 that we were dividing by. This can be expressed as $\frac{2}{3}$. So $137 \div 3 = 45\frac{2}{3}$. Repeat this demonstration with other examples, such as $129 \div 4$; $208 \div 5$ and $211 \div 2$.

Independent work: Explain that the children are going to practise short division by generating three- or four-digit numbers and random one-digit divisors using the number cards you have provided. If the division has a remainder, this should be expressed as a fraction. For example, the children can generate a three-digit number (such as 533) and a divisor 4 ($533 \div 4 = 133$ remainder 1, which is $133\frac{1}{4}$).

Progress check: Check that children understand the process of division by asking: *When dividing do you expect a bigger number or a smaller number as the answer? Why?* Relate division to the multiplication work. Ask: *How can we check our division answers? What is the inverse? Explain to me what exactly you are dividing at each stage.*

Review

Check the children's understanding of how remainders can be expressed as fractions by asking for volunteers to demonstrate these examples: $151 \div 2$; $216 \div 5$ and $417 \div 10$. Ask: *How do you know what the numerator will be? How do you know what the denominator will be?* (The numerator is the number remaining; the denominator is the divisor.)

Curriculum objectives

● To divide numbers up to four-digits by a one-digit number using the formal written method of short division and interpret remainders appropriately for the context.

Success criteria

● I can use short division to divide numbers.
● I can consider the answers to calculations in context to ensure theu make sense.

You will need

Equipment

Base Ten apparatus

Differentiation

Less confident learners

Base 10 apparatus to demonstrate 3-digit numbers with adult support.

More confident learners

Ask these children to divide a monetary decimal number.

Lesson 4
Oral and mental starter 47

Main teaching activities

Independent and paired work: Tell the children that today they will continue to practise short division and express the remainders as fractions. Write the following short division questions on the board: 170 ÷ 3; 649 ÷ 8; 2113 ÷ 4; 126 ÷ 4; 4119 ÷ 3; 4108 ÷ 8; 5086 ÷ 8; 1309 ÷ 4. Explain that all of the questions will generate answers with remainders and that these should be written as fractions. Once they have completed the questions they should check their answers with a partner and find where any errors have been made, by talking through the short division process. Discuss real-life word problems that might generate these number sentences.

Progress check: Ask: *When there is a zero in the number how do you divide that? What do you do with any 'undivided' remainders? How have you turned the remainder into a fraction?*

Review

Write up a money division calculation such as £402.96 ÷ 4. Ask the children to talk you through the process of dividing this number including what they should do when they reach the zero. This calculation does not have any remainders, but ask the children to consider whether a fraction would be appropriate in the context of money. Ask them to create a word problem that would require this calculation.

Curriculum objectives

● To solve problems involving addition, subtraction, multiplication and division and a combination of these.

Success criteria

● I can use all four operations to solve number problems.

You will need

Photocopiable sheets

'The electronic game championship'

General resources

'Multiplication square'

Equipment

Base 10 apparatus, straw bundles or bead strings

Differentiation

Less confident learners

These children should work in a group with an adult.

More confident learners

These children should suggest additional questions.

Lesson 5
Oral and mental starter 46

Main teaching activities

Independent and paired work: Distribute photocopiable page 'The electronic game championship' from the CD-ROM. Explain to the children that they will need to use all four operations to complete the results table and answer the questions. Remind them of the methods for addition and subtraction and multiplication and division that they have learned so far and the need for careful recording and lining up of digits to avoid place value errors. Remind them also of the language clues used in word problems.

Progress check: Ask: *What operation did you use to calculate the totals? Show me the method you chose to divide by 5. How did you choose to double? Did you round and estimate the totals first?*

Review

Ask: *Who was the overall winner? Who came last? What strategies did you need to calculate Jemima's score? Which questions involved a two-step calculation? Which words indicated the operation you should use? Did anybody make up any further questions? Tell me what I have to do to solve your question.*

 SCHOLASTIC

Calculating with fractions

Expected prior learning

Children should be able to:

- recognise and name simple fractions of shapes
- understand fractions are equal parts of a whole
- know that whole numbers and fractions may be combined and are known as mixed numbers.

Topic	Curriculum objectives	Expected outcomes
Fractions (including decimals and percentages)	**Lesson 1**	
	To recognise mixed numbers and improper fractions and convert from one form to the other and write mathematical statements > 1 as a mixed number (for example, $\frac{2}{5} + \frac{4}{5} = \frac{6}{5} = 1\frac{1}{5}$).	Counting forwards and backwards with mixed numbers.
	Lesson 2	
	To multiply proper fractions and mixed numbers by whole numbers, supported by materials and diagrams.	Connect multiplying by a fraction to dividing (for example, multiply by $\frac{1}{7}$ is equivalent to dividing by 7). Express a smaller whole number as a fraction of a larger one (for example, recognise that 5 out of 8 is $\frac{5}{8}$).
	Lesson 3	
	To multiply proper fractions and mixed numbers by whole numbers, supported by materials and diagrams.	Calculate with fractions. Connect multiplying by a fraction to dividing (for example, multiply by $\frac{1}{7}$ is equivalent to dividing by 7).
	Lesson 4	
	To add and subtract fractions with the same denominator and denominators that are multiples of the same number.	Solve problems involving fractions.
	Lesson 5	
	To add and subtract fractions with the same denominator and denominators that are multiples of the same number. To multiply proper fractions and mixed numbers by whole numbers, supported by materials and diagrams.	Solve problems involving fractions.

Preparation

Lesson 1: select 1–9 from the '0–30 number cards'; make the 'Fraction families' cards, one set per pair and separate them into families

Lesson 2: prepare some simple fraction of number questions and write them on the board

Lesson 3: prepare some questions that ask for simple and multiple fractions of numbers and write them on the board

Lesson 5: make enlarged copies of 'Blank 100 square', one per pair

You will need

General resources
'0–30 number cards'; 'Fraction families'; 'Blank 100 square'

Equipment
Blank cards; pens; fraction shapes and counters, if needed

Further practice

Provide further examples of questions involving the multiplication of proper fractions by whole numbers. Put them in a problem solving context where possible, for example 'If we slept for ⅛ of a day (24 hours), how long would that be?' If the weather is 24°C in Barbados and the weather is only ⅙ as hot in London, how hot is it in London?' and so on.

Oral and mental starters suggested for week 3

See bank of starters on page 167. Oral and mental starters are also on the CD-ROM.

42 It doesn't make sense

44 Fraction match

45 Fraction line up

Overview of progression

This week's lessons recap on ordering and comparing mixed numbers and improper fractions as well as introducing addition of fractions with a common (the same) denominator. Lesson 2 explores how to find fractions of amounts and demonstrates how this is linked to division and likewise how multiplying by a fraction is linked to division. All of these skills are applied to solve calculations and problems.

Watch out for
Some children find the link with division to find fractions of amounts extremely challenging. It is best to demonstrate this practically with fraction pieces and counters, keeping the numbers quite small so that these children grasp the concept before moving on to solve problems.

Creative context

Fractions are often used in everyday speech, not always accurately. Encourage children to qualify what they mean when they hear phrases such as 'I spent half my time ...'.

Vocabulary

denominator, equivalent, fraction, **improper fraction**, mixed number, **numerator**, proper fraction, unit fraction,

Curriculum objectives
- To recognise mixed numbers and improper fractions and convert from one form to the other.

Success criteria
- I can recognise mixed numbers and improper fractions and can convert from one to another.
- I can order mixed number and improper fractions.

You will need

General resources
'0–30 number cards'; 'Fraction families'

Equipment
Blank cards; fraction shapes

Differentiation

Less confident learners
It would support these children to work initially with halves and quarters only and to use fraction shapes to compare wholes and fractions and their improper fraction equivalents. Then they progress to thirds and sixths.

More confident learners
These children include twentieths and twenty-fifths.

Lesson 1 — Oral and mental starter 42

Main teaching activities

Whole-class work: Separate the fraction cards you have made into three groups: halves, quarters and eighths; fifths and tenths; and thirds and sixths. Select two cards from one group and hold them up. Ask the children to tell you something about them, for example, which is the larger or that they are equivalent, and so on. Ask two children to hold them in size order and select another card to place correctly in the line. Continue until most of the cards have been ordered. Ask the children to tell you something about the comparative size of each new fraction. Repeat with another group of fractions.

Now ask the children to tell you a fraction within the same group which is larger than 1, for example, $^6/_5$. Write it on a blank card and ask them to also tell you the mixed number equivalent and write this on the card too. Repeat to ensure that all the children are clear about ordering fractions which have the same denominator or a multiple of that denominator.

Paired work: Ask the children to use the groups of fraction cards and whole number cards and to draw a number line from one to ten in their books. On this number line they should estimate the position of alternate mixed number and improper fractions of their choosing, for example, $1\frac{1}{2}$; $\frac{9}{4}$; $2\frac{1}{4}$; $1\frac{3}{4}$; $3\frac{1}{8}$; and so on. They will not have all of the improper fractions on cards so they will have to combine and convert some of their mixed number fractions. Repeat with a different set of fraction cards.

Progress check: Ask: *How do I decide on an improper fraction that is bigger than $^{19}/_4$? Which is bigger, $\frac{3}{8}$ or $\frac{1}{4}$? How do you know? What do you have to do to decide? Why have we not mixed thirds and quarters at this stage?*

Review

Say: *Tell me an equivalent fraction for $^6/_{10}$. (for example, $\frac{3}{5}$ or $^{60}/_{100}$) What is the decimal equivalent of $^6/_{10}$? (0.6) What about an equivalent for $^{35}/_{10}$? What would that look like as a decimal fraction? How might this be useful when we are calculating?*

Curriculum objectives
● To multiply proper fractions by whole numbers, supported by materials and diagrams.

Success criteria
● I can find fractions of shapes and amounts.

You will need
Equipment

Fraction shapes and counters

Differentiation
Less confident learners

Encourage these children to use the fraction shapes and counters as demonstrated in the lesson to support their understanding of fractions of numbers.

More confident learners

Encourage these children to work out fractions which are multiples of these, for example, $\frac{1}{3}$ and $\frac{2}{3}$ of 24.

Lesson 2 — Oral and mental starter 44

Main teaching activities

Whole-class work: Introduce finding a simple fraction of a number. Demonstrate using fraction shapes and counters. For example, if I have six counters and want half of these, we can do this by dividing by 2. Place 6 counters onto the two halves of a whole fraction shape, placing three on one half and three on the other. Repeat with one quarter of 12, placing three counters on each quarter of the fraction shape. Explain to the children that the denominator of a fraction is the number of equal parts that either a shape or a number is shared into so finding a third of something is the same as dividing by 3; finding a fifth of something is the same as dividing by 5; and so on. Explain that one way of writing this mathematically is as a multiplication question such as $30 \times \frac{1}{2} = 15$ or $45 \times \frac{1}{5} = 9$.

Paired work: Ask the children to find simple fractions of the numbers that you have written on the board, for example one half of 18, 22, 24 and 32. Extend this process by asking the children to find one third of 9, 12, 18 and 30; then one quarter of 12, 16, 24 and 40.

Progress check: Ask: *What is a half of 7, 17, 23?* (3.5 or $3\frac{1}{2}$, and so on) *Why are odd numbers more difficult? Which numbers can we easily find a simple fraction of?* (Numbers in known times tables)

Review

Write $\frac{2}{3}$ of 18 on the board. Ask the children to explain the denominator and the numerator. Explain further if necessary by saying: *If I eat $\frac{3}{4}$ of a cake, I cut into four equal pieces and eat three of them.* Demonstrate the problem $\frac{2}{3}$ of 18 using fraction shapes. One whole is three thirds so we share all of the 18 counters equally between the three parts, which means I put 6 counters on each third. So one third of 18 is 6. Two thirds of 18 is $\frac{1}{3} + \frac{1}{3} = 6 + 6 = 12$.

Curriculum objectives
● As lesson 2 above.

Success criteria
● I can understand how multiplying by a fraction is related to division.
● I can find fractions of shapes and amounts.

You will need
Equipment

Fraction shapes; counters

Differentiation
Less confident learners

These children may need to use the fraction shapes and counters in order to physically divide the number and then add together the single fraction amounts.

More confident learners

As a further challenge, ask these children how they would find fractions of numbers beyond their known times tables, for example, $\frac{3}{5}$ of 145.

Lesson 3 — Oral and mental starter 44

Main teaching activities

Whole-class work: Remind the children of the work done yesterday on how to find a simple fraction of an amount. Ask: *If we can find $\frac{1}{3}$ of a number, how might we find $\frac{2}{3}$?* (Find $\frac{1}{3}$ and double it.) *What is $\frac{2}{3}$ of 15? 24? 36?* Repeat this process, finding $\frac{1}{4}$ and then $\frac{3}{4}$ of 32, 24 and 40.

Paired work: Provide the children with questions that ask for simple and multiple fractions of numbers. These could include: $\frac{1}{4}$ of 32; $\frac{1}{2}$ of 16; $\frac{3}{4}$ of 24; $35 \times \frac{1}{5}$; $35 \times \frac{3}{5}$; $42 \times \frac{1}{7}$; $42 \times \frac{3}{7}$, and so on. Then ask them to write some simple steps for others to follow that describe how to find a multiple fraction of a number.

Progress check: Ask: *Describe to me how you would find $\frac{3}{7}$ of 42. Is this a one- or two-step calculation? Show me how you are recording this?*

Review

Write the number 5 on the board and ask the children to tell you some division facts that give this answer. Write these up around the number. Repeat for 2, 10 and 12. Encourage the children to use a wide range of times-table facts. Ask: *How did you work this out?*

Now ask the children to tell you some fractions of numbers that give the answers above. Add these to the facts already recorded on the board. Discuss how fractions are closely related to division: the denominator is the divisor and the numerator is the multiple. Ask the children to tell you $\frac{3}{4}$ of 24; $\frac{2}{3}$ of 9; and so on.

Ask: *Is it possible to find $\frac{1}{5}$ of 36? How would you write this?* (7r1 or $7\frac{1}{5}$). Ask the children to read out their step-by-step guides and vote on the clearest and most succinct one to form part of a classroom display.

Curriculum objectives
● To add and subtract fractions with the same denominator and denominators that are multiples of the same number.

Success criteria
● I can add and subtract fractions with the same denominator.
● I can use my knowledge of equivalence to convert between improper fractions and mixed numbers.

You will need

General resources
'Fractions families'

Equipment
Solid fraction pieces

Differentiation

Less confident learners
These children should use only low number, single denominator fractions to add. Solid fraction pieces may be used to demonstrate and track progress more clearly.

More confident learners
These children can begin to calculate with two related fraction families, for example quarters and eighths or fifths and tenths.

Lesson 4 — Oral and mental starter 45

Main teaching activities

Whole-class work: Explain to the children that they are now going to learn how to use their knowledge of fractions to add and subtract fractions. Remind them that they know how to find equivalent fractions where the denominators are multiples and now they are going to find out how to use that knowledge to add and subtract fractions. Use the fraction pieces to demonstrate that $\frac{2}{5} + \frac{1}{5} = \frac{3}{5}$. Explain that it is only the numerator which is added together since the denominator denotes the size or name of the fraction and therefore the denominators should not be added together. Repeat with $\frac{3}{7} + \frac{2}{7} = \frac{5}{7}$ and $\frac{6}{9} + \frac{3}{9} = \frac{9}{9} = 1$.

Now ask: *What happens if we add larger numerators?* Demonstrate with $\frac{3}{5} + \frac{3}{5} = \frac{6}{5}$ or 1 and $\frac{1}{5}$ or $1\frac{1}{5}$. Repeat with other examples.

Extend to a pair fractions, one with a denominator that is a multiple of the denominator of the other, for example $\frac{3}{5} + \frac{1}{10}$. Ask: *How can we add this together?* Remind the children that $\frac{3}{5}$ is equivalent to $\frac{6}{10}$ so we can write the calculation as $\frac{6}{10} + \frac{1}{10}$ and can add to find $\frac{7}{10}$. Emphasise that we cannot add fractions if the denominators are different. We must find an equivalent first.

Paired work: Using photocopiable page 'Fraction families' from the CD-ROM, distribute one fraction 'family' (that is, the fractions with the same denominator) to each pair. Ask the children to use their fractions to make a number sentence to give the answer 2. For example, $\frac{4}{5} + \frac{4}{5} + \frac{2}{5} = \frac{10}{5}$ or 2. More confident learners could also write number sentences involving subtraction, for example, 3 (or $\frac{15}{5}$) − $\frac{5}{5}$ = $\frac{10}{5}$ or 2. The pairs should go on to explore as many ways as they can to create the number 2, using fractions of the same denominator. They should then swap fraction families with another pair and repeat the process.

Progress check: Ask: *If you add all the fractions in the set together does it equal one whole?* (No, more than one.) *What is the total of all your fraction cards?* (This depends on the denominator or 'family') *What will you have to do to make larger numbers?* (Use them more than once.) Once you feel the children are confident, they can use two fraction families, one of which has a denominator which is a multiple of the denominator of the other, to create more adventurous number sentences.

Review

Write up the number sentence $5\frac{1}{4} − \frac{3}{4}$. Ask for a volunteer to come and write the improper fraction equivalent of $5\frac{1}{4}$ on the board. ($\frac{21}{4}$) Ask: *How did you work that out?* Now ask the class to subtract $\frac{3}{4}$ from this number. $\frac{21}{4} − \frac{3}{4} = \frac{18}{4}$ or $4\frac{3}{4}$. Now ask the children to consider how they would subtract a whole number from an improper fraction, for example, $\frac{21}{4} − 2$. They should be able to spot that it would be simpler to convert the improper fraction back to a mixed number to do this, for example, $5\frac{1}{4} − 2 = 3\frac{1}{4}$.

Make sure the children have a clear grasp of the rules for adding and subtracting fractions.

The denominators must be the same.

If the denominators are different, multiply the top and bottom of one fraction by the same number to make an equivalent fraction with the same denominator as the other fraction. For example, when adding $\frac{1}{2}$ and $\frac{3}{4}$, multiply the top and bottom of $\frac{1}{2}$ by 2 to get $\frac{3}{4}$. Now add $\frac{3}{4}$ and $\frac{2}{4} = \frac{5}{4}$ or $1\frac{1}{4}$.

When the denominators are the same you just add or subtract the numerators.

Curriculum objectives

● To add and subtract fractions with the same denominator and denominators that are multiples of the same number.
● To multiply proper fractions and mixed numbers by whole numbers, supported by materials and diagrams.

Success criteria

● I can apply my knowledge of adding, subtracting and multiplying simple fractions to solve problems.

You will need

General resources

'Blank 100 square'

Equipment

Coloured pens and pencils; blank playing cards

Differentiation

Less confident learners

These children may need adult support to create and play the games.

More confident learners

These children should produce more challenging questions.

Lesson 5

Main teaching activities

Paired work: Distribute the enlarged versions of photocopiable page 'Blank 100 square' from the CD-ROM. Explain that they may use any of the other materials that you have provided to make a board game that tests the fractions knowledge that they have acquired so far. They have only the length of the lesson to produce their game.

It must test:

- converting mixed numbers to improper fractions and vice versa
- converting fractions to equivalent fractions with different denominators
- finding fractions of numbers using division
- adding and subtracting fractions.

They need to decide:

- how the questions will be asked – either by landing on a square with it written on or by landing on a square that prompts a question card
- how a person wins, for example, first to reach the final square, first to collect 10 cards, and so on.

Remind them that the maths is the important bit and they may only complete the 'artwork' once the questions are fixed. They also must know the answers, which should be recorded somewhere.

Progress check: Ask: *What skills are you testing? How does a player progress in this game? Who is the winner? Have you recorded the answers? Are you sure these are correct?*

Review

Pairs should swap games, explain the rules to the other pair then play the games. They can then feedback on the difficulty and quality of the games. Ask: *How do you think your game will help children to use and remember fractions? How has it furthered your understanding?*

Percentages

Expected prior learning

Children should be able to:

- use diagrams to identify equivalent fractions – $\frac{6}{8}$ and $\frac{3}{4}$ or $\frac{70}{100}$ and $\frac{7}{10}$
- interpret mixed numbers and position them on a number line
- use decimal notation for tenths and hundredths and partition decimals
- position numbers with one and two decimal places on a number line.

Topic	Curriculum objectives	Expected outcomes
Fractions (including decimals and percentages)	**Lesson 1**	
	To recognise the per cent symbol (%) and understand that per cent relates to 'number of parts per hundred', and write percentages as a fraction with denominator 100, and as a decimal.	Understand percentage as the number of parts in every 100 and relate this to fractions and decimals.
	Lesson 2	
	To recognise the per cent symbol (%) and understand that per cent relates to 'number of parts per hundred', and write percentages as a fraction with denominator 100, and as a decimal.	Understand percentage as the number of parts in every 100 and relate this to fractions and decimals.
	Lesson 3	
	To recognise the per cent symbol (%) and understand that per cent relates to 'number of parts per hundred', and write percentages as a fraction with denominator 100, and as a decimal. To solve problems which require knowing percentage and decimal equivalents of $\frac{1}{2}$, $\frac{1}{4}$, $\frac{1}{5}$, $\frac{2}{5}$, $\frac{4}{5}$ and those fractions with a denominator of a multiple of 10 or 25.	Understand percentage as the number of parts in every 100 and relate this to fractions and decimals.
	Lesson 4	
	To recognise the per cent symbol (%) and understand that per cent relates to 'number of parts per hundred', and write percentages as a fraction with denominator 100, and as a decimal. To solve problems which require knowing percentage and decimal equivalents of $\frac{1}{2}$, $\frac{1}{4}$, $\frac{1}{5}$, $\frac{2}{5}$, $\frac{4}{5}$ and those fractions with a denominator of a multiple of 10 or 25.	Find percentages of amounts by using fractions and division knowledge.
	Lesson 5	
	To recognise the per cent symbol (%) and understand that per cent relates to 'number of parts per hundred', and write percentages as a fraction with denominator 100, and as a decimal. To solve problems which require knowing percentage and decimal equivalents of $\frac{1}{2}$, $\frac{1}{4}$, $\frac{1}{5}$, $\frac{2}{5}$, $\frac{4}{5}$ and those fractions with a denominator of a multiple of 10 or 25.	Calculate a percentage increase or decrease in a 'real' situation.

Preparation

Lesson 1: make copies of photocopiable page 'Blank 100 square', one per child if needed; make copies of 'Fractions, decimals and percentages', one set per pair

Lesson 2: copy 'Fractions, decimals and percentages' onto card, one set per pair

Lesson 3: copy 'Simple percentages', one per child; make copies of 'Multiplication square', one per child if needed

Lesson 4: copy 'Percentages', one per child

Lesson 5: make some labels reading: 10% off; 25% off; 50% off; 10% more; 50% extra; 20% more; collect some packets of cereal or other foodstuffs as well as some items of sports equipment or clothing to denote a shop; label items with either a price or a mass

You will need

Photocopiable sheets

'Simple percentages'; 'Percentages'

General resources

'Blank 100 square'; 'Fractions, decimals and percentages'; 'Multiplication square'; interactive activity 'Percentage points'

Equipment

Calculators; labels and items for a 'shop'; cubes or counters

Further practice

Interactive activity 'Percentage points', offers further practice of recognising percentages and their fraction equivalents.

Oral and mental starters suggested for week 4

See bank of starters on pages 167 to 168. Oral and mental starters are also on the CD-ROM.

43 Hit the target number

48 Kilogram and gram calculator

50 Percentage pairs

Overview of progression

This week's lessons introduce percentages and makes explicit the link between fractions and decimals in a fairly simple way. Some practical applications and games are included to help the children understand the basic principles. For those children who find understanding percentages difficult, revise thoroughly their understanding of simple fractions and the ways in which fractions can be multiplied up. Once children have grasped that anything that can be multiplied up to a denominator of 100, then the progression to percentages is easy.

Watch out for

The most common misconception occurs when children do not relate percentages to a fraction of 'out of 100' and therefore fail to grasp that 100% is all of a number or amount. Instead they look for there to be 100 objects. Provide practical examples with a number of objects, for example 70 counters. Say, *This is 100%. These are all the counters that I have, that is 70/70. I am going to give you 10% or 1/10 of them. How do you think I could work that out?* Repeat with further examples, emphasising that 'all of them' is the starting point and therefore represents 100% or 100 out of 100 (or 70/70 or 80/80 and so on).

Creative context

Encourage children for look for examples of percentages used in daily life and to note the context.

Vocabulary

cancel, decimal, decimal fraction, decimal place, decimal point, **denominator**, equivalent, fraction, **numerator**, **per cent (%)**, **percentage**, proper fraction

Curriculum objectives
● To recognise the per cent symbol (%) and understand that per cent relates to 'number of parts per hundred', and write percentages as a fraction with denominator 100, and as a decimal.

Success criteria
● I can recognise that 'per cent' meant 'out of 100'.
● I can recognise fraction and decimal equivalents of percentages.

You will need
General resources
'Blank 100 square'; 'Fractions, decimals and percentages'
Equipment
Calculators for checking answers

Differentiation
Less confident learners
A 'Blank 100 square' will support these children's understanding of tenths, hundredths and 'out of 100'.
More confident learners
These children could include ⅕, ⅖, ⅗, ¾ and so on.

Lesson 1   Oral and mental starter 48

Main teaching activities

Whole-class work: Revise tenths and hundredths, asking for equivalent decimals: $\frac{1}{10}$ = 0.1; $\frac{2}{10}$ = 0.2; and so on.

Introduce the concept of percentages as parts of 100. Display the 'Blank 100 square'. Shade 10 squares and explain that this is 10% or 10 out of 100. Show that 35 out of 100 = 35%.

Explain how percentages are linked to fractions and decimals: $\frac{1}{10}$ = 0.1 = $\frac{10}{100}$ = 10%. Use the 'Fractions, decimals and percentages' cards to start a class table of equivalents on the board:

Fraction	Decimal	Out of 100	Percentage
$\frac{1}{10}$	0.1	$\frac{10}{100}$	10%

Paired work: Ask the children to use the 'Fractions, decimals and percentages' cards from the CD-ROM to complete the table, working methodically.

Progress check: Ask: *If $\frac{1}{10}$ = 0.1, which other fractions can you complete immediately?* (0.2, 0.3, and so on) *How are you going to find the equivalent percentage for ¼? Can you make this into an equivalent fraction with a denominator of a hundred? How will this help you to decide on the decimal?*

Review

Ask: *How would you obtain $\frac{1}{10}$ of a cake?* (Cut it into ten pieces.) *What percentage is $\frac{1}{10}$ equivalent to? How would you find 10% of a cake? What about 50% of a cake? Or 25% of a cake?* Demonstrate how fractions can be entered into a calculator, for example, for ¼ key in 1 ÷ 4, which will give the decimal 0.25. This can be used to check the equivalents in the table.

Curriculum objectives
● To recognise the per cent symbol (%) and understand that per cent relates to 'number of parts per hundred', and write percentages as a fraction with denominator 100, and as a decimal.

Success criteria
● I can match fraction, decimal and percentage equivalents.

You will need
General resources
'Fractions, decimals and percentages'

Differentiation
Less confident learners
Reduce the set of cards to 4 or 5 trios in the first instance, to build confidence.
More confident learners
Add additional cards to the pack such as ⅖ = 0.4 = 40%. Ask the children to create further trios of equivalents.

Lesson 2   Oral and mental starter 43

Main teaching activities

Paired work: Explain to the children that they are going to practise their knowledge of fraction, decimal and percentage equivalents by playing a version of 'Pelmanism' or a trio of equivalents memory game. Distribute the sets of 'Fractions, decimals and percentages' cards from the CD-ROM. Ask them to shuffle them and spread them out face down on the table. They take it in turns to reveal three cards, trying to find a trio of matching equivalents, for example, $\frac{1}{10}$, 0.1 and 10%. Once a trio has been found, the player keeps those cards. The winner is the person with the most sets of equivalent trios.

Progress check: Listen to the conversations as the children play this game to inform your assessments of how well they have understood and remembered. Ask: *Which are the most difficult equivalents to remember? Which are the easiest? Why?* (The decimals and percentages because they have the same digits.) *What fraction family do all of these cards relate back to?* (Hundredths)

Review

Check that the children have created accurate sets of 'trios'. Pose the further challenge: *What percentage is equivalent to 1$\frac{1}{10}$? Is this possible to have such an amount?* (110%; Yes, for example, prices can rise so the original price is 100% and 110% would mean the new price is 10% more) Ask the children to think of other examples in life where percentages are used. For example, is it possible for people to give 110% effort or commitment to something, as is often heard? Not really, since you can't give more than your full (100%) effort, however they are implying that they are going to work extra hard.

Curriculum objectives

● To recognise the per cent symbol (%) and understand that per cent relates to 'number of parts per hundred', and write percentages as a fraction with denominator 100, and as a decimal.
● To solve problems which require knowing percentage and decimal equivalents of ½, ¼, ⅕, ⅖, ⅘ and those fractions with a denominator of a multiple of 10 or 25.

Success criteria

● I can find simple percentages of amounts.

You will need

Photocopiable sheets

'Simple percentages'

General resources

'Multiplication square'

Differentiation

Less confident learners

An adult may need to support these children with relating percentages to division and then to help the children to calculate. A 'Multiplication square' may help with this.

More confident learners

Encourage them to find 1% of a number and tell you how that may be helpful to find more complex percentages.

Lesson 3   Oral and mental starter 50

Main teaching activities

Whole-class work: Explain to the children that we can use our knowledge of decimal and fraction equivalents to find percentages of numbers. Remind them of the trios game that they played yesterday and ask them to tell you a selection of trios of equivalents that they can remember, for example, ¹∕₁₀, 0.1 and 10% or ½, 0.5, 50%.

Demonstrate finding the percentage of numbers by asking: *What is half of 60?* Most children should be able to answer '30'. Now ask: *What is 50% of 60?* Repeat this with ¼ and 25% and with ¹∕₁₀ and 10%. Ask: *Is there a way of finding 20% of 60?* Show them that this can be achieved by calculating 10% + 10% .

Independent work: Distribute photocopiable page 'Simple percentages' from the CD-ROM. The children find the percentages of numbers and amounts of money.

Progress check: Ask: *How do you calculate 10% of an amount? How do you find 20% or 30% of an amount?* Ask the more confident learners *What about finding 60%? Is there a short cut you can take?* (for example, find 50% = ½ and add 10%.)

Review

Explain that if they have been able to find 10% and 50% they can find more complicated percentages of numbers. Ask the children to consider how difficult it might be to calculate 99%. Encourage them to think flexibly. They should be able to suggest subtracting 1% rather than the longer adding version. Check the accuracy of the children's calculating.

Curriculum objectives
- To recognise the per cent symbol (%) and understand that per cent relates to 'number of parts per hundred', and write percentages as a fraction with denominator 100, and as a decimal.
- To solve problems which require knowing percentage and decimal equivalents of ½, ¼, ⅕, ⅖, ⅘ and those fractions with a denominator of a multiple of 10 or 25.

Success criteria
- I can find percentages of amounts by using fractions and addition.

You will need
Photocopiable sheets
'Percentages'

General resources
Interactive activity 'Percentage points'

Differentiation
Less confident learners

Give children the interactive activity 'Percentage points' to further practice percentages and their fraction equivalents.

More confident learners

Challenge children to find other percentages by calculating them in parts, for example 13% of 130.

Lesson 4 — Oral and mental starter 43

Main teaching activities

Whole-class work: Reinforce that finding a percentage of an amount is linked to division in the same way as finding a fraction of an amount is, and so it can be helpful to remember the equivalent fraction. Demonstrate by asking: *What is 100% of 50? What is 10% of 50? Remember that from the table we made in a Lesson 1, 10% is equivalent to ¹⁄₁₀. To find ¹⁄₁₀ of a number we divide by 10. So to find 10% of a number we divide by 10. So 10% of 50 = 5. From this, I can find 20% because it is twice as much as 10%. What is 20% of 50? What is the equivalent fraction for 50%. How can this help us to find 50% of a number. How can we find 25%?* (25% = ¼, so we can divide by 4.)

Explain that any percentage of an amount can be found by adding other percentages of the amount together. For example, 75% of 36 can be found by adding 50% (18) and 25% (9) to get 27. We can find harder percentages using the same method: 13% of 30 can be made up by finding 10% (3) and 3 lots of 1% (0.3 × 3 = 0.9) and adding them to get 3.9.

Independent work: Ask the children to complete photocopiable page 'Percentages' from the CD-ROM, using the equivalents table that they made in lesson 1. Remind them to record which fraction they used each time and show how they calculated the answers.

Progress check: Ask: *What is 10% of 30? So how would you find 15%? What about 17%? How many steps would this take?*

Review

Ask questions that link fractions and percentages, such as: *Which is greater, 50% of 60 or half of 60? Which would you prefer, 25% of £10 or ⅕ of £10? Why?* (Because 25% is equivalent to ¼, which is bigger than ⅕.) Ask the children to think of a comparison question that uses equivalents they have learned. Split the class into two teams to challenge each other. Keep the score and ask the children to explain their reasoning.

Curriculum objectives

• To recognise the per cent symbol (%) and understand that per cent relates to 'number of parts per hundred', and write percentages as a fraction with denominator 100, and as a decimal.
• To solve problems which require knowing percentage and decimal equivalents of ½, ¼, ⅓, ⅔, ⅘ and those fractions with a denominator of a multiple of 10 or 25.

Success criteria

• I can calculate a percentage increase or decrease.

You will need

Equipment

Labels and items for a 'shop'; cubes or counters, if needed

Differentiation

Less confident learners

These children might need adult support and apparatus such as cubes or counters to understand the concept of percentage reductions and increase.

More confident learners

These children could go on to add more items to the 'shop', with different percentage labels.

Lesson 5

Oral and mental starter 50

Main teaching activities

Whole-class work: Discuss with the children the fact that percentages are most commonly seen in shops either to promote a sale or reduction of cost or to suggest greater value for money by offering more of something for the same cost. Show them the labels that you have produced. Ask whether they think people really stop to calculate the true cost.

Indicate the items you have collected. Demonstrate that if a product is marked as '10% off', you need to calculate 10% of the original price and then subtract it from that price to find the reduced price. Similarly, '10% extra free' means they calculate 10% of the original mass and add it to that mass to find the increased mass.

Encourage them to work to this model:

Item	Original price / amount	% less / more	Reduction / extra	New price / amount
Coat	£40	10% off	10% of £40 = £4	£40 − £4 = £36
Cereal	250g	10% extra	10% of 250g = 25g	250g + 25g = 275g

Paired work: In pairs the children select an item, decide on whether it has a percentage reduction or a percentage increase and complete the table using the model to help them.

Progress check: Listen to the conversations as the children work. Ask: *What do you think is the most common error made when working with percentage reductions or increases?* (Only finding the percentage not adding or subtracting it from the original figure.) *Tell me how you have calculated 20%. What is the equivalent fraction?*

Review

Display the following: 'Coat reduced by 75%! Original price £400. Now only £300'. Ask: *Is this correct? Why not? What has this person done incorrectly?* (Only calculated the percentage, not the new price) *Where else do we see percentages used in real-life?* (Interest rates, rates of improvement, surveys) Explain that this area of mathematics is much used and is therefore good to understand.

Capacity

Expected prior learning

Children should be able to:

- know that there are some imperial measures still used in the UK
- have some experience of measuring liquids using millilitres and litres.

Topic	Curriculum objectives	Expected outcomes
Measurement	**Lesson 1**	
	To convert between different units of measure (for example, kilometre and metre; centimetre and metre; centimetre and millimetre; gram and kilogram; litre and millilitre).	Convert between litres and millilitres. Understand the practical application of capacity.
	Lesson 2	
	To convert between different units of measure (for example, kilometre and metre; centimetre and metre; centimetre and millimetre; gram and kilogram; litre and millilitre).	Convert between litres and millilitres. Understand the practical application of capacity.
	Lesson 3	
	To understand and use approximate equivalences between metric units and common imperial units such as inches, pounds and pints.	Represent a puzzle or problem by identifying and recording the information or calculations needed to solve it; find possible solutions and confirm them in the context of the problem.
	Lesson 4	
	To estimate volume [for example, using 1 cm³ blocks to build cubes and cuboids] and capacity [for example, using water].	Solve one-step and two-step problems involving whole numbers and decimals and all four operations, choosing and using appropriate calculation strategies, including calculator use.
	Lesson 5	
	To use all four operations to solve problems involving measure [for example, length, mass, volume, money) using decimal notation, including scaling.	Solve one-step and two-step problems involving whole numbers and decimals and all four operations, choosing and using appropriate calculation strategies, including calculator use.

Preparation

Lesson 1: copy 'How much? How much more?', one per child; assemble the 'Place value table' and associated number cards, if needed

Lesson 2: copy 'Equal capacity', one per child; assemble the 'Place value table' and associated number cards, if needed

Lesson 3: copy 'Imperial/ metric capacity conversion chart', one per child

Lesson 4: assemble a selection of containers, enough for the whole class and provide dry sand or water, if needed

Lesson 5: assemble the selection of containers from the last lesson also dry sand or water and capacity measuring equipment, such as jugs and measuring cylinders with a variety of different scales

You will need

Photocopiable sheets

'How much? How much more?'; 'Equal capacity'; 'Imperial/metric capacity conversion chart'

General resources

'Place value table'; interactive teaching resource 'Measuring jug'

Equipment

A selection of containers; dry sand or water; capacity measuring equipment, such as jugs and measuring cylinders with a variety of different scales

Further practice

The interactive activity 'How much?' offers additional capacity problems.

Oral and mental starters suggested for week 5

See bank of starters on page 167. Oral and mental starters are also on the CD-ROM.

41 Ordering measures

42 It doesn't make sense!

43 Kris-cross 100 square

Overview of progression

This set of lessons is designed to be very practical in order for children to understand the measurement of capacity and to be able to measure accurately, estimate and scale measures up and down. There is reference to imperial measures (pints and gallons) that are still in common usage in the UK and an opportunity to solve problems.

Watch out for

Measurement in any unit is often an area of difficulty for children, especially estimating and ordering measures. They need practical experience of reading scales and comparing amounts to get a feel for how much is a litre or a millilitre and for appropriate units of measure for different capacities.

Creative context

It is a good idea to encourage children to make their own 'measures' display and keep it for regular reference when measurements occur in daily activities and other areas of the curriculum.

Vocabulary

imperial measures (pints and gallons), litres (l), millilitres (ml)

Curriculum objectives
- To convert between different units of measure.

Success criteria
- I can convert between litres and millilitres.

You will need
Photocopiable sheets
'How much? How much more?'

General resources
Interactive teaching resource 'Measuring jug'; 'Place value table' and associated number cards

Differentiation
Less confident learners
'Place value table' and number cards will help children to understand place value. They may need adult support to work out the divisions of the scale and to read the scales accurately. They could use water or dry sand in containers to check their answers.

More confident learners
Further challenge these children to work out how many cylinders it would take to fill the jug.

Lesson 1
Oral and mental starter 42

Main teaching activities

Whole-class work: Remind the children that 1000ml = 1 litre and tell them that they are going to practise this by reading the scales and then writing the capacities in both millilitres and litres. For those children who find understanding percentages difficult, revise thoroughly their understanding of simple fractions and the ways in which fractions can be multiplied up. Once children have grasped that anything that can be multiplied up to a denominator of 100, then the progression to percentages is easy. If necessary, show the interactive teaching resource 'Measuring jug' on the CD-ROM and fill to different levels to check children's understanding of litres and millilitres.

Independent work: Distribute photocopiable page 'How much? How much more?' from the CD-ROM. Ask the children to read the scales accurately and then calculate how much more would need to be added in order to fill the container to its maximum. They should write their answers in both millilitres and litres.

Progress check: Ask: *How much is equivalent to 0.2 litres? What about 567ml? 350ml? 500ml? How much is the 5 digit worth in 0.5 litre? What about in 0.05 litre?*

Review

Share answers and ensure that the place value of the decimal fractions of litres is correct. Check especially conversion such as 0.04 litres and 6ml. Ask: *How can we ensure that we have the correct place value for 1.5 litres?* (Use zeros to show place value, for example 1.500 litres)

Curriculum objectives
- To convert between different units of measure.

Success criteria
- I can convert between litres and millilitres.

You will need
Photocopiable sheets
'Equal capacity'

General resources
'Place value table' and associated number cards

Differentiation
Less confident learners
These children might find the 'Place value table' and associated number cards helpful to understand the place value of these equivalent measures.

More confident learners
Create their mixture of capacities in millilitres and litres for a friend to order.

Lesson 2
Oral and mental starter 47

Main teaching activities

Whole-class work: Remind the children that it important to be able to convert between measures as both are used in real life and also when it comes to calculating by asking: *How many more millilitres would I need to add to 0.56l to make a whole litre?* (440ml) Likewise ask: *Which container holds more, one containing 0.4 l or one with 40ml? Explain why?*

Independent work: Distribute photocopiable page 'Equal capacity' from the CD-ROM. Explain to the children that they are going to further practise their equivalent measures by converting from millilitres to litres and vice versa. They will then use their skills to order a mixture of capacities given in litres and capacities given in millilitres.

Progress check: Ask: *When ordering mixed measures how do you know which is the smaller amount? Do you always have to convert one to another? Which are the more tricky ones to decide about?*

Review

Check that the children are all able to convert capacities accurately. Ask: *If I have a paddling pool containing 20,000 litres of water which empties at a rate of 750ml per minute, how long will it take to empty? How will you attempt to solve this problem? Are there any short cuts rather than counting in lots of 750?*

Curriculum objectives

● To understand and use approximate equivalences between metric units and common imperial units such as inches, pounds and pints.

Success criteria

● I can approximate equivalence between imperial and metric measures.

You will need

Photocopiable sheets

'Imperial/metric capacity conversion chart'

Differentiation

Less confident learners

These children should work in a small group with adult support.

More confident learners

These children can complete the photocopiable sheet independently.

Lesson 3   Oral and mental starter 41

Main teaching activities

Whole-class work: Remind the children that they have already learned about imperial and metric equivalents for length and mass. The common imperial units still used in the UK when talking about capacity are pints and gallons. Although by law liquids are usually sold in metric measures, it is still legal, by way of a local (non-European) law, to sell milk and beer in pints when the containers are returnable. Petrol and diesel are now sold in litres but many people, car manufacturers included, still refer to the efficiency of car engines using 'miles per gallon'.

Independent and paired work: Distribute photocopiable page 'Imperial/metric capacity conversion chart' from the CD-ROM and ask the children to consider the two typical problems that are on it. Talk through the problems with the children to ensure that they understand and can plan a way of working.

Progress check: Ask: *Which equivalents are you using? What do you need to find out first? What operation will you need?*

Review

Ask the children to talk you through their strategies for solving these problems. At first glance imperial and metric equivalents can be very confusing but it becomes clearer when you substitute one unit for another in the question, for example My car travels 45 miles on 4.5 litres of petrol.

Curriculum objectives

● To recognise and estimate capacity [using water].

Success criteria

● I can compare quantities and choose appropriate equipment to measure capacity.

You will need

Equipment

A selection of containers, for the class; dry sand or water

Differentiation

Less confident learners

These children should work with an adult with fewer containers, all of which have a clear scale. They may find that using dry sand or water to measure helps their understanding.

More confident learners

These children should use a wider variety of containers, including ones with widely-spaced graduations and ones with very small gradations and unusually-shaped ones without scales.

Lesson 4   Oral and mental starter 41

Main teaching activities

Whole-class work: Revise with the children what they know about units of measure for capacity, for example 1000ml = 1 litre. Establish how well they understand quantities by asking: *What would you measure in millilitres? Or in litres? Tell me something that is approximately 5 litres.*

Group and paired work: Distribute the different containers you have collected to the groups. Ask the children to sort them into two or more groups and to be willing to explain their decisions. For example, they might sort the containers into those with scales and those without; or containers labelled with a capacity and those without. Ask questions to provoke debate such as: *Which of these containers would you use to measure milk for a recipe? Which would you use to fill a paddling pool? Which give you the capacity in millilitres and which litres?* Finally ask them to order the containers, smallest to largest.

Give out sticky labels and ask the children to number the containers in size order as a record for tomorrow. Also ask them to label the scaled ones with the maximum capacity and the scale gradations. Encourage them to look at both the main divisions and the smaller ones.

Progress check: Ask: *What is the maximum capacity of this container? How do you know? Show me the large divisions. What do they represent? What do the small divisions represent? How did you work that out?*

Review

Choose a few of the measuring containers to show the markings and the maximum capacity. Ask: *What capacities and sort of liquids would this be useful for?* Give an example, for example, a small cylinder or spoon would be used for small quantities of liquids such as medicines. Ask: *How are very large quantities measured, for example to fill a swimming pool or to deliver oil? Why do we not have a container larger than a bucket?* (Large capacities have to be measured by a metred pump because liquids are very heavy.)

Curriculum objectives

● To solve problems involving measure (for example length, mass, volume, money) using decimal notation, including scaling.

Success criteria

● I can read scales accurately and compare different amounts.
● I can convert between millilitres and litres.
● I can solve capacity problems.

You will need

Equipment

The selection of containers from the last lesson; dry sand or water; capacity measuring equipment, such as jugs and measuring cylinders with a variety of different scales

Differentiation

Less confident learners

These children should work with an adult on the smaller selection of containers from the last lesson.

More confident learners

These children work on the more challenging selection of containers from the last lesson.

Lesson 5

Oral and mental starter 41

Main teaching activities

Group and paired work: Ask the children to arrange their containers from yesterday, starting with the smallest estimated capacity. Explain that they are going to use the marked measuring equipment to check whether they have correctly ordered all of their containers. Remind them that it would be sensible to use a range of containers because to try to fill a bucket with a medicine spoon would not be formal or accurate. They should label the unmarked containers with the capacity, written in both litres and in millilitres, for example, 0.5 litres = 500ml.

Progress check: Ask: *Are you able to use more than one type of measuring container to measure accurately? What do you have to do if your jug is not big enough to fill the bucket?* (Use it more than once) *How many litres is that? Is it an accurate measure if you are holding the jug up in the air to look at the amount?*

Review

On completion of the measuring ask the groups to report back on their original ordering. Were there any surprises? Discuss which shapes of container are the most difficult to estimate (for example, ones that are very different in shape from the marked jugs). Ask: *What is the average capacity of a coffee mug based on your findings? What about a bucket? For a pool holding approximately 2500 litres, how many buckets would you need to fill it? Which marked measuring container did you find the most useful? Why? Was it always the largest one or the smallest one?*

Line graphs and comparative graphs

Expected prior learning

Children should be able to:

- construct frequency tables, pictograms, bar charts and bar line graphs to represent the frequencies of events and changes over time
- collect, select and organise data to answer questions, draw conclusions and identify further questions to ask.

Topic	Curriculum objectives	Expected outcomes
Statistics	**Lesson 1**	
	To solve comparison, sum and difference problems using information presented in a line graph.	Construct frequency tables, pictograms and bar and line graphs to represent the frequencies of events and changes over time.
	Lesson 2	
	To solve comparison, sum and difference problems using information presented in a line graph.	Plan and pursue an enquiry; present evidence by collecting, organising and interpreting information; suggest extensions to the enquiry.
	Lesson 3	
	To solve comparison, sum and difference problems using information presented in a line graph.	Plan and pursue an enquiry; present evidence by collecting, organising and interpreting information; suggest extensions to the enquiry.
	Lesson 4	
	To solve comparison, sum and difference problems using information presented in a line graph.	Answer a set of related questions by collecting, selecting and organising relevant data; draw conclusions, using ICT to present features, and identify further questions to ask.
	Lesson 5	
	To solve comparison, sum and difference problems using information presented in a line graph.	Answer a set of related questions by collecting, selecting and organising relevant data; draw conclusions, using ICT to present features, and identify further questions to ask.

Preparation

Lesson 1: copy 'The Archimedes Science and Technology Centre', 'Thrills and spills' and 'Fair's Fair?', one of each per child; they use these throughout the week

Lesson 5: enlarge some of the children's graphs for display to allow them to share their findings

You will need

Photocopiable sheets

'The Archimedes Science and Technology Centre'; 'Thrills and spills (1) and (2)'; 'Fair's fair?'

Equipment

Squared paper

Further practice

Create line graphs of their own continuous data, for example, distance travelled on a walk, recorded every 5 minutes.

Oral and mental starters suggested for week 6

See bank of starters on page 168. Oral and mental starters are also on the CD-ROM.

49 Multiplication snap

50 Percentage pairs

51 Fraction problems

Overview of progression

During this week children have the opportunity to explore different sorts of graph and chart to record information for three different but related data handling activities evaluating the school visits undertaken by one school in a year. They have to plan their activities and work as a group or in pairs to record their findings and present their results. The children will have to assess the type of data and consider the most appropriate way to present it. They will have to move between bar charts and line graphs and make comparisons. They will also have to evaluate their data and make a persuasive report to others, giving reasons supported by their findings.

Watch out for

The most common error with data handling is not understanding the different types of graph and how they present information. Most particularly, many children try to present all information as a bar chart, which is incorrect for presenting continuous data where the points between the identified points still have meaning. This is true for any kind of information that is recorded over time. This should be represented as a continuous line graph. It is for this reason that the three different data representations are used in this one week's activities.

Creative context

Once the children have an understanding of the different types of graph they should be encouraged to present information in Science and other areas of the curriculum in graphical form.

Vocabulary

analyse, axes, bar chart, bar line chart, calculate, calculation, chart, classify, data, explain, graph, horizontal axis, information, interpret, label, line graph, maximum/minimum value, method, mode, pattern, pictogram, predict, problem, questionnaire, reason, reasoning, relationship, represent, scale, solution, survey, table, title, vertical axis

Curriculum objectives
- To solve comparison, sum and difference problems using information presented in a line graph.

Success criteria
- I can understand the difference between a bar chart and a line graph and when it is appropriate to use each.
- I can represent data on a line graph.
- I can represent data on a bar chart.
- I can extract information from graphs in order to answer questions and draw conclusions.
- I can pose questions to interrogate a graph.

You will need
Photocopiable sheets

'The Archimedes Science and Technology Centre'; 'Thrills and spills (1) and (2)'; 'Fair's fair?'

Equipment

Squared paper

Differentiation
Less confident learners

Children should solve problems as a group with the support of an adult.

More confident learners

These children can use photocopiable page 'Thrills and spills (2)', which have more complicated numbers. However the real challenge comes from being able to work independently and methodically, changing between the different representations.

Lesson 1 — Oral and mental starter 49

Main teaching activities

Whole-class work: Explain to the children this week they will carry out three different, but related, data-handling activities. These activities are all about investigating and evaluating the school visits undertaken by one school in a year. Revise the way in which different graphs are used for different types of data: bar charts or bar line graphs for comparisons of discrete data (data that can be counted) and line graphs for continuous data (data that are measured). Explain that anything that is measured over time, such as your heart rate when you are in hospital, is represented on a continuous line graph, because at any point along the line, the heart is still beating (hopefully) and so has a value, even if it is not at a point that you have actually recorded.

Paired and independent work: Set groups of children to work independently or in pairs on the activities. Talk through each activity with the group beforehand. You may wish to set up a carousel of simultaneous activities and work with different groups each day.

● Activity 1: The Archimedes Science and Technology Centre

The children use the table of data on photocopiable page 'The Archimedes Science and Technology Centre' from the CD-ROM to create a bar line graph showing the number of visitors to the Centre each month in a year and then use the graph to answer the questions.

Progress check: The children's answers should reflect some reasoning about fluctuating numbers at different times of the year. Ask: *Why might December be a relatively quiet month at the centre? Who do you think would be most likely to visit during term time? Why is the centre busy in August?* Encourage the children to see that the information extracted from a graph can be used to make hypotheses and even to predict.

● Activity 2: Thrills and spills

A Year 5 class visits the Speed and Sound science fair each year. Their favourite features are the rides demonstrating speed. Photocopiable page 'Thrills and spills' from the CD-ROM has a line graph showing the speed of the Rocking Roller Coaster. The children draw a similar line graph for the Hill and Dale Dipper and answer the questions.

Progress check: Ask: *How can the line graphs help us to compare the speeds for the two rides? When is each ride travelling the fastest? How long does this last for? How can you tell when a ride is accelerating?*

● Activity 3: Fair's fair?

Use the data from the tables on photocopiable page 'Fair's fair?' from the CD-ROM to draw one comparative bar chart showing all the information. Use all the data to compare the rides. List them in order of value and write a report commenting on the waiting times, the ride times and the value for money of each ride.

Progress check: The children's decisions about value for money should use all of the available data, not just one or two parameters. Ask: *What information are you using to help you decide whether these rides are good value for money? Do you think different people might have varying views?*

Review

Each day, check the progress of each group and correct any misconceptions. Ask questions such as: *Why does this activity use a bar line chart when this activity uses a line graph? How do you access information that falls between the marked points on a line graph. Can you obtain any information from between two bars on a bar line chart?*

Curriculum objectives

● To solve comparison, sum and difference problems using information presented in a line graph.

Success criteria

● I can understand the difference between a bar chart and a line graph.
● I can represent data on a line graph.
● I can represent data on a bar chart.
● I can extract information from graphs.

You will need

Photocopiable sheets

'The Archimedes Science and Technology Centre'; 'Thrills and spills'; 'Fair's fair?'

Equipment

Squared paper

Differentiation

Less confident learners

These children can work as a group with the support of an adult.

More confident learners

These children should work independently.

Lesson 2   Oral and mental starter 50

Main teaching activities

Whole-class work: Ask the children to continue with the carousel of activities (see lesson 1).

Paired and independent work: Revise when a bar or bar line graph is appropriate and when to use a line graph. (The latter measures something over a period of time, such as the temperature of a person over a 24-hour period.)

Progress check: Refer back to the progress checks in lesson 1. Ensure that the children are interpreting the data correctly and representing it accurately on each type of graph.

Review

Invite a group who have been working on 'The Archimedes Science and Technology Centre' activity to share their work so far. Ask questions such as: *What was difficult about drawing this graph? Why would it have been inappropriate to draw a line graph for this? Why do you think there were more visitors in some months than in others? How might a graph like this help the Centre to organise its publicity and special events? Who might be interested in this data?*

Curriculum objectives

● As lesson 2.

Success criteria

● As lesson 2 above.

You will need

Photocopiable sheets

'The Archimedes Science and Technology Centre'; 'Thrills and spills'; 'Fair's fair?'

Equipment

Squared paper

Differentiation

Less confident learners

These children can work as a group with the support of an adult.

More confident learners

These children should work independently.

Lesson 3   Oral and mental starter 49

Main teaching activities

Whole-class work: Ask the children to continue with the carousel of activities (see lesson 1).

Progress check: Refer back to the progress checks in lesson 1.

Review

Ask a group who have been working on the 'Thrills and spills' activity to report back about their work to the rest of the class. Then ask: *What sort of graph did you draw? Why? Which of the questions would you have been unable to answer if you had drawn a bar chart?* (The ones that involve reading intermediate points.) *Who might find this information of value?*

Ask a group who have been working on 'Fair's fair?' activity to report their findings and views. Some other groups who have looked at this activity may have different views, and can be invited to discuss these. Ask: *What facts do we need to look at when deciding which is the 'best' ride? Does it depend on your own preferences? Do some people value the thrill of a longer ride more than not having to wait a long time? How can you calculate the price per minute of a ride?*

Curriculum objectives
● As lesson 1.

Success criteria
● I can extract information from graphs in order to answer questions and draw conclusions.
● I can pose questions to interrogate a graph.

You will need

Photocopiable sheets
'The Archimedes Science and Technology Centre'; 'Thrills and spills'; 'Fair's fair?'

Equipment
Squared paper

Differentiation

Less confident learners
These children can work as a group.

More confident learners
These children can work independently.

Curriculum objectives
● As lesson 1.

Success criteria
● I can extract information from graphs in order to answer questions and draw conclusions.
● I can pose questions to interrogate a graph.

You will need

Photocopiable sheets
'The Archimedes Science and Technology Centre'; 'Thrills and spills'; 'Fair's fair?'

Equipment
Squared paper

Differentiation

Less confident learners
These children could do a group presentation of their findings.

More confident learners
These children should be able to produce a more in-depth comparison and use higher level reasoning skills.

Lesson 4   Oral and mental starter 51

Main teaching activities

Whole-class work: Ask the children to continue with the carousel of activities (see lesson 1). Explain that you want to display their data-handling work and also that they need to be able to present their findings to the class as if they were talking to the owners of the Science Centre or the Speed and Sound Fair or, alternatively, to teachers who might be planning school trips. Divide the class to match these two audience groups. They will need to have clear results and explanations, and be ready to answer questions. Each audience will have a different interest and this should be considered when preparing the presentation. They should prepare a statement to go with each activity sheet. The statement might be a comparison of length of ride or value for money or popularity.

Progress check: Ask: *How confident are you that you have a clear view to share with the others about the most successful trip? Do your graphs back up what you want to say? If not, why not? Do you need to review the scale that you used?*

Review

Ask the children to consider how data can be presented to show the same results in different lights, for example by increasing the vertical scale on a bar chart, differences can be made to look visually bigger. Demonstrate using differences of waiting time on a vertical scale of 1 square = 1 minute and compare this to a vertical scale of 1 square = 5 minutes.

Lesson 5   Oral and mental starter 50

Main teaching activities

Whole-class work: This lesson should be the culmination of the children's work on handling data. Before the lesson, if possible, select a variety of the children's graphs to enlarge for display. Use these to allow the children to share their results and findings. Compare the appearance of some graphs that are showing the same information but look different due to a larger or smaller scale being used on the y-axis. Ask various groups to present their findings as if they were talking to either the owners of the Science Centre or the owners of the Speed and Sound Fair or teachers planning a school trip. Invite the class to ask each group questions as if they were representatives of each audience.

Progress check: Ask: *Who is your audience for this research. If you were talking to the owner of the Science Centre, might you be emphasising different points?*

Review

Use this session to gather and reinforce all the children's learning about data handling in this unit of work. Ask:

- *Why are graphs and charts useful? When are they most often used? Who might find these graphs and charts useful?*
- *What action might the owner of the Speed and Sound Fair want to take after seeing this data? Should visitors be given this kind of data as part of their guide book? Would it encourage or discourage visitors?*
- *Can you think of any other information about the Speed and Sound Fair that would be useful? (For example, a line graph showing price increases over the last five years.) Who might be interested in this?*
- *Can the 'picture' conveyed by a graph sometimes be deceptive? How? Why might someone want to manipulate the data?*

Give the children strips of paper to write down what they have learned from this work or what they know now about data handling that they didn't know before. Display these or store them as a record.

 SCHOLASTIC

Curriculum objectives
● To add and subtract fractions with the same denominator and denominators that are multiples of the same number.

You will need
1. Check
Oral and mental starter
44 Fraction match

2. Assess
Individual whiteboards

3. Further practice
General resources
'Fraction families'

Adding fractions

Most children should be able to add fractions with the same denominator to make mixed number answers and add fractions by converting to equivalent fractions with a common denominator.

Some children will not have made such progress and will require practice to recognise equivalents and then convert them before adding the fractions.

1. Check
44 Fraction match

Use the oral and mental starter to remind children of equivalent fractions, including mixed numbers and improper fractions. Observe the children who instantly recall simple fraction equivalents such as ½ and ¼ and those who are able to convert to equivalent fractions with a common denominator before adding. Less confident learners may need extra practice with this.

● *Can you find a match for ½? How do you know? What do you have to do to check? Which fractions from the list could you add together? What would you have to do with ones that have different denominators?*

2. Assess

Extend the oral and mental starter to ask children to choose two fractions from the list to add together. Note their choices and reasons and the resulting answer. They convert improper fractions to mixed numbers. Less confident learners will need practice with the rules for adding fractions together and with recognising that improper fractions are more than one whole. Record the outcomes.

3. Further practice

Use the fraction cards and shapes for children to match fractions that are of the same 'family', and practise converting them in order to add them together.

Curriculum objectives
● To recognise the per cent symbol (%) and understand that per cent relates to 'number of parts per hundred', and write percentages as a fraction with denominator 100, and as a decimal.

You will need
1. Check
Oral and mental starter
50 Percentage pairs

2. Assess
'Fractions, decimals and percentages'

3. Further practice
General resources
'Fractions, decimals and percentages'; 'Blank 100 square'

Percentages as fractions of 100

Most children should be able to recognise and use percentages and their fraction and decimal equivalents.

Some children will not have made such progress and will require practice in matching fractions with their percentage equivalents

1. Check
50 Percentage pairs

Use the oral and mental starter to check the children's recall of equivalents and their understanding of 'parts of 100'. Observe how they convert percentages to fractions and vice versa.

● *Express this percentage as a fraction. Which percentages do you instantly recognise as a simple fraction? How might the decimal equivalent help with this?*

2. Assess

Extend the oral and mental starter by using the 'Fractions, decimals and percentages' cards to make trios of equivalents. Confident learners will be able to explain how they know that they are equivalent and be able to describe their calculations. Less confident learners will need further practice with expressing a percentage as a fraction of 100 and then simplifying. Record the outcomes.

3. Further practice

Use a 'Blank 100 square' to help convert the percentage to a fraction 'out of 100' and then divide to simplify the fraction.

You will need

1. Check

Oral and mental starter

 Multiplication snap

2. Assess

'Testing times'

3. Further practice

Oral and mental starter

37 Fast times

Written methods of multiplication: 2-digits × 2-digits and 3-digits × 2-digits

Most children should be able to use a formal written calculation to multiply larger numbers.

Some children will not have made such progress and will require additional practice with 2-digit × 1-digit calculations to build confidence.

1. Check

49 Multiplication snap

Use the oral and mental starter to check children's dexterity in multiplying using known multiples or factors. Some children will confidently choose different factors to multiply and recognise that products can be found in a variety of ways. Less confident learners will need to calculate each one to find a pair and may need to practise mental multiplication.

- *Explain how you chose that number sentence? What are factors? How can they help us to solve tricky multiplication questions?*

2. Assess

As the children complete photocopiable page 169 'Testing times', observe the methods that they use. For children using long multiplication watch that they carry any digits correctly and that they use a place-holding zero when multiplying by tens. Some children may need further practice with expanded methods such as the grid method or expanded vertical calculations. They may also need to perfect their known times tables. Record the outcomes.

3. Further practice

Use the oral and mental starter for children to further practise their multiplication knowledge to assist with accurate written calculations.

You will need

1. Check

Oral and mental starter

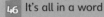 It's all in a word

2. Assess

'The word is the key'

3. Further practice

Oral and mental starter

47 Kris-cross 100 square

Photocopiable sheets

'Lots to think about'

Interpreting mathematical language in word problems

Most children should be able to make decisions about the correct operation to use to solve a problem.

Some children will not have made such progress and will require extra practice with understanding the vocabulary of problem solving.

1. Check

46 It's all in a word

The oral and mental starter can be used with differentiated numbers to assess the understanding of the mathematical vocabulary. Most children will be confident about their chosen operation but some may need practice with different words for the same operation.

- *Tell me how you are going to solve this question. What is the key word? Talk me through what you did to get your answer. Is there a way you could check it?*

2. Assess

Observe the children completing photocopiable page 170 'The word is the key'. Their choices of numbers will give you valuable information about their confidence with calculation. As they solve the problems, some children will confidently calculate whereas others may need further practice with mixed operation questions. Record the outcomes.

3. Further practice

Photocopiable page 171 'Lots to think about' can be reused to give further practice in using mathematical vocabulary.

Oral and mental starters

Number and place value

41 Ordering measures

Remind the children that measurements may be expressed in different ways. Revise all the units of measure that they know and categorise them into length, weight and capacity. They may mention imperial measures too, which can be added to the categories and a discussion may be had about the difference. Explain that for this exercise you are concentrating on metric units of measure.

Challenge the children to write a list of lengths, in ascending order of size but using mixed units.

For example: 0.001km;   500cm;   6m;   0.8km

Swap with a partner to check for accuracy.

Repeat with capacity and weight mixed units.

42 It doesn't make sense!

Ask the children to solve the following problem:

215 children are to visit a music festival. 45 children can fit onto a bus. How many buses do I need?

Explain that sometimes it is not sufficient to simply do a calculation but it is important to give an answer that is possible given the context. In this case, 215 divided by 45 is 4 remainder 35. However, this is not a sensible answer in terms of a number of buses. Unless they are going to leave 35 children behind, the correct answer is that they need five buses.

Ask the children to make up similar context-based questions to share with the class.

43 Target number

Using number cards 0–9, ask children to select four digits and display them as a four-digit number. Ask the children to read the number and explain the value of each digit. Ask: How many more would I need to make the next whole thousand? *How many less to make 500? How many more to make ten thousand?*, and so on. Repeat with other four- and five-digit numbers.

Fraction

44 Fraction match

Write the following fractions on the board. Ask the children to find equivalent pairs and join them with a line. Ask them to explain how they worked out that they were equivalent.

$\frac{10}{25}$ $\frac{7}{3}$ $\frac{5}{4}$ $4\frac{1}{5}$ $\frac{2}{6}$ $\frac{1}{4}$ $\frac{2}{10}$ $\frac{2}{5}$ $\frac{1}{3}$ $\frac{1}{5}$ $\frac{4}{16}$ $1\frac{1}{4}$

$2\frac{1}{3}$ $1\frac{2}{3}$ $2\frac{1}{5}$ 4

45 Fraction line up

Write the following fractions on the board:

$\frac{1}{3}$ $\frac{2}{5}$ $1\frac{1}{5}$ $\frac{1}{10}$ $\frac{2}{3}$ $\frac{7}{4}$ $\frac{9}{10}$ $\frac{20}{10}$ $1\frac{5}{5}$

Draw a number line like the one below. Ask the children to consider where they would place each of the given fractions on the number line, giving you their reasons.

0_____1_____2_____3

50 Percentage pairs

Ask the children to convert fractions into percentages and vice versa. Remind them that 'percentage' means 'out of 100'. You could use the following:

$\frac{1}{10}$; $\frac{1}{20}$; $\frac{1}{5}$; $\frac{1}{25}$; $\frac{3}{4}$; $\frac{1}{2}$; $\frac{4}{20}$; $\frac{4}{10}$; $\frac{5}{50}$

20%; 25%; 10%; 75%; 40%; 80%; 23%; 12%

46 It's all in a word

Ask the children to listen carefully to the vocabulary used in the following questions as it gives clues about the type of calculation required. Ensure that the children can explain the meaning of the 'clue' words.

- *What is the product of 3 and 5?*
- *Give me the sum of 135 and 246.*
- *205 subtract 67.*
- *Multiply 10, 6 and 2.*
- *What are the factors of 24?*
- *Give me three multiples of 12.*
- *Tell me the difference between 938 and 833.*
- *What is 30 fewer than 921?*
- *What is 55 more than 297?*
- *What is the quotient of 27 and 3?*

This activity can be repeated with different numbers.

47 Kris-cross 100 square

Distribute the photocopiable page sheet '100 square' from the CD-ROM, one per child (or pair). Explain that you are going to call out some rules of multiples and division for the children to cross through.

Use statements such as:

- *Cross out all the multiples of 5.*
- *Cross out factors of 50.*
- *Cross out any two numbers that add up to 11.*
- *Cross out any numbers that are divisible by 8.*

Check the children's understanding of the vocabulary and the numbers that they have selected.

Measurement

48 Kilogram and gram calculator

Ask questions such as:

- *If 450 grams of flour is taken from a 1 kilogram bag, how much will be left in the bag?*
- *If 2.5 kilograms of flour is used from a 10 kilogram bag, how much is left?*
- *I am weighing out flour for a cake. I have 125g. How much more do I need to make 1kg?*

Continue to mix kilograms and grams in questions to make 1kg , 5kg or 10kg.

Multiplication and division

49 Multiplication snap

Explain to the children that you are going to write a multiplication fact on the board. The children must write an equivalent but different sentence and shout 'snap' as they hold it up for you to check.

For example: You say 12 × 3 and a child might suggest 6 × 6. (Both equal 36.)

Try: 6 × 4;   4 × 3;   20 × 5;   4 × 8;   0.8 × 100;   0.04 × 1000;   15 × 2; and so on.

Oral and mental starter 51 continues on the CD-ROM.

Testing times

- Solve these questions.

I. 39 × 17

2. 73 × 26

3. 176 × 28

4. 285 × 28

5. 296 × 24

6. 402 × 39

I can do formal written calculations to multiply larger numbers.

How did you do?

Name: _____   Date: _____

The word is the key

■ Using the numbers below write a number sentence and a word question for each of the 'key words' in the boxes.

| 2018 | 1937 | 23 | 31 | 4 | 856 | 716 | 52 |

Sum / Total	Difference / Subtract

Share	Product / Lots of

■ Now give your questions to a partner to check.

I can understand and use mathematical language to solve problems.

How did you do?

PHOTOCOPIABLE

SCHOLASTIC
www.scholastic.co.uk

Lots to think about

- On another sheet of paper, solve the following problems.

1. A man cycles 5 miles to work and the same on his return.
He works 5 days a week. How far does he cycle each week?

2. Alex scored 5834 points in his game in the first round and another 1992 in the second round. His total only just failed to reach the highest score ever achieved by his brother Mark, who achieved just 179 points more. What was Mark's score?

3. Joe has collected 245 football stickers. He buys 59 more. How many stickers does he have in total?

4. Felicity decides that she has far too many hair clips and gives half of them to her sister. If she started with 152 hair clips, how many hair clips does Felicity have left?

5. Fruity chews are sold in bags of 84. Each bag has equal numbers of the four different flavours and costs £1.09. How many chews of each flavour are there?

6. Multi-packs contain five bags of chews and cost £4.99.
How many chews are there altogether in a multi-pack?
How many of any single flavour? What is the saving per bag if you buy the multi-pack?

I can select the correct mathematical operations to solve problems.

How did you do?

Negative numbers and Roman numerals

Expected prior learning

Children should be able to:

- order whole numbers up to 1000
- round numbers to the nearest 10, 100 or 1000
- have some experience of negative numbers as distances from zero.

Topic	Curriculum objectives	Expected outcomes
Number and place value	**Lesson 1**	
	To count forwards or backwards in steps of powers of 10 for any given number up to 1,000,000. To round any number up to 1,000,000 to the nearest 10, 100, 1000, 10,000 and 100,000.	Count from any given number in whole-number steps, extending beyond zero when counting backwards; relate the numbers to their position on a number line.
	Lesson 2	
	To interpret negative numbers in context, count forwards and backwards with positive and negative whole numbers, including through zero.	Explain what each digit represents in whole numbers and decimals with up to two decimal places, and partition, round and order these numbers.
	Lesson 3	
	To solve number problems and practical problems that involve all of the above.	Represent a puzzle or problem by identifying and recording the information or calculations needed to solve it; find possible solutions and confirm them in the context of the problem.
	Lesson 4	
	To read Roman numerals to 1000 (M) and recognise years written in Roman numerals.	Explain what each numeral represents and combine in order to create representations of larger numbers.
	Lesson 5	
	To solve number problems and practical problems that involve all of the above. To read Roman numerals to 1000 (M) and recognise years written in Roman numerals.	Represent a puzzle or problem by identifying and recording the information or calculations needed to solve it; find possible solutions and confirm them in the context of the problem.

■SCHOLASTIC

Preparation

Lesson 1: make copies of 'Number lines', one per pair; assemble the '0–30 number cards', one set per pair; assemble the 'Place value arrow cards', one set per pair if needed

Lesson 2: make copies of 'Number lines', one per pair; organise access to the internet for research

Lesson 4: copy 'Roman numeral game cards' onto card, one set per pair

Lesson 5: copy 'Roman numeral years', one per child

You will need

Photocopiable sheets

'Roman numeral years'

General resources

'Number lines'; '0–30 number cards'; 'Place value arrow cards'; 'Roman numeral game cards'

Equipment

Internet access for research

Further practice

Give children further opportunities to play the 'Roman numerals game' (see lessons 4) to consolidate their understanding of roman numerals to 1000 (M).

Oral and mental starters suggested for week 1

See bank of starters on page 208. Oral and mental starters are also on the CD-ROM.

52 Multiplication challenge

53 Division challenge

54 Round and estimate

Overview of progression

This week offers an opportunity for the children to explore, round and order larger numbers to 1,000,000 and to find out about temperature extremes around the world to support understanding of negative numbers in context. They will then go on to learn about Roman numeral representations and their more familiar equivalents. They should be able to embed this learning by playing games such as 'Snap' and 'Pairs' (Pelmanism) in order that they can recognise years written in Roman numerals.

Watch out for

Some children may inaccurately read the place value or not use the appropriate number of place-holding zeros, thereby misreading the value of the numbers. When combining Roman numerals, some children will find the conventions of combining them difficult to remember, for example, 19 = XIX not XVIIII. In this instance, refer the children back to the rules for combining Roman numerals which state that no letter can be repeated more than 3 times in a row.

Creative context

There is the opportunity to use computers to further understanding and knowledge of the world and numbers in context.

Vocabulary

ascending, between, descending, digit, greater than (>), hundred thousands, hundreds, less than (<), million, numeral, partition, pattern, place value, **Roman numerals**, sequence, ten thousands, tens, thousands, ones

Curriculum objectives

● To round any number up to 1,000,000 to the nearest 10, 100, 1000, 10,000 and 100,000.
● To count forwards or backwards in steps of powers of 10 for any given number up to 1,000,000.

Success criteria

● I can round any number up to 1,000,000.
● I can count forwards and backwards in steps of powers of 10.

You will need

General resources

'Number lines'; '0–30 number cards'; 'Place value arrow cards'

Differentiation

Less confident learners

The size of the numbers may be daunting so it may help this group to work with an adult, starting with four-digit numbers and building up to larger ones. They may also find using the 'Place value arrow cards' helpful when building numbers.

More confident learners

These children should be able to describe and place numbers very accurately and to calculate differences between numbers.

Lesson I

Main teaching activities

Whole-class work: Tell the children that they are going to practise their rounding and estimating positions on a number line, but this time they are going to be working with much larger numbers. Ask them to divide a blank number line so that it shows 100,000 to 1,000,000 and the divisions between in jumps of 100,000. Discuss how this is dividing the line into tenths.

Ask a volunteer to select six digits from the set of number cards 0–9 and order them to make a six digit number, for example 721,835. Revise with the children the place value of each of the digits by asking another volunteer to make the same number from place value arrow cards, such as:

700 000 + 20 000+ 1000 + 800 + 30 + 5.

Return to the number lines that the children started with and ask them to discuss with a partner between which two 100 000 divisions this number will sit, for example between 700,000 and 800,000. Ask: *Will it be nearer the 700,000 or the 800,000?* Explain that it would be rounded to 700,000. Encourage them to mark the 750 000 division and from there the 725,000. In this way they can estimate the position of 721,835 quite accurately. Repeat with other examples as necessary.

Paired work: In pairs the children should repeat this exercise selecting six digit numbers to place onto their blank number line by rounding and estimating. Each pair should be able to select at least 4 different numbers, avoiding ones that are too close to ones already placed. They should be able to explain their reasoning and the decisions that they made when rounding up or down

Progress check: *How are you deciding where to place your numbers? Which digit are you looking at when you round to the nearest 10,000? What about when you round to the nearest 1000? How do you decide whether to round up or down? What is the largest number that you have made? Read it out to me.*

Review

Ask one pair to select one of their rounded numbers but not say what it is. The other children should then try to work out what the number is by asking questions that determine its position on the number line, for example, *Is it in the first half of the number line or the second? Is it larger than 200,000 but smaller than 300,000?*

Curriculum objectives

- To interpret negative numbers in context, count forwards and backwards with positive and negative whole numbers, including through zero.

Success criteria

- I can read and understand the value of negative numbers in real-life contexts.
- I can count forwards and backwards through zero.

You will need

General resources

'Number lines'

Equipment

Internet access for research

Differentiation

Less confident learners

These children may need some specific facts to research.

More confident learners

Encourage these children to pursue a line of enquiry, for example, the three coldest places on earth compared to the extreme temperatures of the planets and the sun.

Lesson 2 — Oral and mental starter 52

Main teaching activities

Whole-class work: Draw a vertical number line on the board and mark the mid-point with a zero. Remind the children that numbers that are less than zero are called negative numbers, the minus indicating the distance away from zero of a value. Ask for the children to estimate where -3, -20 and -10 might fall as well as estimating 5, 18 and 30. Explain that the most common place to see a vertical number line showing both positive and negative number is on a thermometer. However, demonstrate how this information can also be shown as a horizontal number line.

Paired work: Explain to the children that they are to use the internet to find out six temperature facts about the natural world such as the hottest or coldest place on earth; the boiling or freezing point of water; the average summer temperature in Britain or in the Sahara desert. They are to place these temperatures on a blank number line to display these facts, so they will have to divide up their number line from the extremes and work out some equal division points in order to estimate accurately.

Progress check: Ask: *What is the range of your number line? How are you going to divide it up to assist you to estimate the position of the different temperatures? What marker will you need to divide negative and positive numbers? What is the lowest temperature that you have found? Is this closer or further away from zero than your highest temperature?*

Review

Share some of the facts that they children have discovered. Discuss how it is important to understand the relative size of negative numbers as distance from zero. Use the extremes to calculate differences and use the vocabulary of hotter and colder to embed understanding of negative numbers. Ask: *How much hotter is the temperature on a summer's day in Britain than the temperature at the North Pole? How much colder is the South Pole than water's freezing point?*

Curriculum objectives

- To solve number problems and practical problems that involve number and place value.

Success criteria

- I can recognise a linear number pattern.
- I can create number patterns for others to solve, justifying the rule.

You will need

Equipment

Squared paper

Differentiation

Less confident learners

Children work with adult support to create patterns of only 3s, 4s and 8s.

More confident learners

These children should create more complex patterns, for example using negative or decimal numbers.

Lesson 3 — Oral and mental starter 53

Main teaching activities

Whole-class work: Write these number patterns on the board:

105,	90,	75,	60,	...,	...,	...
2.0,	1.5,	1.0,	0.5,	...,	...,	...
-8,	-5,	-2,	...,	...,	...	

Discuss the patterns and how to continue them. State a rule for each one, such as: 'This pattern is decreasing by 15 each time'.

Paired work: Explain that you want each pair to create a number pattern 'wordsearch' on squared paper. They should use a run of four numbers in the same number pattern, for example, -10, -7, -4. These may run vertically, horizontally or diagonally. On completion, swap with another pair and solve the puzzle.

Progress check: Ask: *What pattern are you using? Do you have to stick to differences? Are there other number patterns that you know? Have you used a number more than once in your puzzle? Is it part of the same number pattern?*

Review

Check that everyone has found all the number patterns in their paired work activity. Ask: *Do all number patterns have to be made by adding or subtracting? What is the pattern here: 1.0, 0.1, 0.01, 0.001, ... or 3, 0.03, 0.0003, ...? What is the rule?* Ask each pair to create a number pattern that uses division or multiplication. In turn, each pair can hold up their pattern for the rest of the children to continue and state a rule.

Curriculum objectives
● To read Roman numerals to 1000 (M) and recognise years written in Roman numerals.
Success criteria
● I can read Roman numerals to 1000.

You will need
General resources
'Roman numeral game cards'

Differentiation
Less confident learners
These children should revisit and embed the understanding of 1–100 in Roman numerals.
More confident learners
These children should use numbers above 100 for their game.

Lesson 4

Oral and mental starter 54

Main teaching activities

Whole-class work: Explain to the children the concept of a different number recording system from our own. Display the Roman numerals from photocopiable page 'Roman numeral game cards' from the CD-ROM and discuss the rules for recording numbers using Roman numerals (below) and demonstrate how to write the numbers 20 (XX), 50 (L), 100 (C), 500 (D) and 1000 (M).

● The letters should be arranged from the one with the largest value to the one with the smallest.
● Each letter's value is added to the previous ones (III).
● Only powers of ten (I, X, C and M) can be repeated (LXX).
● You cannot repeat any letter more than three times in a row (VIII).
● Because of the preceding rule, certain numbers must be written using subtraction. In this case, a letter with a smaller value precedes one with a larger value and the value of the smaller is subtracted from the larger. The result is then added to the rest of the letters (IX).

The following rules apply to subtraction:

● Only powers of ten (I, X, C, M) can be subtracted (LXL).
● The smaller letter must be one fifth or one tenth of the larger one (LD).
● The smaller letter must be either the first letter or preceded by a letter at least ten times greater than it (MLD).
● If another letter follows the larger one, it must be smaller than the number preceding the larger one (MD).

Illustrate these rules by revising simpler numbers for example XIX (19) and XXVII (27). Then ask the children to attempt to work out numbers higher than 100, for example 104 (CIV) and 404 (CDIV) or DCCCXLVI (500 + 300 + 40 + 6 = 846). Each time work through the representations to build the number. Roman numerals are read from left to right in sections so that parts of the whole number can be worked out separately. Tell the children that for longer numbers, recording as a number sentence (as shown) is helpful. Distribute generals resources 'Roman numeral game cards' (3) and (4) from the CD-ROM to help illustrate the above.

Paired word: Give out one set of photocopiable page 'Roman numerals game cards' to each pair from the CD-ROM. Explain the rules of playing 'Snap' except the matched pair must be a number and its equivalent Roman numeral. As for ordinary 'Snap', the winner is the person who ends up with all the cards. The children can then change the game to 'Pairs' or 'Pelmanism' where they spread all the cards face down on the table and turn over two cards, trying to find a number and its equivalent Roman numeral. When they turn them face downwards again they must try to remember where the cards are. The winner is the person who collects the most pairs.

Progress check: Ask: *What number are you looking for? What might help you remember the number equivalents? Where might you see Roman numerals still used?*

Review

Call out a number and ask the children to write the Roman numeral equivalent on their whiteboards or write a roman numeral on the board and ask the children to write the ordinary number. Ask the children to work out what other numbers might look like when written as Roman numerals, for example, CCXII (212), CCCXXXVI (336), CMXI (911) They should be able to explain how they worked them out.

 SCHOLASTIC

Curriculum objectives
- To read Roman numerals to 1000 (M) and recognise years written in Roman numerals.
- To solve number problems and practical problems that involve number and place value.

Success criteria
- I can read Roman numerals.
- I can recognise years written in Roman numerals.

You will need

Photocopiable sheets
'Roman numeral years'

General resources
'Roman numeral game cards'

Differentiation

Less confident learners
These children may need support to remember the rules for making some numbers.

More confident learners
On complete of the activity on the photocopiable sheet, these children can go on to challenge a partner to make the largest number possible using only L, C, D and M.

Lesson 5

Oral and mental starter 52

Main teaching activities

Whole-class work: Revise how larger Roman numerals can be combined to make numbers to 1000.

Ask the children to explain their reasoning about converting these Roman numerals:
- DLII is 500 plus 50 plus 2 = 552
- CM is one hundred less than 1000 = 900
- CMXXVI is therefore 900 plus 20 plus 6.

Next demonstrate how to convert numbers in reverse for example, write the following as Roman numerals, 306, that is 300 (CCC) plus 6 (VI) = CCCVI.

Now ask the children to convert other numbers, explaining their thinking:
- 265 (200 + 60 +10 +5) = CCLXV
- 838 (800 made up of 500 plus 300 + 30 +8) = DCCCXXXVIII

Explain that Roman numerals can still be seen in use to denote the year a film or television programme was made. for example MM = the year 2000 so MMXIV = 2014 or MCCCX = 1310.

Paired work: Distribute photocopiable page 'Roman numeral years' from the CD-ROM. The children write the equivalents either in Roman numerals or ordinary numbers and then order the years from the earliest to the latest, discussing with their partner how to translate the numbers.

Progress check: Ask: *Which digit or letter are you starting with to translate these numbers? Do you read these numbers from the left or the right?* Say: *Do not forget to refer to the rules we have discussed for creating and reading Roman numerals.*

Review

Ask the children to share their answers and to discuss the most difficult ones. Correct misconceptions by asking children to talk through their decisions. Ask: *Which digit do they notice is missing from Roman numerals? (0) Why does this not cause a problem in Roman notation?*

Adding and subtracting large and small numbers

Expected prior learning

Children should be able to:

- add and subtract whole numbers to 100
- use a written method for addition and subtraction for whole numbers, either an informal, expanded method or columnar addition and subtraction.

Topic	Curriculum objectives	Expected outcomes
Addition and subtraction	**Lesson 1**	
	To add and subtract whole numbers with more than four-digits, including using formal written methods (columnar addition and subtraction). To use rounding to check answers to calculations and determine, in the context of a problem, levels of accuracy.	Use formal written methods to add and subtract whole numbers with up to five digits.
	Lesson 2	
	To solve addition and subtraction multi-step problems in contexts, deciding which operations and methods to use and why. To solve problems involving number up to three decimal places.	Represent a puzzle or problem by identifying and recording the information or calculations needed to solve it; find possible solutions and confirm them in the context of the problem.
	Lesson 3	
	To add and subtract numbers mentally with increasingly large numbers. To solve addition and subtraction multi-step problems in contexts, deciding which operations and methods to use and why.	Represent a puzzle or problem by identifying and recording the information or calculations needed to solve it; find possible solutions and confirm them in the context of the problem.
	Lesson 4	
	To add and subtract numbers mentally with increasingly large numbers. To solve addition and subtraction multi-step problems in contexts, deciding which operations and methods to use and why.	Represent a puzzle or problem by identifying and recording the information or calculations needed to solve it; find possible solutions and confirm them in the context of the problem.
	Lesson 5	
	To solve problems involving addition, subtraction, multiplication and division and a combination of these, including understanding the meaning of the equals sign.	Solve one-step and two-step problems involving whole numbers and decimals and all four operations, choosing and using appropriate calculation strategies.

■SCHOLASTIC

Preparation

Lesson 1: copy 'Sum, total and difference', one per child

Lesson 2: write the calculations and column headings on the board

Lesson 3: assemble '0–30 number cards', one set to demonstrate and one set per pair, if needed

Lesson 4: write the number puzzles on to board

Lesson 5: copy 'Problems with measures (2)', one per child

You will need

Photocopiable sheets
'Sum, total and difference'; 'Problems with measures (1), (2) and (3)'

General resources
'0–30 number cards'

Further practice

Give children photocopiable page 'Journey between the planets' to practice the addition and subtraction of whole numbers with four or more digits using formal written methods.

Oral and mental starters suggested for week 2

See bank of starters on pages 208 to 209. Oral and mental starters are also on the CD-ROM.

55 The tall and the small

56 You know for a fact!

57 Mystery number

Overview of progression

This week provides opportunities to solve puzzles and problems using mental and written calculations for addition and subtraction. There is an emphasis on reasoning, looking for patterns in number and explaining thinking. The week begins with a revision of columnar addition and subtraction and the related mathematical vocabulary and then encourages children to assess the most efficient ways of calculating which may not always be a written method. There is an opportunity to develop reasoning and systematic ways of thinking through solving the number puzzle and to apply reason about sensible answers in real life contexts.

Watch out for

Children need to be able to work systematically in order to be sure of exploring all possibilities. Some children will need support to do this since they are unable to plan ahead with their mathematical thinking. In this instance the teacher might give step by step guidance, for example in a two-step word problem give assistance with which part needs to be solved first in order to access the next step. In working through the puzzle pose questions to scaffold thinking such as, is it possible to get 9 or 8 at the top of the pyramid, using single digit differences? Why not?

Creative context

While some of the puzzles are purely number based, others are examples of real problems in an everyday context. Encourage the children to look for opportunities to apply their mathematical thinking in other areas of the curriculum.

Vocabulary

add, decimal place, decimal point, difference, digit, estimate, hundred thousands, hundreds, hundredth, million, minus, **numeral**, partition, place value, plus, reason, round, subtract, sum, ten thousands, tens, tenth, thousands, **thousandth**, total, ones

Curriculum objectives

• To add and subtract whole numbers with more than four-digits, including using formal written methods (columnar addition and subtraction).
• To use rounding to check answers to calculations and determine, in the context of a problem, levels of accuracy.

Success criteria

• I can use written calculations including columnar addition and subtraction to answer questions and solve problems.

You will need

Photocopiable sheets

'Sum, total and difference'

Differentiation

Less confident learners

Use this time to work with a group who are less secure with columnar addition and subtraction.

More confident learners

Having practised their calculating, these children could make up some problems of their own for a partner to solve.

Main teaching activities

Whole-class work: Revise formal columnar addition and subtraction with the children, highlighting the errors that people often make, such as when 'carrying' digits in addition and incorrect decomposition when subtracting. Use the following example to remind the children about the inverse operation and how it may be used to check answers.

$$\begin{array}{r} {}^3\!4\ {}^9\!0\ {}^1\!1\ 7 \\ -\ 1\ 8\ 9\ 2 \\ \hline 2\ 1\ 2\ 5 \end{array}$$

Revise how to rearrange the 4000 into 3000, 10 hundreds and then move 1 of the hundreds across to make 10 tens, leaving 900.

$$\begin{array}{r} 2\ 1\ 2\ 5 \\ +\ 1\ 8\ 9\ 2 \\ \hline 4\ 0\ 1\ 7 \end{array}$$

Remind the children to take care when carrying digits and to remember to add them into the final total.

Independent work: Distribute photocopiable page 'Sum, total and difference' from the CD-ROM. Explain to the children that the questions use a variety of the vocabulary that is associated with adding and subtracting and has calculations involving money and measures.

Progress check: Ask: *How do you know which operation to use? What is the clue word? Have you checked that your decomposition still makes the original number even though it has been rearranged? Have you added in any 'carried' digits? Have you checked with the inverse?*

Review

Check the accuracy of the children's calculating and then discuss the point at which the children recognise that they need to use a written calculation for efficiency and accuracy. Write some examples such as 24 + 17; 284 + 83; 834 + 3912; £1028.21 + £2778.19; 103 − 87; 1094 − 319; £1201.13 − £628.93. Ask the children to identify the ones where they would prefer to use a written calculation and to say why.

Curriculum objectives

● To solve problems involving number up to three decimal places.
● To solve addition and subtraction multi-step problems in contexts, deciding which operations and methods to use and why.

Success criteria

● I can assess different types of number sentences for addition and subtraction and choose an appropriate operation and strategy, depending on the numbers.

Differentiation

Less confident learners

These children will need adult guidance to choose the formal method since they may rely heavily on one type of calculating method. The children could work as one group with the adult helper demonstrating some alternatives.

More confident learners

These children may be the group least flexible in their choice of methods to solve problems since they will choose a mental calculation the most often. They too may need guidance as to the formal method and how they need an alternative calculation to check their results.

Lesson 2 — Oral and mental starter 56

Main teaching activities

Whole-class work: Write these calculations on the board:

5007 − 2996   1045 − 745   1204 + 1094

£251.89 + £87.68   (25 × 5) + (6 × 4)

Now write these three column headings:

Mental Jottings Written

Ask the children to sort the calculations into the different categories giving reasons for their choice. Some interesting conflicting views may arise since some children will have greater confidence with mental calculations and others will need the security of a written method. Talk about what we mean by choosing a formal method, that is, one that the child can do reasonably quickly but accurately. Use the example of £400.01 − £10.00. Discuss how this calculation would take much too long as a written calculation since it would require a lot of decomposition or redistributing and adjusting, leaving a considerable margin for error, whereas it is possible to do the calculation mentally or with jottings much more efficiently. Talk through also how two-step problems can be made clearer by the use of brackets. Ask the class to write down some suggestions of calculations to fit under each category. Choose two or three to write up underneath the appropriate headings.

Paired work: Ask the children to work along the categories choosing two or three of the problems to solve. Use the method suggested by the category heading but then discuss if any of the other methods might be suitable, or if not, why not. Ask the children to note down their thoughts as they work through the questions.

Progress check: Ask: *Are you selecting the most efficient method, given the numbers? Are you relying on only one method? Why is this not efficient for all numbers? Why is it helpful to have more than one strategy? How would you check your answers?*

Review

Draw together all the opinions discussed in this lesson. Ask: *Did we all have the same ideas or use the same methods? Does this matter? How can an alternative method help us to check our answers?* Write up the following calculation: (£38.91 + £45.07) − £16.20. Ask: *Can you make up a word problem that could be solved by calculating this number sentence?*

Curriculum objectives
● As lesson 4 below.

Success criteria
● I can solve a problem using mental calculations, work systematically and draw conclusions.

You will need
General resources
'0–30 number cards'

Differentiation
Less confident learners
These children can use number cards 0–9 to make the pyramids.

More confident learners
Extend the investigation by allowing two-digit numbers (up to 20) along the bottom row. Does this change the range of possible numbers at the top of the pyramid?

Lesson 3   Oral and mental starter 57

Main teaching activities

Whole-class work: Explain that the children are going to investigate number pyramids. Using the number cards 0–9, put three different non-zero digits in a row. Find the difference between each pair of digits and put these in the second row, then find the difference between these to give the top number. For example:

Paired and independent work: Ask the children to investigate these questions:
- *What is the highest number you can get at the top of the pyramid?*
- *Is there a systematic way of finding the answer?*

They should investigate these, using reasoning and trial and improvement.

Progress check: Ask: *How do you know that you have used all the possibilities and are sure about your answer? Which rule or strategy can you suggest for others to help them to find the answer? What other questions could you investigate?*

Review

Ask: *What is the highest top number anyone has found? Describe your strategy? What would happen if you used the same digit in all three bottom spaces? Would it be easier or harder if you had to use four different digits in the bottom row?*

Curriculum objectives
● To solve addition and subtraction multi-step problems in contexts, deciding which operations and methods to use and why.
● To add and subtract numbers mentally with increasingly large numbers.

Success criteria
● I can use mental addition and subtraction to investigate a problem.
● I can reason and explain my thinking.

Differentiation
Less confident learners
These children will require a lot of support to organise their work and their thinking in a logical way. They may find spotting a pattern difficult. They should use small starting numbers to make this easier.

More confident learners
These children should relish this open-ended task and be able to investigate lots of different starting points, building up a good bank of evidence.

Lesson 4   Oral and mental starter 57

Main teaching activities

Whole-class work: Draw a triangle on the board with a single-digit number at each vertex or corner. Put a dot at the midpoint of each side and join up the dots to make a new triangle. At each dot, write the number which is the difference between the numbers either side of it. Ask the children if they notice any special relationship between the resulting differences. (With triangles, two of the differences will add up to the third.)

Paired work: Explain to the children that they are going to test this theory with other starting numbers and then go on to explore the same test with a quadrilateral starting shape. (For quadrilaterals, two results occur. Either the sum of two opposite midpoint numbers equals the sum of other two, such as 6 + 3 = 8 + 1. Alternatively, three of the resulting numbers can be used in a number sentence to equal the fourth one. 8 = 5 + 1 + 2 or 8 − 5 = 2 + 1. Both of these situations can occur with the same starting digits in different positions, so warn the children that they should not be satisfied with only one relationship or pattern.)

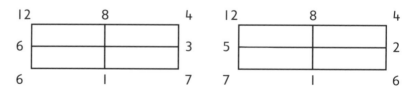

Progress check: Ask: *Have you found that you get the same outcome with different starting numbers on your triangle? What about the quadrilateral? Is there more than one result? Have you tried different numbers?*

Review

Collate patterns and relationships that the children have found. Can they suggest a reason why this should be so? What else might they investigate in this way?

Curriculum objectives
● To solve problems involving addition, subtraction, multiplication and division and a combination of these, including understanding the meaning of the equals sign.

Success criteria
● I can use written addition and subtraction calculation methods to solve one and two-step problems in context.

You will need
Photocopiable sheets
'Problems with measures (1), (2) and (3)'

Differentiation
Less confident learners
Provide photocopiable page 'Problems with measures (1)', which uses simpler numbers and has only one-step problems.

More confident learners
Provide photocopiable page 'Problems with measures (3)', which uses more difficult numbers and has a final challenge for the children to try.

Lesson 5   Oral and mental starter 56

Main teaching activities

Whole-class work: Explain to the children that they are going to use their knowledge of equivalent units of measurement and addition and subtraction to help them solve problems. We sometimes need to convert measurements to the same units in order to work out a problem. For example: *Sally wants to put three shelves up in her kitchen. Each shelf is 80cm long. In the DIY store, wood for shelving is sold in 2m lengths. How many lengths will she have to buy? How much wood will be wasted?* Work through this problem together on the board:

1. These are mixed units. What needs to be converted to make calculating easier? (2m to 200cm)

2. To turn the problem into calculations, identifying the operations needed to solve it: 200cm − 80cm = 120cm and 120cm − 80cm = 40cm. Sally can get two shelves from one piece of wood.

3. To make three shelves, Sally needs to buy two lengths of wood.

4. She will waste 40cm + 120cm = 160cm.

Explain that some of the questions on the activity sheet will need written calculations and some will need informal jottings but they all involve converting between different units.

Independent work: Distribute photocopiable page 'Problems with measures (2)' from the CD-ROM for the children to work through.

Progress check: Ask: *Which method have you selected to solve this problem? What numbers and information do you need? What are the clue words in the problem which tell you which operation to use? Have you remembered to use the same units for the measures when calculating?*

Review

Ask for volunteers to talk you through the methods they used to solve some of the problems. Talk about information in word problems that is redundant or irrelevant, as in the question about the race track: you don't need to know how long the track is to work out its width. Ask the children to work in pairs to write a measures question, including some redundant information, for the others to solve.

Long multiplication and division with remainders

Expected prior learning

Children should be able to:

- recall their times tables up to 12 x 12
- calculate using a written method and have some experience of beginning to use columnar methods for multiplication and division.

Topic	Curriculum objectives	Expected outcomes
Multiplication and division	**Lesson 1** To divide numbers up to four-digits by a one-digit number using the formal written method of short division and interpret remainders appropriately for the context.	Refine and use formal written methods to divide 4-digits ÷ 1-digit. Recall quickly multiplication facts up to 12 × 12 and use them to multiply pairs of multiples of 10 and 100; derive quickly corresponding division facts.
	Lesson 2 To solve problems involving addition, subtraction, multiplication and division and a combination of these, including understanding the meaning of the equals sign.	Solve one-step and two-step problems involving whole numbers and decimals and all four operations, choosing and using appropriate calculation strategies.
	Lesson 3 To multiply numbers up to four-digits by a one- or two-digit number using a formal written method, including long multiplication for two-digit numbers.	Recall quickly multiplication facts up to 12 × 12 and use them to multiply pairs of multiples of 10 and 100; derive quickly corresponding division facts. Refine and use formal written methods to multiply 3-digits × 1-digit and 2-digits × 2-digits up to four digits.
	Lesson 4 To multiply numbers up to four-digits by a one- or two-digit number using a formal written method, including long multiplication for two-digit numbers.	Recall quickly multiplication facts up to 12 × 12 and use them to multiply pairs of multiples of 10 and 100; derive quickly corresponding division facts. Refine and use formal written methods to multiply 3-digits × 1-digit and 2-digits × 2-digits up to four digits.
	Lesson 5 To solve problems involving addition, subtraction, multiplication and division and a combination of these, including understanding the meaning of the equals sign.	Solve one-step and two-step problems involving whole numbers and decimals and all four operations, choosing and using appropriate calculation strategies.

Preparation

Lesson 1: copy 'A short spell of short division', one per child

Lesson 2: copy 'Division word problems (1)', one per child

Lesson 3: assemble '0–30 number cards' or dice, one set/one per child

Lesson 4: copy 'Round, estimate and multiply (2)', one per child

Lesson 5: organise access to ICT: internet, spreadsheet software, and so on

You will need

Photocopiable sheets

'A short spell of short division'; 'Division word problems (1) and (2)'; 'Round, estimate and multiply (1), (2) and (3)'

General resources

'0–30 number cards'

Equipment

Calculators; dice; access to computers: internet, spreadsheet software, and so on

Further practice

Give children photocopiable page 'In the sweet shop' to practice multiplication of decimals in the context of money.

Oral and mental starters suggested for week 3

See bank of starters on page 209. Oral and mental starters are also on the CD-ROM.

58 Pairs to make 10 bingo

59 Visualising shapes

60 Giving change

Overview of progression

This week brings together all of the previous experiences with written and mental calculating with multiplication and division to solve problems in context. This culminates with a significant piece of practical work to research and cost a school trip. There is an opportunity to revise short division including changing remainders into fractions and then their related decimals. Multiplication, both mental and written is extended to include decimals. The context for applying these skills is to plan an outing within a budget, making real life decisions as well as making mathematical choices as to the correct operations to use in order to reach a practical plan.

Watch out for

Some children may still not have a secure understanding of written methods for these operations and may not be secure enough with place value to be accurate when multiplying decimals. Remind these children that the inverse is a way of checking their calculations and that estimating is a good way of ensure that a number is approximately the correct size.

Creative context

There is an opportunity for letter writing, telephoning and research of local places of interest in the last lesson of this week, which provides a real context for multi-operational calculating.

Vocabulary

answer, calculate, calculation, divide, divisible by, divisor, explain, **factor**, **inverse**, method, multiple, multiply, operation, problem, product, **quotient**, remainder, solution

Curriculum objectives

● To divide numbers up to four-digits by a one-digit number using the formal written method of short division and interpret remainders appropriately for the context.

Success criteria

● I can use short division to solve problems.
● I can convert a remainder into a fraction and a decimal.

You will need

Photocopiable sheets

'A short spell of short division'

Equipment

Calculators

Differentiation

Less confident learners

Encourage the children to focus on the top half of the photocopiable sheet.

More confident learners

Challenge children to make up their own 4-digits ÷ 1-digit questions after completing the photocopiable sheet.

Lesson I
Oral and mental starter 58

Main teaching activities

Whole-class work: Explain that today, the children will revisit short division and learn to express the answer as a decimal. Point out that some fraction/decimal equivalents are difficult to remember, for example ⅐.

Write 274 ÷ 7 on the board and ask the children to talk you through how to solve this using short division. The answer is 39 r1 or 39⅐ (by expressing the remainder as a fraction, that is, one remaining divided by the divisor number 7).

Explain that any fraction can be changed into a decimal by dividing the numerator by the denominator. A calculator is helpful to do this for the tricky fraction/decimal equivalents. ⅐ is keyed into a calculator as 1 ÷ 7 and gives 0.1428571. Tell the children to round the answer to two decimal places, so the result is 0.14 and the answer to the short division question can be written as 39.14.

Invite the children to use a calculator to change some known equivalents first, for example, ½ = 1 ÷ 2 = 0.5, before trying unknown fractions such as ⅚ or ⁴⁄₇ which may need rounding. Remind the children that they cannot use the inverse operation for accurate checking if they have rounded an answer to two decimal places.

Independent work: Distribute photocopiable page 'A short spell of short division' from the CD-ROM. Some of the answers will give known fraction equivalents and some will require the use of a calculator to change the fraction to a decimal and may need rounding. Remind the children to use short division first, only using a calculator to determine an unknown decimal equivalent.

Progress check: Ask: *What can we do if we get a fraction remainder where we don't know the decimal equivalent? (Use a calculator) Which fraction/decimal equivalents do you know already? Write them down at the side of your page to remind you. For which fractions did you have to rely on a calculator?*

Review

Ask the children: *Which fractions created unknown equivalents decimals? What do we have to remember when we check these? Have you learned any new equivalents that you think you will remember? What do you notice about ¾? What about ³⁄₁₀?*

Play decimal/fraction match. Call out a fraction or a decimal and ask the children to tell you the equivalent. Give points for correct answers and double points for fractions that need simplifying or multiplying to make them easier to recognise as an equivalent.

Curriculum objectives
- To solve problems involving addition, subtraction, multiplication and division and a combination of these, including understanding the meaning of the equals sign.

Success criteria
- I can solve word problems including money and measures, using short division and understand the answers in context.

You will need
Photocopiable sheets
'Division word problems (1) and (2)'

Differentiation
Less confident learners
Encourage the children to focus on the questions on the sheet rather than making up their own.

More confident learners
Provide photocopiable page 'Division word problems (2)', which has more difficult problems.

Lesson 2   Oral and mental starter 60

Main teaching activities

Whole-class work: Explain that the children are going to apply their skills to solving division word problems that use money and measures. Remind them how to convert a word problem into a number sentence and then calculate the answer, perhaps generating a fraction or decimal remainder. For example: *Mrs Smith has a piece of wood 1945cm long. She wants to make it into four equal-length bookshelves. How long will each shelf be?*

$$4 \overline{) 1\ ^{1}9\ ^{3}4\ ^{5}5} \quad\text{r1} = 486¼\text{cm or } 486.25\text{cm each}$$

with quotient $0\ 4\ 8\ 6$

Independent work: Distribute photocopiable page 'Division word problems (1)' from the CD-ROM. Ask the children to solve the word problems using their division skills.

Progress check: Ask: *What information have you used to create a number sentence from these words? Which ones needed a fraction or decimal answer? Does this make sense in the context of the question?*

Review

Share some of the children's answers with the class and iron out any difficulties or misconceptions that occur. Then ask: *What is the practical reason for rounding long decimal numbers to two decimal places when we are talking about money or measures?* (We cannot usually measure to anything more accurately than two decimal places and money is only available in certain notes and coins.) *Why do we convert fractions of numbers into decimals for money and measures?* (¼ of 1cm or ⅕ of £1 doesn't mean much and isn't easily measurable until converted to mm or pence by using the decimal form.)

Say: *Tell me a word problem that might use the calculation 204 ÷ 3.* This could be any practical problem. Repeat with 274 ÷ 8. Now say: *Tell me a division word problem that has the answer 12. What about the answer 25?* Go through the steps necessary to go backwards from an answer to a calculation and then to a word problem. This is useful for reinforcing how to solve word problems.

Curriculum objectives

● To multiply numbers up to four-digits by a one- or two-digit number using a formal written method, including long multiplication for two-digit numbers.

Success criteria

● I can multiply 1-digit.1s decimal numbers by a one-digit number.

You will need

General resources

'0–30 number cards' or dice

Differentiation

Less confident learners

Provide 1–9 number cards to generate the 1-digit.1s number and a 1–6 dice for the × 1-digit number so that the answers remain smaller.

More confident learners

Children should be able to multiply bigger numbers such as 2-digit.1s × 1-digit or numbers with two decimal places.

Lesson 3 — Oral and mental starter 58

Main teaching activities

Whole-class work: Explain to the children that they are going to use their written multiplication skills to solve problems involving decimals. Write 89 × 5 on the board. Ask the children to solve this calculation using columnar multiplication. Then write up 8.9 × 5. Estimate the approximate size of this answer and solve the calculation, again using columnar multiplication, demonstrating that the decimal point can be put in place first. Repeat using a number of other decimal examples such as: 6.3 × 7 and 8.3 × 8.

Independent work: Ask the children to generate some 1-digit.1s × 1-digit questions using dice or the 0–9 number cards. Tell them to estimate the size of the answer first and then solve the calculation.

Progress check: Ask: *What have you to remember about the place value and the position of the decimal point when multiplying decimal numbers? What does this digit in this calculation represent? Does your answer match the size of your estimate?*

Review

Ask the children to estimate the approximate size of the following: 3.8 × 7; 7.2 × 12. Ask them to explain how this is helpful when solving decimal multiplications. Ask two different children to demonstrate how they would calculate 83.9 × 4, one using the grid method and one using a standard written method. Discuss how a thorough knowledge of place value is essential in each case to avoid mistakes.

Curriculum objectives
• To multiply numbers up to four-digits by a one- or two-digit number using a formal written method, including long multiplication for two-digit numbers.

Success criteria
• I can round and estimate to ensure accurate place value when multiplying decimals.

You will need
Photocopiable sheets

'Round, estimate and multiply (1), (2) and (3)'

Differentiation
Less confident learners

Provide photocopiable page 'Round, estimate and multiply (1)', which uses lower values.

More confident learners

Provide photocopiable page 'Round, estimate and multiply (3)', which uses higher values and requires conversions between units.

Lesson 4 — Oral and mental starter 60

Main teaching activities

Whole-class work: Write the following question on the board:

If one box of chocolates weighs 645g, what would be the mass of six boxes? Give your answer in kg.

Remind the children that they should round and estimate first before calculating this. Ask for someone to explain how to solve this calculation and then how to convert it into a decimal number to give the answer in kilograms (3.87kg). Repeat with another example such as: *My return journey to school is 9.1km. How far do I travel in a school week?* Ask: *What is the estimate? Did you recognise whether to round up or down?* Now calculate.

Independent work: Distribute photocopiable page 'Round, estimate and multiply (2)' from the CD-ROM. Remind children to choose whether to round up or down and estimate before calculating to ensure accurate place value. Also tell them that they must make up some decimal word problems of their own, to demonstrate that they can decode multiplication questions.

Progress check: Say: *Remind me of the rule for rounding up or down. When you compare your answer to your estimate, is it in the same size range? When making up your own questions, think about the answer making sense in the context of the word problem.*

Review

Take examples from the worksheet and ask individuals to talk you through their methods. Write up the following calculation and ask the children to tell you at a glance if it is correct or not and why it must be so: $54.8 \times 6 = 3288$. Ask them to explain to you the misconception about the place value.

Curriculum objectives
• To solve problems involving addition, subtraction, multiplication and division and a combination of these, including understanding the meaning of the equals sign.

Success criteria
• I can solve real-life problems by using all four operations to calculate.

You will need
Equipment

Access to ICT: internet, spreadsheet software

Differentiation
Less confident learners

These children should be supported by an adult.

More confident learners

These children should calculate cost per mile or find out about special offers that might influence the costs.

Lesson 5 — Oral and mental starter 59

Main teaching activities

Group work: Explain to the children that they are going to use a range of maths operations and skills to plan a class day visit. They must work in groups to produce three comparative suggestions, fully costed, including lunch or a snack, transport and any extra activities. They should present their ideas, in writing, with an approximate timetable for the day, to the rest of the class. All the calculations must be included as part of their presentation. This may be an opportunity to combine their maths work with ICT, perhaps using a spreadsheet, as well as using the internet to research venues and costs. Ideally, the children should plan a visit to enhance their learning or to fit in with the theme or topic that is being covered at school and then be allowed to go on the visit you (or they) choose, if practicable.

Progress check: Ask: *Is the place you are considering possible to visit in one day? What calculations are you including in your plan? What operations are needed? Are you recording all parts of your calculations clearly so that others can read and understand them? How much are you charging for transport per person? How have you calculated that fairly?*

Review

Display all of the groups' findings and give time for the children to read all of the suggestions. Ask the children to explain how they calculated and check for accuracy. Encourage the children to ask questions of each other and decide on the trips that seem the best value for money. Ask: *If we feel it is too expensive, what could we cut down on? How would that alter our calculations? Could we apply for a small grant from school fund? If so how much would that reduce the cost per person? What percentage of the whole cost could we apply for?*

Working with fractions

Expected prior learning

Children should be able to:

- order fractions whose denominators are the same, including mixed numbers
- recognise and convert mixed numbers and improper fractions
- find simple fractions of shapes and numbers.

Topic	Curriculum objectives	Expected outcomes
Fractions (including decimals and percentages)	**Lesson 1**	
	To recognise mixed numbers and improper fractions and convert from one form to the other and write mathematical statements > 1 as a mixed number [for example, $\frac{2}{5} + \frac{4}{5} = \frac{6}{5} = 1\frac{1}{5}$].	Find equivalent fractions by multiplying and dividing. Order and compare fractions.
	Lesson 2	
	To recognise mixed numbers and improper fractions and convert from one form to the other and write mathematical statements > 1 as a mixed number [for example, $\frac{2}{5} + \frac{4}{5} = \frac{6}{5} = 1\frac{1}{5}$].	Identifying mystery fractions using the vocabulary of equivalents and comparison.
	Lesson 3	
	To add and subtract fractions with the same denominator and denominators that are multiples of the same number.	Convert fractions to equivalent fractions with a common denominators in order to add them together.
	Lesson 4	
	To add and subtract fractions with the same denominator and denominators that are multiples of the same number.	Make decisions about converting fractions in order to estimate and calculate to solve a puzzle.
	Lesson 5	
	To recognise mixed numbers and improper fractions and convert from one form to the other and write mathematical statements > 1 as a mixed number [for example, $\frac{2}{5} + \frac{4}{5} = \frac{6}{5} = 1\frac{1}{5}$]. To add and subtract fractions with the same denominator and denominators that are multiples of the same number.	Using fraction knowledge and skills to devise and play a game.

Preparation

Lesson 1: copy 'Bags of fractions', one per child; assemble 'Multiplication square', one per child, if needed

Lesson 2: assemble the 'Number lines' and '0–30 number cards', if needed

Lesson 3: copy 'Fraction pond', one per child

Lesson 5: assemble blank playing cards and pens

You will need

Photocopiable sheets
'Bags of fractions'; 'Fraction pond'

General resources
'Multiplication square'; 'Number lines'; '0–30 number cards'

Equipment
Blank playing cards; pens

Further practice

Photocopiable sheets
'Multiples snap'; 'Improper fractions and mixed numbers (1) and (2)'

Oral and mental starters suggested for week 4

See bank of starters on page 209. Oral and mental starters are also on the CD-ROM.

61 Even steps

62 Multiples of 10

63 Sorting circles

Overview of progression

This week consolidates work on ordering and comparing fractions and converting between improper fractions and mixed numbers. The children use this knowledge to solve simple fraction addition problems in a variety of contexts.

Watch out for

A common problem when multiplying or cancelling to find equivalence is simple calculating errors. Remind the children that whatever operation they use to convert to an equivalent fraction must be applied to both the numerator and the denominator. This does not apply when adding fractions together, however. $\frac{1}{4} + \frac{1}{4} = \frac{1}{2}$, but a common error is to write $\frac{1}{4} + \frac{1}{4} = \frac{1}{8}$. You may need to demonstrate using fraction shapes how this cannot be correct.

Creative context

Encourage the children to think about real-life contexts for using fractions rather than calculating in isolation.

Vocabulary

denominator, equivalent fraction, fraction, **improper fraction**, mixed number, **numerator**, proper fraction, unit fraction

Curriculum objectives
- To recognise mixed numbers and improper fractions and convert from one form to the other.

Success criteria
- I can multiply and divide to find equivalent fractions.

You will need

Photocopiable sheets
'Bags of fractions'

General resources
'Multiplication square'

Differentiation

Less confident learners
These children may need additional support to recognise factors and multiples to calculate the equivalents. A multiplication square may be helpful.

More confident learners
These children could extend the fraction bag 'families' by thinking of some additional fractions that could be ordered.

Lesson 1 — Oral and mental starter 61

Main teaching activities

Whole-class work: Remind the children that to compare the size of fractions they need to have the same denominator, which is called a common denominator. Write on the board ⅝ and ¾. Ask the children how they would make these two fractions comparable. (Change to equivalent fractions with a common denominator, so multiply both the numerator and the denominator of ¾ by 2, giving ⅝, which they can then see is larger than ⅝.) Repeat with other fractions that have denominators that are all multiples of the same number, for example, ⅔, ⅙ and ⁷⁄₁₂. (Convert them all into twelfths.)

Independent and paired work: Distribute photocopiable page 'Bags of fractions' from the CD-ROM. Explain that in each bag is a selection of fractions that need to be converted into equivalent fractions with a common denominator so that they can be written in order of size. Emphasise that they must multiply or divide both the numerator and the denominator by the same number.

Progress check: Ask: *What helps you to decide whether you should multiply the fractions up or simplify them by dividing? How did you decide which common denominator would be the most useful? Is it always the largest denominator? What sort of errors do you think people make when doing this activity? Are any fractions more tricky than others to compare?*

Review

Write ¹⁸⁄₂₄ on the board. Ask the children: *What is a factor? How does a knowledge of factors help us to compare and simplify fractions? What is the smallest equivalent form for this fraction? What number are you dividing by to find this? Are there any other fractions that are equivalent to this one? How do you know when the fractions are in the simplest form?*

■SCHOLASTIC

Curriculum objectives
● To recognise mixed numbers and improper fractions and convert from one form to the other.

Success criteria
● I can count on and back in fractional steps.
● I can work out a mystery fraction by asking comparison questions.

You will need
General resources
'Number lines'; '0–30 number cards'

Differentiation
Less confident learners
These children might find a blank number line and some 0–9 number cards helpful to visualise and keep track of their line of enquiry.

More confident learners
Once confident, these children could expand their range to larger numbers and more complex fractions.

Lesson 2
Oral and mental starter 61

Main teaching activities

Whole-class work: Explain to the children that they are going to count on and back together in fraction steps. Say for example: *Start at zero and count on to ten in thirds; start at eight and count back in steps of a quarter*, and so on. Once they are confident, repeat with sevenths, this time recording the steps as they count. Ask: *How would 3⅗ look as an improper fraction?* (²⁴⁄₇) *Tell me a rule for converting mixed numbers to improper fractions and vice versa.* Find the equivalent for other mixed numbers using this rule to ensure proficiency.

Play 'I am thinking of a fraction'. Write a mixed number on a piece of paper but do not tell the children, for example 4¾. The children have 20 Yes/No questions to ask you to discover the number. For example, *Is it a number between 1 and 10? Is it an improper fraction? Is it a mixed number? Is the denominator of the fraction 10? Is the fraction part greater than ½?* Once they have guessed the number repeat using an improper fraction.

Paired work: Invite the children to play the game with a partner, recording their questions as they go. Suggest that they start with a mixed number or improper fraction between 1 and 10.

Progress check: Ask: *How are you establishing the range of the number? Is it effective to simply guess at possible answers? What questions can you ask to narrow down the possible denominator number?*

Review

Tell the children that you are going to describe a number and they have to work out what it might be with the least number of clues. After each clue they should write down on their whiteboards a selection of possible answers and then eliminate the incorrect ones as further clues are revealed. For example:

- My number is an improper fraction greater than 2 but smaller than 3.
- The denominator is a factor of 10.
- The numerator is a prime number when the fraction is changed to a mixed number fraction.
- It is equivalent to ⁵⁶⁄₂₀. (Answer: ¹⁴⁄₅)

Check the children's whiteboards for inaccurate detective work.

Curriculum objectives

● To add and subtract fractions with the same denominator and denominators that are multiples of the same number.

Success criteria

● I can add fractions by converting them to equivalent fractions with a common denominator.

You will need

Photocopiable sheets
'Fraction pond'

Differentiation

Less confident learners

These children will probably choose the simpler fractions to add.

More confident learners

These children should be able to add three or four fractions in their number sentences.

Lesson 3 — Oral and mental starter 62

Main teaching activities

Whole-class work: Remind the class about how fractions may be added by counting on, such as ¼ + ¾ = ⁴⁄₄ or 1. Point out that the denominator does not get added; they must just count up the number of the same things – in this case, quarters. Ask: *How can we add different types of fraction?* (Convert to equivalent fractions with a common denominator, such as, ¾ + ½ = ¾ + ²⁄₄ = ⁵⁄₄ = 1¼.)

Repeat with other more difficult examples such as ¾ + ⅜ in which the denominators of one of the fractions has to be changed in order to write them with a common denominator. In this case, ¾ + ⅜ = ⁶⁄₈ + ⅜ = ⁹⁄₈ = 1⅛.

Paired work: Distribute photocopiable page 'Fraction pond' from the CD-ROM. Explain that the children should select two fractions that they feel they could convert into fractions with a common denominator. They then write and complete an addition number sentence.

Progress check: Ask: *What is influencing your choice of fractions to add? What are you looking for? How can your knowledge of factors and multiples help? What are you multiplying by in order to make them have the same denominator? How do you know which number to multiply by?*

Review

Ask the children to explain to you some of their choices of fractions to add and how they converted them to equivalent fractions with a common denominator. Their choices will be revealing for your assessments. Ask if anyone chose fractions with denominators that were not multiples of the same number but simply used the opposite denominators to find equivalent fractions. Ask: *Could we add more than one of these fractions together? Could we add them all together? What would we have to do?*

Curriculum objectives

● To add and subtract fractions with the same denominator and denominators that are multiples of the same number.

Success criteria

● I can make decisions about combining fractions to solve a puzzle.

You will need

Photocopiable sheets
'Fraction pond'

Differentiation

Less confident learners

These children may need adult support to structure their processing and to assist with checking calculations.

More confident learners

These children may finish the challenges but ensure that they have justified every possibility, not just made an educated guess. Ask them to develop the puzzle to form challenges for others to solve.

Lesson 4 — Oral and mental starter 62

Main teaching activities

Paired work: Explain that today the children are going to extend their addition of fractions to meet a set of challenges. They should use the fractions on photocopiable page 'Fraction pond' from the CD-ROM to make the following target numbers using the smallest number of fractions possible:

● Exactly 1
● Exactly 2
● Nearest to 5
● The largest possible total

Progress check: Ask: *How are you going to choose which fractions to add? Can you estimate at all? Might some of the number sentences from yesterday help you? Do you think that you need to add them together in only one number sentence?*

Review

Ask the children to share their answers with you and to explain the steps they took for each challenge. Ask: *If you could add a fraction to the pond that would help you what would it be? Was there a fraction that you could not find a common denominator for? What was the largest possible total? How many steps did you have to take to get there?*

Curriculum objectives

- To recognise mixed numbers and improper fractions and convert from one form to the other.
- To add and subtract fractions with the same denominator and denominators that are multiples of the same number.

Success criteria

- I can use my fraction knowledge and skills to devise and play a fractions game.

You will need

Equipment

Blank playing cards

Differentiation

Less confident learners

These children should work as a supported group to produce the questions.

More confident learners

These children should be able to devise higher level questions.

Lesson 5 — Oral and mental starter 63

Main teaching activities

Paired work: Explain to the children that they are going to work in pairs to create a game like Top Trumps™, built around fractions. Ask an 'expert' from the group to explain how 'Top trumps' is played.

Explain that on each playing card the children must write a question in two categories:

A: Mixed numbers and improper fractions, for example, 'What is the improper fraction equivalent of 1 and $\frac{9}{10}$?' ($1\frac{9}{10}$) or 'How many more fifths do I need to add $1\frac{1}{5}$ to make 3?' ($\frac{9}{5}$)

B: Adding and subtracting fractions, for example, $\frac{3}{5} + \frac{2}{10}$ ($\frac{8}{10}$) or $3 - \frac{3}{4}$ ($1\frac{3}{4}$).

When playing, the cards are divided equally between the players and they are placed face down in front of them. Each turns over and looks at their first card. One person starts by choosing the category that they think will beat the other player. They both read out the question in the chosen category and answer each other's. The holder of the card with the higher answer wins. They win both cards and take the next card on their pile, choose a category and give the question and answer. If they lose, the other player chooses the category. The winner is the person who wins all the cards. The challenge is to write a variety of questions for each category.

Distribute at least 20 blank playing cards to each pair for them to create their questions. There should be two questions on each card, one category A and one category B.

Progress check: Ask: *How are you deciding what questions to pose? Remember that they cannot all have the highest answers. Don't forget you need to put the answers in brackets too. Have you used comparisons as well as straightforward equivalents? Will you provide a whiteboard with your game for people to do their jottings for calculations?*

Review

Once the children have completed their questions they need to discuss the rules of how to play and whether they could develop further categories or ways to play. They should play their game and evaluate whether any of the questions need adjusting, before offering it to another pair to play.

Investigating shapes

Expected prior learning

Children should be able to:

- recognise and name acute, obtuse and right angles
- have some understanding of how a protractor is used to measure angles
- understand angles as a measurement of the 'amount of turn'.

Topic	Curriculum objectives	Expected outcomes
Geometry: properties of shapes	**Lesson 1**	
	To know angles are measured in degrees; estimate and compare acute, obtuse and reflex angles.	Measure angles to 1° accuracy.
	Lesson 2	
	To know angles are measured in degrees; estimate and compare acute, obtuse and reflex angles. To identify: • angles at a point and one whole turn (total 360°) • angles at a point on a straight line and ½ a turn (total 180°) • other multiples of 90°.	Draw angles to 1° accuracy.
	Lesson 3	
	To use the properties of rectangles to deduce related facts and find missing lengths and angles. To distinguish between regular and irregular polygons based on reasoning about equal sides and angles.	Investigate regular and irregular shapes.
	Lesson 4	
	To distinguish between regular and irregular polygons based on reasoning about equal sides and angles.	Investigate diagonals.
	Lesson 5	
	To distinguish between regular and irregular polygons based on reasoning about equal sides and angles.	Investigate similarities and differences in shapes with an equal number of sides.

Preparation

Lesson 1: copy 'The rounders match: fielders', one per child

Lesson 2: copy 'The rounders match: the batting', one per child; write the following angles on the board: 55°, 90°, 110°, 35°, 140°, 78°, 128°, 177°, 155°

Lesson 3: make copies of 'Isometric dotty paper', three or more sheets per child to be used in this and the next lesson

Lesson 5: copy 'Regular polygons', one per child

You will need

Photocopiable sheets

'The rounders match: fielders'; 'The rounders match: the batting'

General resources

'Angles'; 'Shapes'; 'Isometric dotty paper'; 'Regular polygons'

Equipment

Protractors, rulers

Further practice

Give children some practical angle measuring activities to further practice the accurate use of the protractor.

Oral and mental starters suggested for week 5

See bank of starters on pages 208 to 209. Oral and mental starters are also on the CD-ROM.

56 You know for a fact!

57 Mystery number

63 Sorting circles

Overview of progression

These lessons revisit accurate measuring of angles and the application of this knowledge to investigate the similarities and differences of shapes. A further investigation into the properties of different polygons explores the patterns of diagonals in regular polygons.

Watch out for

It is very important that children learn to use a protractor effectively in order to measure angles accurately. The first two lessons give specific practice in this and should be used to correct any difficulties. The most common errors are poor alignment of the protractor and reading from the wrong scale. The latter can be corrected by asking children whether an angle is acute or obtuse before measuring, so that they can check the approximate size of their measurement.

Creative context

Patterns and shapes are an important artistic feature in life. Encourage the children to look for them all around them, both man made and in the natural world.

Vocabulary

acute angle, angle, angle measurer, **bisect**, degree (°), diagonal, **intersect**, irregular, obtuse angle, polygon, protractor, **reflex angle**, regular, right angle

Curriculum objectives
● To know angles are measured in degrees; estimate and compare acute, obtuse and reflex angles.

Success criteria
● I can estimate and measure angles using a protractor.

You will need

Photocopiable sheets
'The rounders match: fielders'

General resources
'Angles'

Equipment
Protractors

Differentiation

Less confident learners

These children may need adult support when measuring angles to ensure accurate orientation of the protractor.

More confident learners

These children could extend the activity by adding additional fielders and by measuring to 1mm accuracy how far away each person is standing from the batsman.

Lesson 1

Main teaching activities

Whole-class work: Display photocopiable page 'Angles' from the CD-ROM. Ask the children to define and identify the right angle (exactly 90°), the acute angles (0° to 90°), the obtuse angles (90° to 180°) and the straight line (exactly 180°), and introduce the term 'reflex angle'. Explain that this is an angle of between 180° and 360°. Explain to the children that if they use these terms to identify an angle before measuring it, they will not make the mistake of reading the incorrect scale on the protractor as they can check that their final answer falls within their estimated range.

Revise the use of a protractor, stressing the importance of placing the protractor on the correct line, even if it is not horizontal. Encourage the children to turn their page in order to orientate the protractor to make one line horizontal for measuring purposes. Also emphasise the importance of reading the correct scale and that estimating first will help with this.

Paired work: Distribute photocopiable page 'The rounders match: fielders' from the CD-ROM which requires children to estimate and measure angles to 1° accuracy. They should take it in turns to check their partner's measurements.

Progress check: Ask: *What is an angle? What type of angle are you measuring? Can you estimate what the measurement might be? How accurate was your estimate? Show me which scale on the protractor you are using for this measurement.*

Review

Share the children's results and ask them to suggest a list of steps to help someone measure an angle correctly. Revise once more the names of the different types of angles, including reflex angles. Discuss how a reflex angle might be measured or calculated. (Measure the inside angle and subtract from 360° if you do not have a 360° protractor.)

Oral and mental starter 56

Lesson 2

Main teaching activities

Whole-class work: Explain to the class that it is important to be able to draw angles accurately as well as measure them. Demonstrate how to do this with both acute and obtuse angles. Encourage the children to turn their page so that the base line of the angle is in a horizontal position to make drawing the angle easier.

Paired work: Distribute photocopiable page 'The rounders match: the batting' from the CD-ROM. Tell the children that they are going to look at the rounders match from yesterday again but this time they are to draw the lines to mark where the batman hits the ball, using the angles that you have written on the board (55°, 90°, 110°, 20°, 140°, 78°, 128°, 177°, 155°). Remind them to carefully line up the protractor with the batting line and place the centre on the X where the batsman is actually standing. Once complete, they should check their measurements with a partner.

Progress check: Ask: *Tell me the steps that you are taking to measure and mark these angles. Where is your starting point? How can you check that you are correctly using your knowledge of acute and obtuse angles?*

Review

On the board draw two intersecting lines. Ask the children to estimate the angles. Ask what they remember about angles on a straight line from a previous lesson. Ask for a volunteer to come and measure the angles and mark them on the diagram. What do the children notice? (Angles on a straight line add up to 180°. Angles around a complete turn add up to 360°.)

Oral and mental starter 57

Lesson 3

Main teaching activities

Whole-class work: Give each pair a rectangle from photocopiable page 'Shapes'. Tell them that you wish to draw a perfect rectangle on the board but they need to give you a detailed, step-by-step set of instructions to do so. Revise with the children the properties of the rectangle that they should be using as part of their instructional vocabulary. Draw a rectangle to their instructions. Now display a square and ask them to tell you how it is different. Remind them that a square is a special kind of rectangle. Reinforce the concept of regular and irregular shapes. A square is regular because it has equal length sides and equal angles.

Paired work: Give each pair two pieces of dotty paper. Ask them to label one 'regular shapes' and the other 'irregular shapes'. Ask them to try to draw shapes to match the label, starting with quadrilaterals but moving on to six-sided shapes once these have been exhausted. After 10 minutes they should swap their papers, check each other's work so far and attempt to draw different shapes from those of their partner.

Progress check: Ask: *How many regular quadrilaterals did you draw? Is this shape the same as another but simply rotated (through 45°)? Do you have more irregular shapes than regular? If you are unsure of the angles, mark them on your diagram.*

Review

Explain that there is only one regular quadrilateral and one regular hexagon because of their given properties; they differ only in size. Display the irregular polygons and pick out some of the more interesting ones. Discuss concave shapes and how this affects the internal angles. Ask: *Is a rectangle/ parallelogram/kite a regular shape?* (No, but some incorrectly think so because they are recognised and named shapes that we see often). Indicate a particular shape and ask the children to use the vocabulary of shape to describe it.

Curriculum objectives

• To know angles are measured in degrees; estimate and compare acute, obtuse and reflex angles. Identify reflex angles.

Success criteria

• I can draw angles to 1° accuracy.

You will need

Photocopiable sheets
'The rounders match: the batting'

Equipment
Protractors, rulers

Differentiation

Less confident learners
These children may need adult support to ensure accurate drawing.

More confident learners
These children could challenge a partner to draw additional angles of their choosing.

Curriculum objectives

• To use the properties of rectangles to deduce related facts and find missing lengths and angles.
• To distinguish between regular and irregular polygons based on reasoning about equal sides and angles.

Success criteria

• I can describe and identify shapes by their properties.
• I can recognise regular and irregular polygons.

You will need

General resources
'Shapes'; 'Isometric dotty paper'

Equipment
Rulers; protractors

Differentiation

Less confident learners
Working in a mixed ability pair will build confidence with the vocabulary of shape.

More confident learners
Expect a greater variety of irregular shapes including convex and concave shapes.

Curriculum objectives
- To distinguish between regular and irregular polygons based on reasoning about equal sides and angles.

Success criteria
- I can investigate the diagonals of shapes and make comparisons.

You will need
General resources
'Isometric dotty paper'
Equipment
Rulers; protractors

Differentiation
Less confident learners
Working in a mixed ability pair will generate discussions which will build confidence with the vocabulary of shape.
More confident learners
Expect higher level reasoning and hypothesis. They may move on to regular and irregular pentagons if time allows.

Curriculum objectives
- To distinguish between regular and irregular polygons based on reasoning about equal sides and angles.

Success criteria
- I can recognise patterns in diagonals in regular shapes.

You will need
Photocopiable sheets
'Regular polygons'
Equipment
Rulers

Differentiation
Less confident learners
Working in a mixed ability pair will generate discussions which will build confidence with the vocabulary of shape.
More confident learners
These children may begin to look for a relationship between the numbers of sides and the number of diagonals in shapes with odd and even numbers of sides.

Lesson 4
Oral and mental starter 57

Main teaching activities

Whole-class work: Explain to the class that they are going to work in pairs to investigate diagonals in various polygons of the same number of sides. Establish that everyone understands that a diagonal is a line that runs between two vertices (or corners) of a polygon, but doesn't include the perimeter lines. Effectively, it is a line that crosses the polygon. When two diagonals cross each other, they are said to 'intersect'.

Paired work: Tell the children that they are going to investigate the diagonals of regular and irregular shapes of the same number of sides and look for patterns. They should start with the regular quadrilateral, the square, and draw and record the number of diagonals, how many times the diagonals intersect and whether they bisect each other. Then they should choose at least three or four special quadrilaterals, such as the kite, rhombus and parallelogram, and an irregular quadrilateral to test with the same questions. The results should be presented in a table. Are there any similarities?

Progress check: Ask: *What is special about the diagonals in a square. Are there any similarities with other quadrilaterals? Are there any differences?*

Review

Make a class list of observations and discuss the children's theories as to why this is. Ask: *Do only regular shapes have diagonals which intersect in exactly the centre?*. (Mostly yes, except rectangles which have equal angles and rhombuses which have equal sides which make this happen.) *Do all quadrilaterals have the same number of diagonals? Is the rule the same in concave shapes?* (Yes) *What do you notice about the angles where they intersect?* (They add up to 360°.) *Which 2D shape which does not have any diagonals?* (Triangle.)

Lesson 5
Oral and mental starter 57

Main teaching activities

Paired work: Explain to the children that they are to repeat the investigation on diagonals from yesterday, but this time they are going to investigate patterns that emerge when comparing the diagonals of regular shapes only, that is, a square, a regular pentagon, a regular hexagon, a regular heptagon, a regular octagon and a regular nonagon. They should mark in the diagonals and tabulate their results as follows:

Name of polygon and drawing	Number of sides	Number of diagonals

Progress check: Ask: *Are there any patterns emerging? Do any of the diagonals intersect in exactly the centre of the shape? In which of the shapes?*

Review

Again record the class observations, looking for patterns and generalisations, such as shapes with an odd number of sides generate an even number of diagonals. Each corner of a regular shape will generate $n - 2$ diagonals, that is one to each corner except the two adjacent to it. The shapes with an even numbers of sides have some diagonals which intersect exactly in the centre. The shapes with an odd number of sides do not, but the diagonals recreate a smaller version of the original shape, rotated inside the lines.

■ SCHOLASTIC

Volume and time

Expected prior learning

Children should be able to:

- tell the time using the 12-hour clock
- understand the formula area = length × breadth.

Topic	Curriculum objectives	Expected outcomes
Measurement	**Lesson 1**	
	To estimate volume [for example, using 1cm³ blocks to build cuboids (including cubes)] and capacity [for example, using water].	Understand volume as expressed in cubic centimetres.
	Lesson 2	
	To solve problems involving measure (e.g. length, mass, volume and money) using decimal notation, including scaling.	Solving practical problems involving volumes in cubic centimetres.
	Lesson 3	
	To solve problems involving converting between units of time.	Convert between times in 12- and 24-hour clock notation.
	Lesson 4	
	To solve problems involving converting between units of time.	Tell the time and calculate with units of time to solve problems.
	Lesson 5	
	To solve problems involving converting between units of time.	Tell the time and calculate with units of time to solve problems.

Preparation

Lesson 1: assemble clear plastic 1000cm³ cube containers, one per pair; wooden or plastic centimetre cubes, such as Diennes apparatus, enough for the whole class and a variety of cubic and cuboid containers, enough for the whole class

Lesson 2: assemble wooden or plastic centimetre cubes or cubes that clip together, such as Multilink apparatus, enough for the whole class

Lesson 3: copy 'A day in the life', one per child; assemble clock faces with moveable hands, one per group if needed

Lesson 4: copy 'Time and tide', one per child; assemble clock faces with moveable hands, one per group if needed

Lesson 5: copy 'Steam train times', one per child; assemble selection of bus or train timetables; assemble clock faces with moveable hands, one per group if needed

You will need

Photocopiable sheets

'A day in the life'; 'Time and tide'; 'Steam train times'

Equipment

Clear plastic 1000cm³ cube containers; wooden or plastic centimetre cubes; a variety of cubic and cuboid containers; Multilink apparatus; clock faces with moveable hands; bus and train timetables

Further practice

Adapt the 'Steam train times template' to give further practice of calculating time differences and converting between 12- and 24-hour times.

Oral and mental starters suggested for week 6

See bank of starters on pages 208 to 209. Oral and mental starters are also on the CD-ROM.

52 Multiplication challenge

54 Round and estimate

58 Pairs to make 10 bingo

Overview of progression

There are two parts to this week's lesson. The first explores volume as expressed as cubic centimetres, with an opportunity to understand this practically by building cubes and cuboids using centimetre cubes. The second part of the week is devoted to time and solving time and money problems. Children should be able to convert between different units of time and understand both 12- and 24-hour clock notation. They should be able to calculate the difference between given times.

Watch out for

The topic of time does not seem to follow the usual ability groupings so assessment of the children's prior learning is particularly important. Many children struggle to read both analogue and digital times and also find understanding of the 24-hour clock tricky. These children may need extra practice with an adult and some hand-held clock faces.

Creative context

Encourage the children to put a 'story' to the study of time to make the numbers mean something in context.

Vocabulary

12-hour clock, 24-hour clock, am and pm; cubes, calendar, cubic centimetres (cm³), cuboid, day, days of the week, hour (h), minute (min), month, months of the year, second (s), timetable, volume

Curriculum objectives
- To recognise and estimate volume.

Success criteria
- I can understand that volume is measured in cubic centimetres.

You will need
Equipment
Clear plastic 1000cm³ cube containers; wooden or plastic centimetre cubes, – Base 10 apparatus; a variety of cubic and cuboid containers

Differentiation
Less confident learners
These children may need the support of an adult to make the connection between the cubes and the measurement to find volume.

More confident learners
These children may spot the connection with measurement more quickly and go on to calculate rather than count.

Lesson 1 — Oral and mental starter 54

Main teaching activities

Whole-class work: Hold up a clear plastic 1000cm³ cube container. Explain that this is a measuring container which measures both liquid, which is known as capacity, and solids, which is known as volume. Explain to the children that volume is measured in cubic centimetres because the container has length, breadth and height, and that this container can hold 1000 centimetre cubes, which they are going to prove by packing the container with the small cubes provided.

Paired work: Let the children do this. Explain that 10 × 10 × 10 = 1000 and it is expressed as 1000cm³. Ask the children to investigate other cubic and cuboid containers to work out their volume. They could use multiples of the centimetre cubes, for example the 10s, 100s and 1000s from Base 10 apparatus rather than individual cubes if you feel that they have understood the principle.

Progress check: Ask: *How many cubes fitted along the length and breadth of your container? How many cubes altogether cover the bottom area of the container? How many layers high is the container?*

Review

Ask: *We have found the volume of these shapes using cubes. Is there another way in which we could find the volume?* (By measuring the dimensions of the container in centimetres and multiplying length × breadth × height) *Can anyone explain why the unit of measure is called cubic centimetres?*

Curriculum objectives
- To solve problems involving measure (volume).

Success criteria
- I can count and calculate in cubic centimetre and look for patterns.

You will need
Equipment
Wooden or plastic centimetre cubes or cubes that clip together, for example Multilink apparatus

Differentiation
Less confident learners
The practical activity related to the number sentence is most important to embed understanding of volume.

More confident learners
These children should quite quickly realise that they can calculate numerically and do so beyond 10 × 10 × 10.

Lesson 2 — Oral and mental starter 58

Main teaching activities

Whole-class work: Explain to the children that they are going to continue to count and calculate the volume of cubes but this time they are going to work systematically to record a pattern. Hold up a one centimetre cube. Explain that its measurements are 1cm × 1cm × 1cm. Ask: *What would be the size of the next sized cube?* (2cm × 2cm × 2cm) *How many centimetre cubes would I need? So what is the volume?* (8cm³)

Paired work: Ask the children to make and record the number sentence and volume of at least the next five cubes. Encourage them to work systematically and record their results in a table.

Progress check: Encourage the children to make the first few cubes so that they explore practically. As soon as children realise that they are going to need an enormous number of cubes, and they have understood how to work out the cube numbers numerically, encourage them to do so, recording each one on their table. Look for the children who establish a link with the pattern of squared numbers.

Review

Establish how far the children got with their table. Ask: *Did anyone reach 1000cm³ or beyond? What method of calculating did you use when the numbers got too high? Why would this be incorrect: 2 × 2 × 2 = 6? What has this person done wrong? Has anyone else made this mistake? Does anyone know what this pattern of numbers is (1, 8, 27, 64, 125, 216, 343, 512, 729, 1000)?* Tell them this number pattern is the pattern of cubed numbers.

Curriculum objectives
● To solve problems involving converting between units of time.

Success criteria
● I can express times in both the 12- and 24-hour clock and convert between the two.

You will need
Photocopiable sheets
'A day in the life'

Equipment
Clock faces with moveable hands

Differentiation
Less confident learners

Give the group clock faces to help them convert 12-hour clock times to 24-hour clock times and let them work with a clock face in order to understand the two revolutions of the hour hand.

More confident learners

Expect these children to be more imaginative with the time intervals and to add some extra of their own.

Lesson 3 — Oral and mental starter 52

Main teaching activities

Whole-class work: Tell the children that they are going to revise telling the time in both the 12- and 24-hour clock and convert between them. Revise how to convert from one to the other and the correct written notation such as 4.21pm is 16:21 and 03:17 is 3.17am.

Distribute one clock face between each pair and ask them to show you accurately the following times and also to say in words when the time is 00:17, it is 17 minutes past midnight or 0.17 am. Use 05:13; 17:27; 11:42; 23:43.

Independent work: Distribute photocopiable page 'A day in the life' from the CD-ROM. Explain to the children that this is a piece of narrative that makes time references and they must read it carefully and fill in the missing times, using the 24 hour notation, in the spaces provided. The second paragraph is for them to create a similar piece of writing to match the given times.

Progress check: Ask: *Tell me the time 7 minutes after 22:57. Explain the difficulty some people might find with bridging into the next hour/day. Which system do you find easier to use, 12 hour or 24 hour? Why do you think people find time telling difficult* (possibly because we use three different methods interchangeably, 12- and 24-digital time as well as analogue clock faces – some of which use Roman numerals in place of digits.)

Review

Share the children's answers for part one and correct any misconceptions. Ask for volunteers to read out their ideas for part two of the photocopiable page. Invite the rest of the class to listen carefully and to challenge any time intervals that are incorrect or do not make sense. Ask: *Where in everyday life would you expect to see the 24-hour clock used to this level of precision?* (Transport timetables where every minute counts when avoiding accidents. Hospital waiting times, sports times – for example, lap times.)

Curriculum objectives
- To solve problems involving converting between units of time.

Success criteria
- I can solve problems relating to time.

You will need

Photocopiable sheets
'Time and tide'

Equipment
Clock faces with moveable hands

Differentiation

Less confident learners
These children might need to count on the time using a clock face with moveable hands.

More confident learners
These children should use real life timetables on the internet to calculate times of train/bus or plane journeys for given destinations.

Lesson 4
Oral and mental starter 52

Main teaching activities

Whole-class work: Remind the children of the work they did yesterday, where they were calculating time forwards and backwards using 24 hour notation. Ask them to consider the difficulties in calculating time as a traditional written calculation. Explain that whereas our usual calculating number systems of addition and subtraction rely on groups or 'base 10' time is calculated in 'lots of 60' or 'base 60'. Ask the children to describe to you how they calculate time differences or times. Use examples such as a film starting at 22:46 and ending at 00:31 or a washing machine cycle of 1 hours 48 minutes ending at 11:27. Many will describe counting on or back up to the next 60 or hour, which enables then to calculate mentally. Remind them of the value of rounding and estimating in any calculation to help with keeping within the correct range of answer. Some children may need the support of informal jottings.

Independent work: Distribute photocopiable page 'Time and tide' from the CD-ROM to give the children an opportunity to practise their skills and enable you to assess those who can work mentally and those who need support to 'jot' then steps.

Progress check: Ask the children to demonstrate their methods to you and to explain how they visualise the 'counting on or back' times. Ask: *If I start a journey at 21:52 and arrive at 03:47, how long have I been travelling?*

Review

Ask the children if any of them found any particular time difficult to calculate and if so how did they do them? Ask if anyone used rounding and estimating first to assist with accuracy and if so how it helped.

Curriculum objectives
- To solve problems involving converting between units of time.

Success criteria
- I can solve problems relating to time.

You will need

Photocopiable sheets
'Steam train times'

Equipment
A selection of bus and train timetables; clock faces with moveable hands

Differentiation

Less confident learners
These children might need to count on the time using a clock face with moveable hands.

More confident learners
Expect these children to be able to work out the cost of each journey.

Lesson 5
Oral and mental starter 54

Main teaching activities

Whole-class work: Distribute the timetables you have collected. Discuss with the children how each timetable is arranged, with places and times cross-referenced. You could also discuss how timetables become more complicated when there are weekend and holiday variations. Explain that timetables always use the 24-hour clock to avoid confusion between morning and evening times, for example, 6pm and 6:00 hours. Ask them to calculate the time taken for each stage of a journey, using the counting on method. Go through a timetable as a class, asking individuals to count on aloud. Build their confidence: *What time does the bus leave Warwick? At what time should it arrive at Coventry? How long does the journey take?* As an additional challenge, tell the children that the ticket price is £12 per hour. Ask: *How much it would cost to visit each separately and then work out the cost for their chosen day out.*

Independent work: Distribute photocopiable page 'Steam train times' from the CD-ROM. Explain that this sheet presents a timetable; the children have to plan a route and answer some questions, using the 24-hour clock.

Progress check: Ask: *Have you considered how long you might want to stay at each place? Is it possible to spend time at every activity along the line? How are you calculating the times?*

Review

Ask for volunteers to describe their planned journey and challenge the rest of the class to calculate how long it will take. Look for consistency and sound judgement. Check the accuracy of the time calculations. (Problems often occur when bridging an hour.) Establish how the children calculated the cost of each journey if a train ticket is calculated to be £12 per hour but not all of the journeys are exactly one hour.

Curriculum objectives
● To solve problems involving converting between units of time.

You will need

1. Check

Oral and mental starter

57 Mystery number

2. Assess

Clock faces

3. Further practice

Photocopiable sheets

'Steam train times template'

Calculating and converting in 12- and 24-hour clock systems

Most children should be able to calculate the difference between two times and convert between times in the different systems. Some children will not have made such progress and will require extra practice using clock faces and the '24-hour clock' to help them.

1. Check

57 Mystery number

Use a version of the oral and mental starter that uses different times as the mystery number. Children should be able to count on and back to work out time differences and also convert from the 12-hour to the 24-hour clock. *If a bus leaves at 11:47 for a journey of 1 hour and 5 minutes, what time does it arrive? A film runs for 2 hours and 11 minutes and finishes at 17:30, what time did it start? Jane played the flute from 14:15 until 14:50, how long was she playing? What is 18:25 as a 12-hour clock time?*

2. Assess

Extend the oral and mental starter by asking the children to plan out an imaginary timetable for a whole day or weekend, putting in as many times as they can, both in the 12-hour and 24-hour clock. More confident learners should use very precise times and convert them confidently. Less able children may need more practice using a clock face to help them convert times and calculate the times between events. Record the outcomes.

3. Further practice

Adapt photocopiable page 'Steam train times template' from the CD-ROM to give further practice of calculating time differences and converting between 12- and 24-hour times.

Curriculum objectives
● To solve addition and subtraction multi-step problems in contexts, deciding which operations and methods to use and why.

You will need

1. Check

Oral and mental starter

55 The tall and the small

2. Assess

'Step by step'

3. Further practice

Oral and mental starter

56 You know for a fact!

General resources

'0–30 number cards' (0–9 only)

Adding and subtracting in context

Most children should be able to use the information given to decide on the steps to take in order to answer the question asked, taking into account the context of the problem.

Some children will require further practice to understand that some problems need to be solved in more than one step and that the answer needs to be interpreted in context.

1. Check

55 The tall and the small

Use the oral and mental starter to observe the way in which children use the given information to solve this problem. *Which piece of information will you use first? Why? How does this help you to work out the final heights? How do you find out ¾ of a measurement? Is it more than one step?*

2. Assess

As the children answer the questions on photocopiable page 210 'Step by step', observe how they select the information and the methods they use to calculate the answer. Less confident learners may not be able to recognise what to do when there is more than one step needed to achieve an answer and some still may not have reliable written methods for addition and subtraction. Record the outcomes.

3. Further practice

The oral and mental starter provides additional practice in recognising the common errors made when calculating and an opportunity to discuss these with an adult in order to avoid repeating them.

Curriculum objectives
• To recognise mixed numbers and improper fractions and convert from one form to the other.

You will need
1. Check

Oral and mental starter

 Fraction line up

2. Assess
'Fraction twins'

3. Further practice

Oral and mental starter

44 Fraction match

Converting between improper fractions and mixed numbers

Most children should be confident converting between improper fractions and mixed numbers and be able to explain how they have done so.

Some children will not have made such progress and will require additional practice to ensure an understanding of an improper fraction and the calculation needed to convert it to a mixed number.

1. Check
 Fraction line up

As the children place the fractions on the number line, ask them to explain their reasoning, especially when placing mixed numbers or improper fractions. Observe their choices and the way they convert between the different forms.

• *Where would you place ⅔? What is this the same as? How would that look using fraction shapes? Is ⅓ bigger or smaller than ¾? How do you know?*

2. Assess

As children match the pairs on photocopiable page 211 'Fraction twins', ensure that they understand how to convert between mixed numbers and improper fractions. Record the outcomes.

3. Further practice

The oral and mental starter consolidates equivalence.

Curriculum objectives
• To round any number up to 1,000,000 to the nearest 10, 100, 1000, 10,000 and 100,000.

You will need
1. Check

Oral and mental starter

54 Round and estimate

2. Assess
'0–30 number cards'; 'Rounding chart'

3. Further practice

General resources

'0–30 number cards' (0–9 only); 'Number lines'

Rounding to the nearest 10, 100 and 1000

Most children should be able to round any number up to 1,000,000 to the nearest 10, 100 or 1000 and use the result to estimate.

Some children will not have made such progress and will require additional practice with number lines in order to understand how to round a number to the nearest 10 and nearest 100.

1. Check
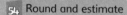 Round and estimate

Use the oral and mental starter to check the children's understanding of how to round to the nearest 10, 100 and 1000 and then how they can use the result to estimate.

• *Look at this number. Round it to the nearest 1000. What are you looking for to do this? Is it always necessary to start at the smallest digit? What is the rule for rounding numbers to the nearest 10 or the nearest 100? How could this help you to estimate the result of calculations?*

2. Assess

Ask the children to generate four- and five-digit numbers using the 0–9 number cards and then round the number and record the results on photocopiable page 212 'Rounding chart'. As the children work, observe their strategies for rounding. Record the outcomes.

3. Further practice

Children who find this difficult can use 'Number lines' to demonstrate the distance from the nearest 10 in the first instance and then, by placing the number on different number lines, demonstrate the nearest 100 and the nearest 1000. This helps less confident learners to understand rounding.

Oral and mental starters

Multiplication and division

52 Multiplication challenge

All the children stand in a circle. Explain that one child challenges another with a quick-fire times table question. The second child either answers immediately or sits down. If the answer given is correct, the challenger sits down and the second child becomes the new challenger. If there is no answer or an incorrect answer, the rest of the class call out the answer and the challenger asks another child a new question. The last child standing is the winner. You could produce a 'handicap' system to level up the abilities: ask some groups about the 3-, 4-, 6- and 8-times tables and others about the 7-, 8-, 9-, 11- and 12-times tables.

53 Division challenge

This is the same as Multiplication challenge, above, but the children ask division questions based on times-tables facts. As before, a 'handicap' system may be operated.

Number and place value

54 Round and estimate

Write these or similar numbers on the board:

2018   3864   4503   2845   3699   2330   4440   5500   7193   5883   2911

Ask the children to challenge each other with questions such as: *I can see two numbers that total approximately 6500. Can anybody see which they are? Can anybody find a pair of numbers with a difference of approximately 1100?* Remind the children about rounding to the nearest 100 or nearest 1000.

57 Mystery number

Ask the children to listen carefully to your description of a mystery number, then to raise their hands to offer the answer. Explain that they can use jottings to note important pieces of information. They must be sure of their answer, not just guessing. Say each question twice.

- I am thinking of a number under 100 that is an even number. It is a multiple of 10. Its digits add up to the name of the times table it belongs to. Its factors include 5 and 18 (90).
- This is an odd number. It is a multiple of 7. It is a square number (49).
- I am thinking of an even number that appears in four different times tables in a 10 × 10 grid. Half of this number is an even number. One of this number's factors is 6 (24).

Repeat with other clues or ask the children to make up ones of their own to test each other.

62 Multiples of 10

Ask the children: *Think of the number 3. Multiply it by 10. What does it become? Now multiply it by 10 again, and again.* Ask the children to suggest another way we could have got from 3 to 3000 (such as 3 × 1000 or 3 × 100 × 10). Show how the number 3 grew to 3000 using 'Place value arrow cards'. Ask the children to notice how the place value moved up one space each time the number was multiplied by 10. Repeat the process, starting at 5, then 8. Each time, ask the children to record the number pattern.

Repeat but this time, divide repeatedly by 10. Start with 10,000, then 9000. Now try 8750 and 7945, going on to at least one decimal place.

SCHOLASTIC

Measurement

55 The tall and the small

Provide the children with the following information and ask them to make up a variety of questions using the information for the others to solve, using accurate mathematical vocabulary.

Jane is 1.35m tall.

Aziz is 152cm tall.

Karen is 40mm taller than Jane.

Ali is ¾ of the height of Sue.

Sue is 174cm tall.

This activity can be repeated with different measures.

Addition and subtraction

56 You know for a fact!

Say to the children: *I have a problem to solve. It contains quite large numbers and I don't think that the answer is correct so I need you to use your knowledge of number and number facts to help me.*

22,419 + 12,583 = 34,993

Ask for their ideas. If necessary, remind them about odd and even numbers, rounding, estimating and crossing the hundred barrier. Ask the children to do a written calculation to find the actual answer.

This can be repeated with other numbers or with a subtraction such as:

8927.77 − 2498.01 = 6429.76.

60 Giving change

Ask the children to imagine that they have £10.00 to spend. Ask: *How much change would you have if you spent 752p? What about 58p? £3.23? £1.45? 91p? £8.33? 17p? £6.29p? 67p?* The children should raise a hand to volunteer the answer.

Repeat with other amounts or with a total of £20.00.

Fractions

58 Pairs to make 10 bingo

Write 15 two-digit decimals between 0.1 and 9.9 on the board.

Indicate the list of decimals. Ask the children to jot down any five of them. Call out the pair to make 10 of one of the numbers on the board, for example, if 6.2 is on the board, say: *3.8.* The children who have the matching pair on their board cross it out. Repeat for the remaining decimals. The winner is the first to cross out all their numbers and shout 'BINGO!'

Oral and mental starters 59, 61 and 63 continue on the CD-ROM.

Step by step

■ Complete these questions using the strategies that you have been learning. Show the calculations where necessary on a separate piece of paper.

1. 5028 + 1887

2. I went to the shop twice today! On the first occasion I spent £30.14 and on the second I spent £18.96. How much did I spend altogether?

3. 21,402 − 2953

4. I paid for two shirts in the shop and it cost £39.25. My friend paid me back £12.56 for her shirt. How much did mine cost?

5. A 54-seat coach and 16-seat minibus came to take Classes 5M and 5C on a school trip. There are 32 children in Class 5M and 29 in Class 5C. What is the maximum number of adults who can go?

6. My cat weighs 3.4kg and my dog weighs 12.52kg. What is their combined mass?

7. Find two numbers between 5 and 6 that total 11.26.

8. Find the missing numbers.

a) _____ − 1.3 = 25.8

b) 54.9 − _____ = 36

9. Two numbers have a difference of 156. One of the numbers is 792. What is the other number? Is there only one answer? Why?

10. In the morning, Mum drives 8km to drop Dan at his friend's house and to pick up my friend Ann. She then takes Ann and me 5km to school. Finally she drives another 8.4km to her office. In the afternoon she does the trip in reverse. How far does she drive altogether?

> I can interpret and solve addition and subtraction problems in context.
>
> How did you do?

Fraction twins

- Join the matching pairs in each group with a line.

$1\frac{1}{3}$	$\frac{4}{8}$
$\frac{1}{2}$	$\frac{9}{12}$
$\frac{3}{4}$	$\frac{4}{3}$
$2\frac{1}{2}$	$\frac{14}{20}$
$\frac{7}{10}$	$\frac{5}{2}$

$\frac{4}{5}$	$\frac{4}{16}$
$\frac{5}{6}$	$\frac{11}{8}$
$\frac{1}{4}$	$\frac{20}{14}$
$\frac{10}{7}$	$\frac{10}{12}$
$1\frac{3}{8}$	$\frac{12}{15}$

I can convert between improper fractions and mixed numbers.

How did you do?

PHOTOCOPIABLE

Name: _____   Date: _____

Rounding chart

- Select digits to form 4- and 5-digit numbers and complete the chart.

Number	Nearest 10	Nearest 100	Nearest 1000	Nearest 10,000

I can round numbers to the nearest 10, 100, 1000, or 10,000.

How did you do?

Addition and subtraction of money

Expected prior learning

Children should be able to:

- securely make number bonds to 10
- add and subtract two-digit numbers mentally
- have some experience of adding and subtracting using a written method.

Topic	Curriculum objectives	Expected outcomes
Addition and subtraction	**Lesson 1**	
	To add and subtract whole numbers with more than four-digits, including using formal written methods (columnar addition and subtraction).	Add and subtract numbers with up to two decimal places in the context of money.
	Lesson 2	
	To add and subtract whole numbers with more than four-digits, including using formal written methods (columnar addition and subtraction).	Add and subtract numbers with up to two decimal places in the context of money.
	Lesson 3	
	To add and subtract numbers mentally with increasingly large numbers.	Represent a puzzle or problem by identifying and recording the information or calculations needed to solve it; find possible solutions and confirm them in the context of the problem.
	Lesson 4	
	To solve addition and subtraction multi-step problems in contexts, deciding which operations and methods to use and why.	Solve one-step and two-step problems involving whole numbers and decimals and all four operations, choosing and using appropriate calculation strategies.
	Lesson 5	
	To solve addition and subtraction multi-step problems in contexts, deciding which operations and methods to use and why.	Solve one-step and two-step problems involving whole numbers and decimals and all four operations, choosing and using appropriate calculation strategies.

Preparation

Lesson 1: write the question on the board; copy 'Shopkeeper shuffle', one per child

Lesson 2: copy 'A mixed bag of problems', one per child

Lesson 4: copy 'Maths mobiles', one per child

Lesson 5: assemble a selection of shapes from 'Shapes', one per pair if needed

You will need

Photocopiable sheets

'Shopkeeper shuffle'; 'A mixed bag of problems'; 'Maths mobiles'

General resources

'Shapes'

Further practice

Interactive activity 'Round, estimate and check' can be used to practice addition and subtraction of four-digit numbers using formal written methods.

Oral and mental starters suggested for week 1

See bank of starters on pages 249 to 250. Oral and mental starters are also on the CD-ROM.

64 Place value elimination game

68 Pick your measure

70 A fraction or a percentage?

Overview of progression

This week addition and subtraction are used to solve calculations including decimal numbers, in a variety of contexts. There are opportunities to further develop and practise written subtraction as well as additions of lists of decimal numbers in the context of money. Mental strategies are used to solve problems and to look for patterns such as triangular numbers and 'number mobiles'.

Watch out for

There will still be some children who will need additional support in order to use columnar methods for addition and subtraction, in particular they may have difficulties with 'carrying' digits when adding and decomposition of numbers for subtraction. This can be addressed by representing the numbers using practical equipment such as bundles of straws or 100s, 10s and 1s which can be deconstructed to demonstrate decomposition. Ensure accurate place value for decimals by aligning the decimal point.

Creative context

Any context that encourages the use of calculation across the curriculum helps the mathematical thinking to become 'real'. Children will be more willing to engage in the maths if there is a problem to solve or an end point, for example finding the pattern or balancing the number mobile.

Vocabulary

add, approximate, decimal place, decimal point, decimal, difference, estimate, **integer**, minus, operation, plus, round, subtract, sum, total

Curriculum objectives
● To add and subtract whole numbers with more than four-digits, including using formal written methods (columnar addition and subtraction).

Success criteria
● I can use a written strategy to solve a calculation involving decimals.

You will need
Photocopiable sheets
'Shopkeeper shuffle'

Differentiation
Less confident learners
Work with the children on 'Shopkeeper shuffle (1)' focusing upon the methods of calculation.

More confident learners
Ask the children to explain the methods they used and challenge them to use more compact methods for 'Shopkeeper shuffle (2)'.

Lesson 1
Oral and mental starter 64

Main teaching activities

Whole-class work: Write the following question on the board:

> A school makes a profit of £1524 on a sponsored event. It is decided to spend £257 on a visiting theatre group. How much money remains in the school fund?

Ask: *How would you calculate this?* Encourage rounding and estimating first and then written responses such as:

Estimate: £1500 − £250 = £1250

$$£1524 = £1000 + £500 + £20 + £4$$
$$- £257 = \qquad\quad £200 + £50 + £7$$

Adjusted to:

$$£1524 = £1000 + £400 + £110 + £14$$
$$- £257 = \qquad\quad £200 + £50 + £7$$
$$\underline{£1267 = £1000 + £200 + £60 + £7}$$

Or:

$$£ \quad 1 \quad {}^4\!5 \quad {}^{1}\!\!2 \quad {}^1\!4$$
$$- \qquad 2 \quad 5 \quad 7$$
$$\underline{£ \quad 1 \quad 2 \quad 6 \quad 7}$$

Compare both methods and look for similarities, for example, the calculations for the ones is 14 − 7; the readjusted number actually reads the same for both calculations.

Also revise written addition methods with:

Either:

$$£ \quad 171.28$$
$$+ \quad 138.64$$
$$\quad 200.00$$
$$\quad 100.00$$
$$\quad\quad\; 9.00$$
$$\quad\quad\; 0.80$$
$$\underline{\quad\quad\; 0.12}$$
$$£ \quad 309.92$$

Or:

$$£ \quad 171.28$$
$$+ \quad 138.64$$
$$\underline{£ \quad 309.92}$$

Again, compare similarities.

Independent work: Distribute the photocopiable page 'Shopkeeper shuffle' from the CD-ROM, which provide practice at solving money problems of 3-digit sums with two decimal places.

Progress check: Ask: *Which is your preferred method? Why? Show me the part of the calculation that is the most tricky. Why do people make errors here? Talk me through what you are doing.*

Review

Write the following on the board:

If I earn £1072 per month but my rent costs £350 per month and my supermarket bill is £421 per month, how much do I have left to spend on bills and treats?

Ask: *How would you solve this?* Some may add £350 and £421 together and take it away from £1072. Others may subtract separately. Ask for volunteers to demonstrate their chosen method and discuss the relative merits and margins of error for each. Ask: *How could you estimate first?* Repeat with a similar example.

Curriculum objectives

● To add and subtract whole numbers with more than four-digits, including using formal written methods (columnar addition and subtraction).

Success criteria

● I can round, estimate and use my knowledge of number to check my calculations.

You will need

Photocopiable sheets

'A mixed bag of problems'

Differentiation

Less confident learners

Work with the children on 'A mixed bag of problems' focusing upon the methods of calculation.

More confident learners

Provide some additional two-step problems to challenge the children. For example: *Ellie received £108.25 for her birthday and £49.36 for Christmas. She bought two books, each costing £7.99 and a bag for school costing 12.49. How much money has Ellie got left?*

Lesson 2

Oral and mental starter 64

Main teaching activities

Whole-class work: Remind the children about the checking and estimating techniques practised in previous lessons, for example, even number + even number = even number; odd number + odd number = even number, and so on, and that rounding and estimating gives the approximate size of the answer.

Also remind the children that not every calculation needs to be written, for example 140 + 150 = 290. However, care must be taken if numbers become more complicated or bridge 10, 100, 1000, and so on. such as 497 + 836:

Odd + Even = Odd

Estimate: 500 + 800 = 1300

Either:

```
      4   9   7
+     8   3   6
      1   3   3   3
      |   |   |
```

Or:

```
      4   9   7
+     8   3   6
  1   2   0   0
      1   2   0
              1   3
  1   3   3   3
```

One or two children might be able to tell you this as the mental calculation 500 + 800 + 36 − 3 but for the majority of the children, this should be a written calculation. Emphasise the importance of accurate place value.

Independent work: Distribute photocopiable page 'A mixed bag of problems' from the CD-ROM. Explain that there are a variety of calculations. Some may be solved using mental or informal methods, but many will require a written calculation

Progress check: Ask: *How do we ensure accurate place holding when calculating using decimals? Why does estimating also help? Why would an answer such as £3.7 not be complete in the context of money?*

Review

Ask: *If I were to calculate £741.71 − £314.28, would I expect the hundredths digit to be odd or even?* (Odd − Even = Odd) Ask: *How would I round and estimate this calculation?* (£750 − £300 = £450)

Now ask for volunteers to talk through their methods of calculation.

```
  £741.71 = £700 + £40 +  £1 + 70p +  1p
− £314.28 = £300 + £10 +  £4 + 20p +  8p
```

Adjusted to:

```
  £741.71 = £700 + £30 + £11 + 60p + 11p
− £314.28 = £300 + £10 +  £4 + 20p +  8p
  £427.43 = £400 + £20 +  £7 + 40p +  3p
```

```
£   7  ³4̶  ¹1. ⁶7̶  ¹1
−   3   1   4. 2   8
    4   2   7. 4   3
```

Emphasise the position of the decimal point and how it remains in the same position.

Curriculum objectives

● To add numbers mentally with increasingly large numbers.

Success criteria

● I can add mentally to investigate a pattern.

Differentiation

Less confident learners

It may help these children to have a recording frame or pattern started so that they can simply continue it.

More confident learners

Some children may begin to spot a pattern and start to formulate a rule for predicting triangular numbers higher up the pattern.

Lesson 3 — Oral and mental starter 68

Main teaching activities

Whole-class work: Introduce the principle of triangular numbers, demonstrating using dots on the board. Say: *We start with one, then to add another row that will make a triangle or pyramid so we need two more dots underneath and we have a total of three dots. The next row has three dots so the pattern has six dots in total.*

The triangular numbers are 1, 3, 6, ... (although for the purposes of this investigation one can be ignored since it cannot really be considered a triangle).

| 1 | 3 | 6 |

Independent work: Ask: *How does this series continue?* Ask the children to write it down.

Progress check: Ask: *How are you working to ensure that you record your results systematically?*

Review

Ask: *Has anybody spotted a pattern in the numbers? Have you been able to find the next numbers in the series without drawing them? Can you explain how? Why is your method so successful? Convince me!* (The triangular numbers are generated by adding one more each time: 1, 1 + 2 = 3, 1 + 2 + 3 or 3 + 3 = 6, 6 + 4 = 10, 10 + 5 = 15, and so on. The first ten triangular numbers are 1, 3, 6, 10, 15, 21, 28, 36, 45, 55.)

Curriculum objectives
● To solve addition and subtraction multi-step problems in contexts, deciding which operations and methods to use and why.

Success criteria
● I can use addition and subtraction to solve puzzles.

You will need
Photocopiable sheets
'Maths mobiles'

Differentiation
Less confident learners
These children should use 100 to begin with as the top number to build confidence.

More confident learners
These children could use more challenging numbers for the top number, such as 1226 or 5030.

Lesson 4
Oral and mental starter 70

Main teaching activities

Independent and paired work: Distribute photocopiable page 'Maths mobiles' from the CD-ROM. Explain to the children that for the Maths mobile to balance both sides must equal the number at the top. The rule is that if the shape is the same then the number within it is also the same. Demonstrate with the following example, placing 100 at the top:

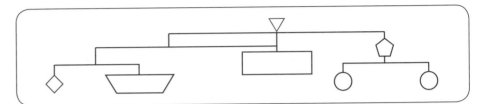

Take suggestions for numbers that might fill the shapes, pointing out that the circles must contain the same number to balance the one above. For example, pentagon = 50 with two lots of 25 in the circles directly below; rectangle = 60, balanced with 15 and 25 in the two quadrilaterals. Both sides total 100 and so the mobile balances.

Explain that using multiples of 10 is a good way to start but then they may need to be more precise and inventive to make the shapes balance. This activity can be differentiated by the complexity of the top number. Repeat using the same mobile but changing the top number to 120 or 1000.

Ask the children to complete the mobiles on the sheet to make 1000 in the first instance. You may wish to change the top number for some groups of children.

Progress check: Ask: *How are you beginning to solve this problem? What do you need to decide first? Is it more helpful to work from the top or the bottom? Show me how each side balances. Is it enough for both sides to total the top number irrespective of the mobile arrangement?* (No some 'arms' need to balance each other it depends on the shapes hanging from them.)

Review
Draw one of the mobiles on the board. Ask the children to talk you through their decision making when placing numbers. Now ask them to suggest a different number to place at the top. Discuss whether some numbers would be more difficult to balance than others (for example odd numbers). Ask them to solve the puzzle using 0.6 as the top number.

Curriculum objectives
● As lesson 4.
Success criteria
● As lesson 4.

You will need
General resources
'Shapes'

Differentiation
Less confident learners
The children could use 'Shapes' to visualise their mobile.

More confident learners
Encourage children to create two or three layer mobiles.

Lesson 5
Oral and mental starter 70

Main teaching activities

Paired work: Explain to the children that they are to create their own mobile puzzles for others to solve. Remind them of how the total of the numbers on each side must both equal the top number and that the same shapes must contain the same numbers. Encourage them to be adventurous in their choices. This time they may need some written calculations if they are going to choose numbers that are not multiples of 10 or 100. Swap puzzles with another pair to check accuracy and difficulty.

Progress check: Ask: *Which numbers are you setting first? How does that influence the choices for the remaining numbers on that side? At what point do you think you might need to check with a calculation?*

Review
Ask if any of the children have created a really challenging puzzle and put it on the board. Ask the children to try to solve it and check its accuracy.

■SCHOLASTIC

Multiplication and division of money

Expected prior learning

Children should be able to:

- exhibit a range of strategies for solving problems based on prior learning
- understand that sometimes real-life problems may require the numbers to be interpreted and may need rounding up or down to make sense in a context.

Topic	Curriculum objectives	Expected outcomes
Multiplication and division	**Lesson 1**	
	To multiply and divide numbers mentally drawing upon known facts.	Recall quickly multiplication facts up to 12 × 12 and use them to multiply pairs of multiples of 10 and 100; derive quickly corresponding division facts.
		Identify pairs of factors of two-digit whole numbers.
	Lesson 2	
	To multiply numbers up to four-digits by a one- or two-digit number using a formal written method, including long multiplication for two-digit numbers.	Recall quickly multiplication facts up to 12 × 12 and use them to multiply pairs of multiples of 10 and 100; derive quickly corresponding division facts.
	To solve problems involving addition, subtraction, multiplication and division and a combination of these, including understanding the meaning of the equals sign.	
	Lesson 3	
	To multiply numbers up to four-digits by a one- or two-digit number using a formal written method, including long multiplication for two-digit numbers.	Solve one-step and two-step problems involving whole numbers and decimals and all four operations, choosing and using appropriate calculation strategies.
	To solve problems involving addition, subtraction, multiplication and division and a combination of these, including understanding the meaning of the equals sign.	
	Lessons 4 and 5	
	To multiply numbers up to four-digits by a one- or two-digit number using a formal written method, including long multiplication for two-digit numbers.	Solve one-step and two-step problems involving whole numbers and decimals and all four operations, choosing and using appropriate calculation strategies.
	To solve problems involving addition, subtraction, multiplication and division and a combination of these, including understanding the meaning of the equals sign.	

Preparation

Lesson 2: copy 'Currency exchange', one per child; arrange internet access or assemble a selection of newspapers giving exchange rates

Lesson 3: copy 'DIY at Number 32', one per child

Lesson 5: copy 'Shopping list', one per child; arrange internet access, if wanted

You will need

Photocopiable sheets

'Currency exchange'; 'DIY at Number 32'; 'Shopping list'

Equipment

Internet access or newspapers giving exchange rates; internet shopping website

Further practice

Provide leaflets from supermarkets or direct children to a supermarket website to compile lists of items with prices and total spend. Ask them to include multiple items to check their multiplication as well as their addition and subtraction skills.

Oral and mental starters suggested for week 2

See bank of starters on pages 249 to 250. Oral and mental starters are also on the CD-ROM.

65 Area calculator

69 Speedy times

71 What's the question?

Overview of progression

In this set of lessons there is a strong element of using and applying skills learned previously. The first two lessons draw on multiplication and division knowledge with rounding and estimating to support written calculation skills.

Through the next three lessons the children use all four operations in problem-solving situations involving measures and money. There is a strong element of decision making in the final lesson, and children may need to use their powers of persuasion to get their first choices.

Watch out for

Some children may get stuck with only one method for calculating and may be unable to progress when that method fails them, particularly when solving problems. For instance, the child who always writes a written calculation for subtraction, but comes unstuck when faced with a small amount to subtract from 30m or 3000cm when counting on or back would have been more efficient.

Creative context

Encourage the children to always create a story around the numbers that they are using for calculations, since a real-life context enables them to understand the actual value and sense of the numbers. If at all possible, have the party planned in lesson 5.

Vocabulary

add, answer, calculate, calculation, calculator, difference, divide, divisible by, divisor, equation, explain, **factor**, **inverse**, method, minus, multiple, multiply, operation, pattern, plus, predict, problem, product, **quotient**, reason, reasoning, relationship, remainder, solution, subtract, sum, symbol, total

SCHOLASTIC

Curriculum objectives
● To multiply and divide numbers mentally drawing upon known facts.

Success criteria
● I can multiply by breaking numbers into factors and rearranging the calculation.

Differentiation

Less confident learners
It is possible that these children will need to revise factorisation with an adult and use simpler numbers, for example 30, 12, 20 and 15 to multiply.

More confident learners
Encourage these children to select additional numbers to multiply beyond 100. They may have to factorise these more than once. For example, $15 \times 144 = 15 \times (12 \times 12)$ may be easier to managed by breaking the 12s into their factors $15 \times (3 \times 4) \times (3 \times 4)$ and then reordering to multiply.

Lesson 1   Oral and mental starter ⑥⑨

Main teaching activities

Whole-class work: Revise multiplying by using factors. Write the following calculations on the board:

35×50 32×40 48×30

Ask the children to simplify these calculations by breaking them down into their constituent factors and re-ordering them for easier multiplying.

For example:

$35 \times 50 = (7 \times 5) \times (5 \times 10)$

$= (5 \times 5) \times 7 \times 10$

$= (25 \times 7) \times 10$

$= 175 \times 10 = 1750$

Ask the children for a selection of numbers from their known times tables which have multiple factors. Jot a selection on the board, such as, 36, 48, 27, 12, 56, 42, 18, asking the children to identify the factors each time.

Independent work: Ask the children to create their own multiplication problems to solve by breaking into factors and reordering to multiply.

Progress check: Ask the children to explain to you how they decided how to factorise. Ask: *Is there another alternative? What is the best order to choose to multiply these together? Do you need to do any jottings in order to help you keep track?*

Review

Write the numbers 13, 19, 23 and 31 on the board. Ask the children what they notice about these numbers. Remind them that they are called prime numbers and that their only factors are 1 and themselves. Write 24×19 and ask the children to tell you how they might solve this. They might suggest $19 \times (6 \times 4)$. Ask if there are any other multiplication strategies that could be used. They might say that 19 is a near multiple of 20. Remind them to adjust their answer: $24 \times 20 = 480$ so $24 \times 19 = 480 - 24 = 456$.

Curriculum objectives
- To multiply numbers up to four-digits by a one- or two-digit number using a formal written method, including long multiplication for two-digit numbers.
- To solve problems involving addition, subtraction, multiplication and division.

Success criteria
- I can solve problems using multiplication and division.

You will need

Photocopiable sheets
'Currency exchange'

Equipment
Internet access or newspapers giving exchange rates

Differentiation

Less confident learners
Children may need adult support with the calculations and checking the place value.

More confident learners
Expect more precise rounding and calculating. These children could rank the currencies in a 'value for money' league table.

Lesson 2
Oral and mental starter 69

Main teaching activities

Whole-class work: Explore with the class how different countries have different currencies from the UK and when people travel abroad they need to exchange their money at the going rate. Give the children time to explore different currencies and their exchange rates using the internet or newspapers. Ask them how they would calculate how many Euros they would get if the exchange rate was €1.82 for every £1. (Multiplying) Ask them to round and estimate approximately how many Euros they would get for £300. (Less than €600) Now ask them to talk you through how to multiply this exactly (€546).

Independent and paired work: Distribute photocopiable page 'Currency exchange' from the CD-ROM. Ask the children to answer the questions on the sheet, which uses imaginary currencies. Alternatively, you may prefer them to use actual currencies and exchange rates that they have researched. Ask them to round and estimate first, in order to check accuracy but also because this is what most people would do when buying something in a foreign country in order to compare the price.

Progress check: Ask: *What is your estimate? Do you expect the answer to be more or less than your estimate? Why? Talk me through how you are calculating. How do you know that you have accurate place value?*

Review

Compare answers and discuss 'value for money' in the various countries. Explain that sometimes goods seem less expensive in different countries partly because of the prices displayed and partly because the exchange rate makes the pound sterling buy more than it would at home.

Curriculum objectives
- As Lesson 2 above.

Success criteria
- I can use all four operations to solve problems involving money and measures.

You will need

Photocopiable sheets
'DIY at Number 32'

Differentiation

Less confident learners
Children may need to work with adult support.

More confident learners
These children can work independently and then create more measurement questions and calculations of their own.

Lesson 3
Oral and mental starter 65

Main teaching activities

Whole-class work: Explain that weights and measures are important in our daily lives and we cannot avoid using them, whether shopping or doing home decoration. Introduce the concept of a house, Number 32, which is in need of some redecoration before the new owners can move in.

Independent work: Distribute photocopiable page 'DIY at Number 32' from the CD-ROM and go through the various measurements. Explain that sometimes the measurements may need converting into smaller units in order to calculate. For example: in the first question the length of the wall in Sally's bedroom is given in metres but one of the shelving lengths is given in centimetres. The children need to decide whether they feel confident to work with decimal numbers or whether they would prefer to convert all the lengths to centimetres, which makes the numbers bigger but eliminates the need to deal with decimals.

Progress check: Ask: *If we have measurements in both metres and centimetres, what must we do to work out the problems? How many centimetres in a metre? Why can I not buy exactly 175cm of wood for a shelf if that is what I need?*

Review

Go through some of the questions, asking individuals what operation they chose and how they created a calculation to solve the problem. Work through some of the questions on the board to iron out misconceptions and confusion. Encourage the children to draw a diagram of anything they cannot visualise.

Curriculum objectives

- To multiply numbers up to four-digits by a one- or two-digit number using a formal written method, including long multiplication for two-digit numbers.
- To solve problems involving addition, subtraction, multiplication and division and a combination of these, including understanding the meaning of the equals sign.

Success criteria

- I can use all four operations to solve problems involving money and measures.

You will need

Photocopiable sheets
'DIY at Number 32'

Differentiation

Less confident learners

These children may experience difficulty in visualising the problems and may need adult support. They should be encouraged to sketch out the different aspects of the problem, for example, draw the tins of paint per room or draw a sketch of the floor area.

More confident learners

These children might like to sketch and redecorate an imaginary bedroom of their own, making up the dimensions. A computer simulation of painting a room on a paint company website might be a starting point.

Lesson 4

Oral and mental starter 65

Main teaching activities

Whole-class work: Explain to the children that mixed units are often found in 'real-life' problems, for example, floors might be measured in square metres whereas tiles are measured in square centimetres. In order to calculate how many tiles you need, a common unit of measure has to be used. Ask: *If a floor area measures 3m × 4m, how do you calculate how many 30cm × 30cm tiles you need?* It is important to think about the problem. You actually need to think about the lengths of the floor and the tiles rather than their areas. Convert the area to 300cm × 400cm. You can fit 300cm ÷ 30cm = 10 tiles along the 300cm length. When you divide 400cm by 30cm, however, you get 13⅓ tiles. Since you have to use a whole tile and cut it to make each row of tiles across the 400cm length, you will need 10 × 14 = 140 tiles.

Independent work: Continue problem solving from yesterday. Ask the children to calculate the area of carpet needed for each room. Calculate the number of tins of paint needed for each room. A tin of paint covers 1½ walls and costs £9.80. Sally wants one wall pink and the rest green. Mum wants the kitchen to have a different colour on each wall. Dad wants their bedroom all cream and the sitting room has one wall covered in wallpaper which Mum doesn't want to change. How much in total will they spend on paint?

Progress check: Ask questions such as: *What are the clues in these questions to help you decide on the operation to use? What formula did you use to calculate area? Why can't you calculate using mixed units? Which operations have you used? Talk me through the different steps you had to make to solve this problem.*

Review

Think of a question, linked to Number 32, which could be solved using this number question: (4.1 × 2.8) ÷ 2. (Sally wants half of her bedroom floor carpeted.) Ask the group of children who made up their own measures questions related to Number 32 in yesterday's lesson to challenge the rest of the class.

Curriculum objectives

● To multiply numbers up to four-digits by a one- or two-digit number using a formal written method, including long multiplication for two-digit numbers.
● To solve problems involving addition, subtraction, multiplication and division and a combination of these, including understanding the meaning of the equals sign.

Success criteria

● I can use my maths skills to plan an activity.
● I can use my maths planning to persuade people to choose my idea.

You will need

Photocopiable sheets
'Shopping list'

Equipment
Internet shopping website

Differentiation

Less confident learners

This group of children may need guidance in the art of negotiation as well as having adult support to calculate their shopping list. It may be a good idea for this group to use a calculator to check their calculations.

More confident learners

These children might use their ICT skills to go 'virtual' shopping on a supermarket's internet shopping site. Remind them that this is only hypothetical and not to place any actual orders!

Main teaching activities

Whole-class work: Explain to the class that as an extension to their 'real-life' word problem activities they are going to plan a barbeque for an end-of-term treat for the whole class. They must calculate what and how much food they need to buy and how much it will cost. They might have to reduce the amount of food and drink if the costs are too high. They must also work out how much to charge per person to cover their costs. This will involve them discussing how much people can afford or would be willing to pay.

Group work: Distribute photocopiable page 'Shopping list' from the CD-ROM, which gives the cost of various items or alternatively access one of the supermarket online shopping websites. The children must work together to plan their menu and use their calculating skills to work out costs. Tell them that you need a detailed costing and evidence of their calculations. Tell them that they have to work democratically and that individuals may have to use their most persuasive language in order to get their choice of menu. Remind the children that they do not want to charge an excessive price for tickets but they must cover their costs.

Progress check: Ask questions such as: *How did you work out the total cost of the sausages? What calculation did you use to decide the ticket price? How are you deciding how much food to provide per person?*

Review

Find out which group has the most inventive menu and which the most reasonable ticket price. Ask questions such as: *Did you have to compromise in order to keep your costs down? How did you decide on your menu if individuals had strong views? What persuaded you to cut out that item?* Take a vote on the best suggestions.

Decimals and fractions

Expected prior learning

Children should be able to:

- recognise simple fractions of shapes such as a half and a quarter
- find simple fractions of an amount, making the link with division
- begin to know simple fraction and decimal equivalents.

Topic	Curriculum objectives	Expected outcomes
Fractions (including decimals and percentages)	**Lesson 1**	
	To read, write, order and compare numbers with up to three decimal places.	Use knowledge of place value and addition and subtraction of two-digit numbers to derive sums and differences and doubles and halves of decimals (for example, 6.5 ± 2.7, half of 5.6, double 0.34).
	Lesson 2	
	To recognise and use thousandths and relate them to tenths, hundredths and decimal equivalents. To read, write, order and compare numbers with up to three decimal places.	Relate fractions to their decimal representations, including thousandths. Explain what each digit represents in decimals with up to three places, and partition, round and order these numbers.
	Lesson 3	
	To recognise and use thousandths and relate them to tenths, hundredths and decimal equivalents. To read, write, order and compare numbers with up to three decimal places.	Relate fractions to their decimal representations, including thousandths. Explain what each digit represents in decimals with up to three places, and partition, round and order these numbers.
	Lesson 4	
	To read and write decimal numbers as fractions [for example, $0.71 = \frac{71}{100}$].	Relate fractions to their decimal representations, including thousandths.
	Lesson 5	
	To read and write decimal numbers as fractions [for example, $0.71 = \frac{71}{100}$]. To recognise and use thousandths and relate them to tenths, hundredths and decimal equivalents. To read, write, order and compare numbers with up to three decimal places.	Relate fractions to their decimal representations, including thousandths. Explain what each digit represents in decimals with up to three places, and partition, round and order these numbers.

Preparation

Lesson 2: copy 'Times and measures', one per child

Lesson 4: copy 'Dicing with decimals', one per child

Lesson 5: copy 'Sir Algernon's fortune', one per child

You will need

Photocopiable sheets

'Times and measures'; 'Dicing with decimals'; 'Sir Algernon's fortune'

Equipment

Dice; digital stopwatches

Further practice

Reinforce children's understanding of thousandths by giving them blank number lines and asking them to complete the numbers between two hundredths. Alternatively, mark two tenths at either end (for example, 0.5 and 0.6). Ask them first to mark in the hundredths and then estimate the position of selected thousandths (for example, 0.521, 0.585).

Oral and mental starters suggested for week 3

See bank of starters on page 250. Oral and mental starters are also on the CD-ROM.

71 What's the question?

72 Doubling and halving

74 On the line

Overview of progression

These lessons extend decimal experience to using thousandths with some reference to where these may be used in real life. There is practise in ordering, comparing and investigating these decimal fractions in a variety of contexts. By the end of the week children should be confidently estimating, converting, ordering and using thousandths.

> ### Watch out for
> Children find converting decimals such as 0.7 to 7/10 easy enough, but struggle to understand that 0.71 is written as 71/100. They may need some practical apparatus such as Base 10 apparatus or a blank 100 square to understand why.

Creative context

Thousandths have less obvious applications since they tend to be used in specialist fields. Precision timing and measuring are the most common. Encourage children to look out for examples in sport.

Vocabulary

add, approximate, decimal fraction, decimal place, decimal point, decimal, difference, divide, divisible by, divisor, double, estimate, **factor**, fraction, halve, **inverse**, minus, multiple, multiply, operation, plus, product, **quotient**, remainder, round, subtract, sum, total

Curriculum objectives

● To read, write, order and compare numbers with up to three decimal places.

Success criteria

● I can use my known whole-number doubles to double decimal numbers.

You will need

Equipment

Dice

Differentiation

Less confident learners

These children can use numbers with one or two decimal places.

More confident learners

These children could start with numbers with three decimal places and go on to numbers with four decimal places.

Lesson 1

Oral and mental starter 71

Main teaching activities

Whole-class work: Explain to the children that during this lesson they will be consolidating the link between whole numbers and decimals, making sure they understand what each digit represents. Write 35 + 37 on the board. Ask the children to suggest ways of calculating this. Hopefully someone will notice that these numbers are near doubles. Explain that we can use this fact to double and adjust: 35 + 35 = 70 so the answer is 70 + 2 = 72. Now apply this in a decimal number context using 0.35 + 0.37. The digits are the same as the previous calculation, but the place value is different: 0.35 + 0.35 = 0.70 so answer is 0.70 + 0.02 = 0.72. It is important to understand the value of each digit to avoid errors. Ask the children to identify the value of each digit in a decimal number with three decimal places, such as 0.801. Demonstrate some other near decimal doubles with two or three decimal places, including some such as 0.801 + 0.803 = 1.604, where doubling a digit results in a two-digit number.

Paired work: Ask the children to generate a number with two decimal places and then write another number to make a near-double calculation. Repeat for several numbers with two decimal places and then with number with three decimal places. Ask them to record their findings using informal jottings.

Progress check: Ask: *What is the value of this digit in this number? When might we use hundredths or thousandths? What number fact are you using to double? Which is the tricky part?*

Review

Write some numbers with two decimal places, such as 0.65, 0.27, 0.33, 0.38, 0.29, 0.17, 0.32, 0.35 on the board. Ask: *Can all these numbers be doubled easily? Which ones are more difficult? Which ones do you know straight away? Why do some numbers greater than 0.5 start to cause difficulty when we are doubling? How could doubling help me to solve this problem: 0.24 × 4?* Ask the children to use repeated doubling to multiply other numbers with two decimal places by four.

Curriculum objectives
● To recognise and use thousandths and relate them to tenths, hundredths and decimal equivalents.
● To read, write, order and compare numbers with up to three decimal places.

Success criteria
● I can order decimal numbers including thousandths.

You will need

Photocopiable sheets
'Times and measures'

Equipment
Blank cards for ordering

Differentiation

Less confident learners

Provide cards so that the children can write the numbers on them and physically move them as they order the numbers.

More confident learners

These children could go on to research the current downhill skiing World records or find out about other sports that rely on split-second timings.

Lesson 2

Main teaching activities

Whole-class work: Distribute photocopiable page 'Times and measures' from the CD-ROM. Explain that some sports and activities rely on split-second timings since the times are so close. Split-second timing involves splitting the seconds into tenths, hundredths and even thousandths of a second. Write 1:45:73 on the board. Explain that a digital stopwatch will time whole minutes and seconds and fractions of a second. Say that this time is 1 minute, 45 seconds and 73 hundredths of a second. Ask the children to identify the value of each digit and then to suggest a time that is 10 seconds faster, 10 seconds slower. Then ask for one which is one thousandth of a second slower. Likewise, precision engineers might measure lengths in hundredths and thousandths of a millimetre.

Independent work: Ask the children to order the times and measures on the photocopiable sheet.

Progress check: Ask: *What is the value of this digit? Which digit are you looking at to decide how to order these numbers? Tell me a rule for helping you to order decimals with a mixture of one, two and three decimal places. How much bigger is this number compared to the previous one?*

Review

Write 3.288 and 3.29 on the board and ask the children to tell you which is the larger number and to explain why. Add a place-holding zero so that both numbers have the same number of decimal places. Explain that errors are easily made by disregarding the value of the digits after the decimal point. Challenge the children to calculate the differences between the largest and smallest numbers in each set.

Curriculum objectives
● To recognise and use thousandths and relate them to tenths, hundredths and decimal equivalents.
● To read, write, order and compare numbers with up to three decimal places.

Success criteria
● I can measure time durations in fractions of a second, compare these and use them to answer questions.

You will need
Equipment
Digital stopwatches

Differentiation
The children should work in mixed-ability groups to encourage discussion and build confidence.

Lesson 3 — Oral and mental starter 72

Main teaching activities

Paired and group work: Give each pair or group a digital stopwatch. Explain how times are measured and displayed, for example, a display showing 4:25:13 means 4 minutes, 25 seconds and 13 hundredths of a second. Explain that they are to use precision timing to find the answer to some practical questions. Questions they could investigate include: Does everyone blink with the same frequency? How long can each person in the group hold their breath? Do they get better with practise? Who in the group can estimate the closest to exactly 1 minute? Explain that they should choose one of the questions or suggest one of their own that they can test. Remind them that scientists and mathematicians would expect to repeat tests at least three times in order to ensure accuracy. They should use the stopwatches to measure times accurately and record their results in a table.

Progress check: Ask questions such as: *What does this time mean? How will these results help you to answer the question? How are you calculating a difference? What might affect the accuracy of your results?*

Review

Ask the groups to report back with the answer to their question, explaining what they did and discussing how accurate their results might be.

Curriculum objectives

● To read and write decimal numbers as fractions [for example, 0.71 = $^{71}/_{100}$].

Success criteria

● I can convert decimal to fractions and vice versa.

You will need

Photocopiable sheets

'Dicing with decimals'

Equipment

Dice; large counters; small counters or coloured pencils, at least two different colours

Differentiation

The children should work in mixed ability groups to encourage discussion and build confidence.

Lesson 4 — Oral and mental starter 74

Main teaching activities

Paired work: Explain to the children that they are going to play a game to practise their skills in converting between fractions and decimals, including thousandths. Ask the children to tell you how they would write 0.643 as a fraction. ($^{643}/_{1000}$) Ask how would they write $^{28}/_{1000}$ as a decimal (0.28).

Distribute photocopiable page 'Dicing with decimals' from the CD-ROM. The children take turns to roll a dice and move their large counter round the track. When they land on a square, they must give the decimal or fraction equivalent. If correct, they cover it with one of their small counters (or shade it with a coloured pencil). If they land on a square already covered, they stay where they are until their next go. The game continues until all the squares are covered or coloured. The winner is the player with the most squares covered or coloured.

Progress check: Ask: *Which fractions have you found the most difficult? Why would you write 0.16 as $^{16}/_{100}$ but 0.161 as $^{161}/_{1000}$?*

Review

Check the accuracy of the conversions by going through the answers altogether.

Curriculum objectives

● To read and write decimal numbers as fractions [for example, 0.71 = $^{71}/_{100}$].
● To recognise and use thousandths and relate them to tenths, hundredths and decimal equivalents.
● To read, write, order and compare numbers with up to three decimal places.

Success criteria

● I can solve problems involving fractions and decimals.

You will need

Photocopiable sheets

'Sir Algernon's fortune'

Differentiation

Less confident learners

An adult may need to support the children to solve this problem.

More confident learners

Once they have understood the principle of this sort of problem these children could attempt to make up one of their own.

Lesson 5 — Oral and mental starter 74

Main teaching activities

Paired work: Explain to the children that they are now going to solve a problem involving decimal numbers and fractions. They will have to work logically and methodically, remembering the relationship between multiplication and division. Distribute photocopiable page 'Sir Algernon's fortune' from the CD-ROM and ask the children to solve the problem.

Progress check: Ask: *How are you going to begin to solve this problem? What do you have to remember about the relationship between division and multiplication? Are you starting with the information at the bottom or the top? If you are finding it tricky try writing the information on the diagram. What is the equivalent fraction? Have you remembered that he actually gave half of his original fortune away, not all of it?*

Review

Ask the children to give you their answers. If there is a difference of opinion? Write some of the alternative answers on the board. Ask the children to describe how they solved the problem. They should have started from the bottom and worked up only using thirds each time. How would they be able to check their answer? (By working through from their answers to see if they reach £0.2 million.) Test some of the answers to find the correct one. (Sir Algernon started with £10.8 million.)

Problems involving percentages

Expected prior learning

Children should be able to:

- recognise the links between fractions, decimals and percentages
- understand percentage as an equivalent fraction 'out of 100'.

Topic	Curriculum objectives	Expected outcomes
Fractions (including decimals and percentages)	**Lesson 1**	
	To recognise the per cent symbol (%) and understand that per cent relates to 'number of parts per hundred', and write percentages as a fraction with denominator 100, and as a decimal.	Understand percentage as the number of parts in every 100 and relate this to fractions and decimals.
	Lesson 2	
	To recognise the per cent symbol (%) and understand that per cent relates to 'number of parts per hundred', and write percentages as a fraction with denominator 100, and as a decimal. To solve problems which require knowing percentage and decimal equivalents of ½, ¼, ⅕, ⅖, ⅘ and those fractions with a denominator of a multiple of 10 or 25.	Understand percentage as the number of parts in every 100 and relate this to fractions and decimals.
	Lesson 3	
	To solve problems which require knowing percentage and decimal equivalents of ½, ¼, ⅕, ⅖, ⅘ and those fractions with a denominator of a multiple of 10 or 25.	Find percentages of amounts by using fractions and division knowledge.
	Lesson 4	
	To solve problems which require knowing percentage and decimal equivalents of ½, ¼, ⅕, ⅖, ⅘ and those fractions with a denominator of a multiple of 10 or 25.	Find percentages of amounts by using fractions and division knowledge.
	Lesson 5	
	To solve problems which require knowing percentage and decimal equivalents of ½, ¼, ⅕, ⅖, ⅘ and those fractions with a denominator of a multiple of 10 or 25.	Find percentages of amounts by using fractions and division knowledge.

Preparation

Lesson 1: make copies of 'Blank 100 square', several per child

Lesson 2: copy 'Fractions, decimals and percentages' onto card, one set per pair

Lesson 3: write some simple percentage questions on the board using only percentages in multiples of 10% and 25%

Lesson 4: copy 'What's the percentage?', one per child

Lesson 5: copy 'Sally's Sports', one per child

You will need

Photocopiable sheets

'What's the percentage?'; 'What's the percentage? template'; 'Sally's Sports'; 'Sally's Sports template'

General resources

'Blank 100 square'; 'Fractions, decimals and percentages'

Equipment

Coloured pencils; squared paper

Further practice

Interactive activity 'Percentage points' gives further practice of recognising simple equivalence between percentages and fractions.

Oral and mental starters suggested for week 4

See bank of starters on pages 249 to 250. Oral and mental starters are also on the CD-ROM.

67 Thirty days ...

70 A fraction or a percentage?

75 It's a matter of scale

Overview of progression

This week begins with some consolidation and practice of the links between fractions, decimals and percentages and their application and requires the children to interchange between them all in order to calculate percentages of amounts to solve problems.

Watch out for

Some children may find the multi-step nature of this work difficult and may need support to work methodically and to understand the links between fractions, decimals and percentages. They should be reminded about the link between fractions and percentages, for example 50% = ½ and 75% = ¾ and the way in which they should use the fraction equivalent to calculate the percentage increase or decrease.

Creative context

Percentages are much in evidence in everyday life. For example, sale prices advertised in shops such as '20% off £30' or to illustrate amounts of improvement such as '25% more people ate apples last year'. Encourage the children to interpret the meaning of the percentages they observe.

Vocabulary

cancel, decimal fraction, decimal place, decimal point, decimal, **denominator**, equivalent, fraction, **improper fraction**, mixed number, **numerator**, **per cent (%)**, **percentage**, proper fraction, unit fraction

Curriculum objectives

● To recognise the per cent symbol (%) and understand that per cent relates to 'number of parts per hundred', and write percentages as a fraction with denominator 100, and as a decimal.

Success criteria

● I can represent fractions and percentages visually and understand their relationship.

You will need

General resources

'Blank 100 square'

Equipment

Coloured pencils; squared paper

Differentiation

Less confident learners

These children may need to revise the concept with an adult.

More confident learners

These children might be able to go on and use blocks of squares of different sizes and still see the fraction/percentage relationship. For example, colouring 2 out of 4 squares = ½ = 50%.

Lesson 1   Oral and mental starter 75

Main teaching activities

Whole-class work: Remind the children of the relationship between percentages and fractions. For example, 10% is the same as ¹⁄₁₀. Ask for a volunteer to explain why this is the case. (¹⁄₁₀ =¹⁰⁄₁₀₀, percentages are numbers 'out of 100') Remind them that 100% describes a whole or the entire amount. Explain that if a person eats 100% of a chocolate bar, they eat all of it. If they eat 10% they eat ¹⁄₁₀ of it. Numerically, if the chocolate bar is made up of 20 squares, ¹⁄₁₀ will be 2 squares. Repeat with different percentages which are known equivalents, for example ½ = 50%, ¼ = 25%, ¾ = 75%, ⅕ = 20%, and so on.

Paired work: Provide each child with a number of copies of photocopiable page 'Blank 100 square' and explain that they are going to practise their knowledge of equivalent fractions and percentages. Ask them to colour a number of the squares and then express the shaded area as both a fraction and a percentage, to be verified by their partner.

Progress check: *Ask: How you express the number of squares that you have coloured as a fraction of the whole square. How does this relate to percentages? What does per cent mean? Why do we not say ⁵⁰⁄₁₀₀? Would that be incorrect? How is ¼ expressed as a percentage?*

Review

Ensure understanding of the relationship between finding a fraction and turning it into a percentage. *What is the equivalent percentage of ½? Can you show how you convert 50% to a fraction? (⁵⁰⁄₁₀₀ = ½) How would I find ⅓ of a number? Why is this more difficult? If I coloured 23 squares on my 100 square, what fraction would that be? Why can't I make the denominator any smaller?*

Curriculum objectives
- As lesson 1.
- To solve problems which require knowing percentage and decimal equivalents and fractions with a denominator of a multiple of 10 or 25.

Success criteria
- I can match fraction, decimal and percentage equivalents and explain their relationship.

You will need
General resources
'Fractions, decimals and percentages'

Differentiation
Less confident learners
Let them rehearse finding the trios face up first before shuffling.

More confident learners
These children should explain why the three cards are equivalent.

Lesson 2 — Oral and mental starter 67

Main teaching activities
Paired work: Explain to the children that just as they know fraction equivalents of percentages, they can also apply their knowledge of decimal equivalents to convert between percentages and decimals, for example, 0.25 is the same as $\frac{25}{100}$ or 25%.

Use a set of 'Fractions, decimals and percentages' cards from the CD-ROM to play the matching game 'Trios' finding all three equivalents.

Progress check: Ask questions such as: *How do you know that $\frac{3}{4}$ is equivalent to 75%. What do you have to do to $\frac{3}{4}$ to prove this? What about $\frac{2}{5}$? What is the percentage equivalent of 0.01? How do you know?*

Review
Check the trios and discuss how some fractions might need multiplying to make them 'out of 100' thereby adding an extra step to the process, for example, $\frac{3}{5}$ has to be multiplied by 20 in order to give $\frac{60}{100}$.

Explain to the children that knowing these equivalents means we can find percentages of amounts. We do this by replacing the percentage with its fraction equivalent and then finding the fraction of the amount using division. Ask: *What is half of 60?* Most children should be able to answer '30'. Now ask: *What is 50% of 60?* Repeat this with other fraction/percentage equivalents.

Curriculum objectives
- To solve problems which require knowing percentage and decimal equivalents of $\frac{1}{2}$, $\frac{1}{4}$, $\frac{1}{5}$, $\frac{2}{5}$, $\frac{4}{5}$ and those fractions with a denominator of a multiple of 10 or 25.

Success criteria
- I can find percentages of amounts using simple fraction equivalents.

Differentiation
Less confident learners
Children may need adult support making explicit the links between percentages, decimals, fractions and finally division. They should refer back to the 100 squares that they coloured earlier in the week. Ask simple fraction questions such as: *How would you find $\frac{1}{4}$ of 8?*

More confident learners
The children should work with more challenging numbers and giving decimal answers.

Lesson 3 — Oral and mental starter 67

Main teaching activities
Whole-class work: Explain to the children that to find some percentages of amounts it is simply a matter of remembering the fraction equivalent, for example, 50% = $\frac{1}{2}$. To find $\frac{1}{2}$ of an amount, they know to divide by 2. Ask some simple percentage questions such as 50% of 90 and 25% of 16, ensuring that the children can explain the fraction/ percentage relationships. Then ask: *Can we find any percentage, from 1% to 100%, using fractions? What about 20% or 75%?* Discuss what fraction/percentage equivalents the children know. They can find 20% of an amount if they remember that 20% = $\frac{20}{100}$ = $\frac{2}{10}$ = 0.2 = $\frac{1}{5}$, so they can divide the number by five. (Note: not all children will need to make all of these steps. Some will recognise $\frac{20}{100}$ as $\frac{1}{5}$ straightaway. Others may need more options to choose from.) They can find 75% of an amount if they know that 75% = $\frac{3}{4}$; they work it out by finding $\frac{1}{4}$ of the amount and then multiplying the result by three. Alternatively, they can find 50% and 25% and add the results.

Independent work: Ask the children to find percentages of numbers and amounts of money using even amounts and percentages in multiples of 10, and 25%.

Progress check: Ask questions such as: *What is 10% of 50. What about 10% of 15? Describe how you divided by 10. How would you use this to find 40%? What is the fraction equivalent of 40% that might help you? Can this be simplified further?* ($\frac{40}{100}$ = $\frac{4}{10}$ = $\frac{2}{5}$).

Review
Ensure that the children are clear about the simple percentage and fraction equivalents. Make a list on the board of the ones that they are confident about, for example, 10% = $\frac{1}{10}$, 50% = $\frac{1}{2}$, and so on.

Curriculum objectives

● To solve problems which require knowing percentage and decimal equivalents of ½, ¼, ⅓, ⅔, ⅕ and those fractions with a denominator of a multiple of 10 or 25.

Success criteria

● I can find more complex percentages by using my known facts and calculating.

You will need

Photocopiable sheets

'What's the percentage?'; 'What's the percentage? template'

Differentiation

Less confident learners

Ask a more confident 'talk partner' to explain the calculations required. Alternatively, adapt the 'What's the percentage? template' with percentages that are mostly multiples of ten.

More confident learners

Adapt the 'What's the percentage? template' to reflect more complex numbers and percentages. Use the context of money if appropriate.

Lesson 4   Oral and mental starter 67

Main teaching activities

Whole-class work: Explain to the children that to find some percentages, we need to use two or more stages. For example, to find 5% we could find 10% and then halve it.

For example: Find 5% of 60.

                10% of 60 = 6

So   5% of 60 = 6 ÷ 2 = 3

Ask the children if they can suggest any alternative methods to find 5% (for example find 1% then multiply by five or find 50% and then divide by 10).

Ask the children to suggest ways of finding 15%, 75%, 30%, 90%, and so on. Demonstrate some examples on the board.

Independent work: Distribute photocopiable page 'What's the percentage?' from the CD-ROM. Ask the children to calculate the percentages, showing how they found them by setting their work out in the way as you have modelled on the board.

Progress check: Ask questions such as: *How did you find 15%? Is there an alternative method? What might influence your decision? What about 58% or 99%? What are the basic 'building blocks' that you need to know to find any percentage?*

Review

Ask: *How would you find 35% of 70?* Demonstrate a method:

1. Find 10% of 70:   70 ÷ 10 = 7
2. Find 30% by multiplying 10% by 3:   7 × 3 = 21
3. Find 5% by dividing 10% by 2:   7 ÷ 2 = 3.5
4. Find 35% by add 30% and 5%:   21 + 3.5 = 24.5

Ask similar questions, encouraging the children to explain their answers:

- *How would you find 12% of 96?*
- *How would you calculate 5% of 150?*
- *If a pair of trainers costing £55 has been reduced in price by 8%, how would you calculate the new price? Can anyone suggest a different method?*
- *How could I quickly calculate 95% of 300?*

Curriculum objectives

● To solve problems which require knowing percentage and decimal equivalents of ½, ¼, ⅕, ⅖, ⅘ and those fractions with a denominator of a multiple of 10 or 25.

Success criteria

● I can solve problems that involve percentages.

You will need

Photocopiable sheets

'Sally's Sports'; 'Sally's Sports template'

Differentiation

Less confident learners

Ask a more confident 'talk partner' to explain the calculations required. Alternatively, adapt the 'Sally's Sports template' with percentages that are mostly multiples of ten.

More confident learners

Adapt the 'Sally's Sports template' to reflect more complex prices.

Lesson 5

Oral and mental starter 70

Main teaching activities

Whole-class work: Remind the children that shops often use percentages when they advertise price reductions in sales. Distribute photocopiable page 'Sally's Sports' from the CD-ROM. Explain that the prices in a sports shop have been reduced by the percentages shown. The children have to find the sale price for each item. Work through one example. Remind the children that to find the sale price, they have to subtract the discount from the original price.

Independent work: Ask the children to work out the sale prices of the items on the photocopiable page.

Progress check: Ask: *What is meant by 25% off a price? How would you calculate this? What do you think is the most common error made when solving this type of problem? How many steps have you taken to arrive at this answer?*

Review

Ask: *Can anyone suggest some different ways I might calculate 70% of a number?* Methods for finding 70% might include: find 10% and multiply by 7; find 50% and 20% and add them; find 50%, add 10%, then add another 10%; find 75% and subtract 5%. Repeat with 35% and 12%.

Play 'Percentage consequences'. Ask each child to write a number smaller than 100 on a whiteboard. Now write on the board a series of percentage additions or subtractions for them to apply to their number and then each successive new number, for example: Add 10%. Add 25%. Add 60%. Take off 5%. Add 100% (and so on). After each new percentage has been added or taken away, they should pass their board to the next child, who continues, applying the next percentage to the new number. The first player to pass 500 holds up their board for the class to check.

■ SCHOLASTIC

Perimeter, area and scale drawing

Expected prior learning

Children should be able to:

- recognise the formula area = length × breadth for finding the area of a rectangle or square
- understand perimeter as a linear measure around the edge of a shape
- know that area is measured in square units such as centimetres squared or metres squared.

Topic	Curriculum objectives	Expected outcomes
Measurement	**Lesson 1**	
	To measure and calculate the perimeter of composite rectilinear shapes in centimetres and metres.	Measure and calculate the perimeter of regular and irregular polygons including the perimeter of composite shapes.
	To calculate and compare the area of rectangles (including squares), and including using standard units, square centimetres (cm²) and square metres (m²) and estimate the area of irregular shapes.	Use the formula for area of a rectangle to calculate the rectangle's area, using standard units of measure.
	Lesson 2	
	To measure and calculate the perimeter of composite rectilinear shapes in centimetres and metres.	Measure and calculate the perimeter of regular and irregular polygons including the perimeter of composite shapes.
	To calculate and compare the area of rectangles (including squares), and including using standard units, square centimetres (cm²) and square metres (m²) and estimate the area of irregular shapes.	Use the formula for area of a rectangle to calculate the rectangle's area, using standard units of measure.
	Lesson 3	
	To solve problems involving multiplication and division, including scaling by simple fractions and problems involving simple rates.	Understand scale.
	Lesson 4	
	To solve problems involving multiplication and division, including scaling by simple fractions and problems involving simple rates.	Understand scale and use this to draw shapes to scale.
	Lesson 5	
	To solve problems involving multiplication and division, including scaling by simple fractions and problems involving simple rates.	Understand scale and use this to draw shapes to scale.

Preparation

Lesson 2: write the problem on the board; assemble measuring equipment: rulers, metre rules and tape measures

Lesson 3: assemble measuring equipment: rulers, metre rules and tape measures; organise access to the playground and assemble washing line or rope in case of inclement weather

You will need

General resources

'Blank grid paper'

Equipment

Measuring equipment: rulers, metre rules and tape measures; centimetre-squared paper; chalk (or washing line or rope if weather is inclement)

Further practice

Set the interactive activity 'Perimeter and area' to check children's understanding.

Oral and mental starters suggested for week 5

See bank of starters on pages 249 to 250. Oral and mental starters are also on the CD-ROM.

65 Area calculator

66 Reversing area

72 Doubling and halving

Overview of progression

During this week the children recap on their understanding of area and perimeter and then go on to explore drawing shapes to scale and understanding how a scale can be used to represent much bigger or smaller things on paper.

Watch out for

Some children may still confuse area and perimeter and their units of measure. Also the concept of scale can be difficult, particularly multiplying by a fraction which makes an object or shape smaller. For example, 1cm = ½cm means a square with sides of 1cm will actually become smaller.

Creative context

You could expand the island theme to further studies of maps and scales and islands all over the world. Also the activities in Lessons 4 and 5 could be further expanded to include coordinates to pinpoint landmarks. There is also scope here for some creative writing links.

Vocabulary

area, perimeter, scale, scale factor

■ SCHOLASTIC

Curriculum objectives

• To measure and calculate the perimeter of composite rectilinear shapes in centimetres and metres.
• To calculate and compare the area of rectangles (including squares), and including using standard units, square centimetres (cm²) and square metres (m²).

Success criteria

• I can demonstrate an understanding of questions relating to area and perimeter.

Differentiation

Less confident learners

These children may need adult support to work through these questions.

More confident learners

Ask these children to suggest two-step questions. For example, if the answer is 4.2m², the question could be: 'If one of the sides of a rectangle is 0.7m and the other is 600cm, convert them to a common unit and find the area.

Lesson 1   Oral and mental starter 66

Main teaching activities

Whole-class work: Remind the children that area is a two dimensional measure. Ask the children to tell you how to find the area of a rectangle. (Use the formula, area = length × breadth.) Draw a rectangle and label its area as 28m². Ask: *What lengths might the sides be? Is there more than one possible answer? Why?* List all the possible answers. Ask the children to think about the area of the classroom floor, their living room and bathroom floors, and the playground. Ask: *What units would it be measured in? How would you measure it?* Ask the children to estimate each area.

Now ask: *If the answer is 24cm², what could the question be?* Take suggestions (such as 'What is the area of a rectangle with sides measuring 2cm and 12cm?') and record some on the board. Repeat with some perimeter questions such as: *The answer is 25cm, what could the question be?* (such as 'A regular pentagon has sides of 5cm. What is its total perimeter?)

Paired work: The children work in pairs to generate another four answers each, then swap and write three possible questions to match each answer.

Progress check: Ask: *What is the unit of measure for area? How is this different from measuring perimeter? Can you think of a question which would give the same number for the perimeter and the area? How would you calculate the perimeter of an irregular shape?*

Review

Write on the board: 64.2cm × 5. Ask the children to imagine that they work in a DIY store and this is a problem they need to solve. Ask them to note down a possible scenario that requires this calculation. Share some ideas and record them for a display. Ask: *Is there another way this answer could have been reached? Could you change your question to make a two-step problem?* For example: 'I am making five bookshelves for my bedroom. Each shelf has to be 64.2cm long to fit into an alcove. How much wood will I need to buy? If wood costs £5 a metre, how much will I need to spend?'

Curriculum objectives

● To measure and calculate the perimeter of composite rectilinear shapes.
● To calculate and compare the area of rectangles (including squares), and including using standard units, square, cm² and m².

Success criteria

● I can measure objects and draw them using a simple scale.
● I can calculate the area of composite shapes.

You will need

General resources
'Blank grid paper'

Equipment
Measuring equipment: rulers, metre rules and tape measures; centimetre-squared paper

Differentiation

Less confident learners
Provide shapes which have measurements in whole centimetres.

More confident learners
Ask these children to draw and measure composite shapes.

Lesson 2

Oral and mental starter 65

Main teaching activities

Whole-class work: Write the following problem on the board:

> A farmer has a field 6m long and 9m wide. What is its total area?
> He then buys a smaller square field adjoining the first one, with a side length of 4m. What is the total area of the farmer's land?

Display 'Blank grid paper' and ask a child to visualise and draw the two adjoining fields (with a shared boundary line) and to label the sides of each field. Drawings should be to scale with the scale marked clearly as a key (for example, 1cm = 1m). Remind the children that the length × breadth formula only works for squares and rectangles, so the field's areas need to be calculated separately and then added together. What could the perimeter be? Remind them that the line where the fields join is not part of the perimeter.

Paired work: Ask the children to work in pairs to measure the dimensions and calculate the perimeter and area of some classroom objects, both rectangles and composite shapes made up from squares and rectangles, such as exercise books, the floor, the corridor, two tables together making an 'L' shape, and so on. Ask them to draw the shapes on squared paper to scale, mark the measurements and write the calculations they used to find the perimeter and the area next to each shape.

Progress check: Ask: *How did you work out the area? What units do we use for area? What units do we use for perimeter? What scale have you used to draw the object in your book? What dimensions does your drawing have if the original lengths were 3.4m and 2.7m?*

Review

Recap on the children's understanding of area. Ask: *How can I find the area of a rectangle? What is the formula or rule that we use?* Now draw a shape consisting of a joined square and rectangle and label with the dimensions given below. Ask: *How can we find the area of this shape? Why can it not be solved using one calculation?*

6m × 9m	= 54m²
4m × 4m	= 16m²
Total area	= 70m²

Curriculum objectives

● To solve problems involving multiplication and division, including scaling by simple fractions.

Success criteria

● I can use scale to draw larger items accurately on paper.

You will need

Equipment
As per lesson 2, plus chalk (or washing line or rope if weather is inclement)

Differentiation

Less confident learners
Provide adult support to draw and measure accurately.

More confident learners
Children could attempt scale drawings of irregular shapes.

Lesson 3

Oral and mental starter 66

Main teaching activities

Whole-class work: Explain the concept of scale drawing by explaining that to fit things such as houses, roads, towns and cities onto plans and maps, a measurement on the page represents a larger equivalent on the ground and vice versa. Now explain that we can use different scales. Ask: *If every 1cm on my page represents 5m in real life, what would the line look like now?* Repeat with other scales. Ask the children to draw a plan of a flower bed on their page. It can be any shape as long as it is drawn using only straight lines following the lines of the squares on the paper (with no diagonals). Ask them to measure and mark the length of each line of the perimeter of their flowerbed. Then, weather permitting, go outside and draw it to the scale of 1cm = 1m or 1cm = 50cm, with chalk on the playground. (In inclement weather you can demonstrate this inside using washing line or rope.)

Progress check: As the children draw, ask questions about the scale such as: *What is the scale you are using? If something is twice as big, what are you multiplying by? Is this the size of flowerbed that you imagined?*

Review

Draw an 'H' shape, 10cm tall, on the board. Ask the children to outline the steps they would take to draw it again either five times bigger or half the size. Discuss where scales are most often seen (maps and technical drawings).

Curriculum objectives

● To solve problems involving multiplication and division, including scaling by simple fractions and problems involving simple rates.

Success criteria

● I can draw a diagram to scale.

You will need

Equipment

Centimetre-squared paper; rulers

Differentiation

Less confident learners

These children should work in a supported group in order to check measuring accuracy.

More confident learners

These children could draw the island using a more challenging scale such as 1km = 2.5cm.

Lesson 4 — Oral and mental starter 66

Main teaching activities

Whole-class work: Explain to the children that you are going to describe an island and they are to draw it to scale on the paper. Revise directions: North, South, East and West and draw the compass points on the board. Explain that land features are rarely drawn with straight lines and so the dimensions are given describing the longest or widest part of the island.

Independent work: Ask the children to draw their island to the scale 1km = 2cm, unless you suggest a different one. Indicate the measurements and instructions written on the board, as below:

- 10km wide by 6.5km long.
- There is a lighthouse 1km to the North of the island.
- Along the south coast there is a beach which is 1.5km long.
- 2.5km north of the beach is a hotel set in 1km square grounds.
- 3.5km to the west of the hotel is a 500m circular pond.

Once completed the children should swap diagrams with a partner to check accuracy. Remind them that the islands may not look exactly the same since the positions of the details are not exact, although the measurements should be.

Progress check: Ask: *How long is the beach on your diagram? How long is the pond? How did you decide on this measurement? Tell me how wide a field measuring 1.5cm on your diagram would be in real life? What is the approximate area of the island?*

Review

Draw a version of the island on the board. Ask for the children to talk to a partner to make up an instruction for you to follow and add to your diagram. Ask them to explain how you should place it correctly. What other information do they need to give?

Curriculum objectives

● To solve problems involving multiplication and division, including scaling by simple fractions and problems involving simple rates.

Success criteria

● I can draw a diagram to scale.

You will need

Equipment

Centimetre-squared paper; rulers

Differentiation

Less confident learners

These children should continue to work on the island started in the previous lesson, adding further landmarks and writing their dimensions and position.

More confident learners

Expect more detail and use of a more challenging scale.

Lesson 5 — Oral and mental starter 72

Main teaching activities

Independent and paired work: Ask the children to devise their own island and write appropriate instructions for a partner to follow to produce a scale drawing. They should draw a scale drawing of their own island and then swap the instructions with a partner. They draw their partner's island following the instructions. They can then compare the interpretations and check the scale measurements. Ensure that everyone includes the scale on their drawings.

Progress check: Ask: *How are you describing the position of each land mark? What is the approximate area and perimeter of your island? Why can we not be precise about these? What scale are you using? Have you checked that it will fit on the page?*

Review

Make a class display of the islands with an explanation of how to use scale for future reference.

Using tables and line graphs

Expected prior learning

Children should be able to:

- know the difference between the data recorded on line graphs and bar charts
- construct bar charts and line graphs.

Topic	Curriculum objectives	Expected outcomes
Statistics	**Lesson 1**	
	To complete, read and interpret information in tables, including timetables.	Using knowledge from previous weeks, plan and present a significant extended piece of research with persuasive evidence for an issue relevant to school.
	Lesson 2	
	To complete, read and interpret information in tables, including timetables.	Using knowledge from previous weeks, plan and present a significant extended piece of research with persuasive evidence for an issue relevant to school.
	Lesson 3	
	To complete, read and interpret information in tables, including timetables.	Plan a presentation relevant to end of school year and present evidence in a variety of different ways and assess how data can look very different depending on the graph or chart used and the choice of scale.
	Lesson 4	
	To solve comparison, sum and difference problems using information presented in a line graph. To complete, read and interpret information in tables, including timetables.	Plan a presentation relevant to end of school year and present evidence in a variety of different ways and assess how data can look very different depending on the graph or chart used and the choice of scale.
	Lesson 5	
	To solve comparison, sum and difference problems using information presented in a line graph. To complete, read and interpret information in tables, including timetables.	Plan a presentation relevant to end of school year and present evidence in a variety of different ways and assess how data can look very different depending on the graph or chart used and the choice of scale.

Preparation

Lesson 1: prepare examples of a bar chart, comparative bar chart and a line graph; interactive teaching resource 'Graphing tool' can be used for recording and displaying data in bar chart or line graph format; copy 'Every picture tells a story', one per child

Lesson 2: set aside time and assemble appropriate equipment for any measuring or timing of sports activities, either in the lesson or before it

Lesson 3: organise access to computers with graphing software for example Number box or Microsoft Excel®

Lesson 4: organise access to computers with graphing software for example Number box or Microsoft Excel®

You will need

Photocopiable sheets
'Every picture tells a story'

General resources
Interactive teaching resource 'Graphing tool'

Equipment
Various measuring equipment, depending on the children's investigations, for example, stopwatches, measuring tapes, trundle wheels, pedometers, sports heart rate monitors (if available), plus appropriate sports equipment; computers with graphing software, for example Number box or Microsoft Excel® or squared paper

Further practice

Give children plenty of practical experience in comparing data in different table formats.

Oral and mental starters suggested for week 6

See bank of starters on pages 249 to 250. Oral and mental starters are also on the CD-ROM.

64 Place value elimination game

69 Speedy times

73 Four operations

Overview of progression

This week children need to make enquiries for themselves in a real-life context, to research some data and to present it in a graphical form for the use by others. The suggestion is that they base their data collection around summer sports activities, and they may already have begun to track their own performance information or conversely they will have to plan some activities where they collect data appropriate for presenting in three different ways. This is obviously a more meaningful activity if the results are presented to the relevant people in school.

Watch out for

Some groups may find making independent decisions about what sort of data to collect difficult and need more guidance. Also be aware of the children's time management. The emphasis for the majority of the week should be on presenting their data in graphical form, not spending all week collecting sporting performance data.

Creative context

There is a clear link here between PE and an extension to the maths may be to find out about sporting records and Olympic achievements of international athletes.

Vocabulary

axes, bar chart, bar line chart, chart, comparative data, data, graph, horizontal axis, information, label, line graph, maximum/minimum value, **scale**, table, title, vertical axis

Curriculum objectives
● To complete, read and interpret information in tables, including timetables.

Success criteria
● I can plan investigations to collect data that can be represented using different types of graph.
● I can collect and record appropriate data for presentation in different types of graph.

You will need
Photocopiable sheets
'Every picture tells a story'
Equipment
Prepared graphs

Differentiation
Less confident learners
These children should work in a small group supported by an adult to plan and collect the data.

More confident learners
These children should work together to plan their investigations, making independent group decisions and being able to rationalise and explain their thinking.

Lesson 1 — Oral and mental starter 73

Main teaching activities

Whole-class work: Show the children your prepared graphs and ask them to revise the different type of graphs that they know and to recall their appropriate use and any information that they can tell you about them. Record their ideas on the board or a large sheet of paper and save it for display throughout the week.

Bar chart: To show amounts or performance of different people or events. Scale can be altered going up in ones, twos or more depending on the size of the sample. Bars or blocks are independent of one another and can be compared. Bar lines (vertical lines) can also be used. They can be orientated either vertically or horizontally, one axis labelled as object, activity or person and other axis showing the amount or value.

Comparative bar charts: Similar to above but for each activity there could be more than one group represented, for example boys' and girls' attendance at a club over a five-day period.

Line graph: Used for representing continuous data over a period of time. Points are marked at time intervals and joined by a line, anywhere along the line has a value. More than one line can be placed on the same axis for comparison, for example temperature in different places over a 24-hour period or heart rates of different people when exercising.

Organise the children into groups of four to six. Explain that they are to plan some sports activities which will result in data that can be represented by one of each of the graphs you have been discussing. They may already have some recorded sports data from their PE work. If not they must plan activities and collect the data, recording it in a table for their group. Suggestions might be:

Bar chart: collect long jump attempts of the group.

Comparative bar chart: Each member of the group to throw a ball three times and measure each throw to represent on a graph.

Line graph: Heartbeat before, during and after exercise over a five-minute period or during a ten-minute walking race, how far was covered by each person at two-minute intervals.

Group work: The children must plan what activities they are going to do and what data they are going to measure, make a list of the equipment they are going to need, devise recording tables for each and be able to explain what sort of graph they will use to represent the information.

Progress check: Ask: *Which graph is most appropriate to represent this information? Why? What are the alternatives? How will your table help you to represent this information when you come to draw your graph? How are you going to ensure that your measurements are as accurate as possible? What measuring equipment will you use? Is that the most accurate/helpful?*

Review

Display your sample graphs without labels or titles (or display photocopiable page 254 'Every picture tells a story'). Ask the children to suggest the sort of information that they would represent on these graphs, what the titles would be and what the labels for each axis would be.

Curriculum objectives

- To complete, read and interpret information in tables, including timetables.

Success criteria

- I can plan investigations to collect data that can be represented using different types of graph.
- I can collect and record appropriate data for presentation in different types of graph.

You will need

General resources

Interactive teaching resource 'Graphing tool'

Equipment

Measuring equipment, depending on investigations

Differentiation

Less confident learners

Children should work in a small group supported by an adult to plan and collect the data.

More confident learners

Children should work together to plan their investigations, making group decisions and being able to explain their thinking.

Curriculum objectives

- To complete, read and interpret information in tables, including timetables.

Success criteria

- I can decide on appropriate scales to present data graphically.

You will need

Equipment

Computers with graphing software, or squared paper

Differentiation

Less confident learners

Some children may need assistance when deciding on an appropriate scale and creating their graphs.

More confident learners

Children may manipulate the 'look' or style of their graphs if using a software package, making group decisions about the clearest representation.

Lesson 2   Oral and mental starter 64

Main teaching activities

Group work: The children should use this lesson to complete their sports activities and record their measurements. Remind them that it is important to measure accurately and record on the tables that they have prepared since their graphs can only be as good as the data they collect. The interactive teaching resource 'Graphing tool' can be used for recording and displaying data in bar chart or line graph format. Also remind them to use their time wisely.

Progress check: Ensure that the children are 'on task' and will, by the end of the session, have appropriate data for their graphs.

Review

Use this time to check the children's progress and iron out any difficulties. Ask: *How are you going to turn the data into a graph? What type of graph will it be?*

Lesson 3   Oral and mental starter 73

Main teaching activities

Whole-class work: Before the children go on to create their graphs, either by hand or with a computer software such as *Number Box* or *Microsoft Excel*, they need to establish a viable and manageable scale for the x- and y-axes. You may need to revise the use of computer software packages in order to help them do this. The necessary scale will depend on the data collected and the size of the sample. Remind the children that the graph must fit on one page and that changing the scale can make the data look very different.

Group work: The children should create graphs to represent their data.

Progress check: Ask: *How have you decided on the scale for your graph? Will it fit on the page? Will each bar be different enough for a reader to be able to distinguish between very close measurements? Are you able to put all the lines graphs for each person in your group on one graph or will it be too confusing? What could you do instead?*

Review

Remind the children that the reason we use graphs to represent information is that they give a pictorial representation of data and they should be able to be read quickly and easily. Comparisons should be clear. Ask the children to look at the graphs that they have produced so far in their group and to evaluate their clarity. Ask: *How can you improve on them? Do they show what you wanted?*

Curriculum objectives

- To complete, read and interpret information in tables, including timetables.
- To solve comparison, sum and difference problems using information presented in a line graph.

Success criteria

- I can understand how the information represented on graphs can look very different when different scales are used.

You will need

Equipment

Computers with graphing software or squared paper

Differentiation

Less confident learners

Children may need support to complete their graphs.

More confident learners

Children should produce a number of graphs that look quite different despite the information being the same.

Lesson 4
Oral and mental starter 69

Main teaching activities

Group work: Remind the children how graphs can look very different when the scale is manipulated and that this is often used by the media or industry to make an argument or point more obvious. Ask the children to complete their original graph first and then to go on to represent the same information but change the scales. Ask them to consider how this changes the 'look' of the information.

After completing their graphs the children should experiment with changing the scales on the y-axis to manipulate the 'look' of their graph. This can be linked to the Computing curriculum.

Progress check: Ask: *How has changing the scale altered the look of your graphs? Which one is easier to read? Which one makes the winner of the competition look best? Which one makes the winner look worst? What might someone think at first glance at your graph, if they didn't read the scale carefully?*

Review

Ask the children to share their alternative graphs with the class and to talk about the differences that they have found. Discuss how this might be used in the commercial world to sway opinion.

Curriculum objectives

- To complete, read and interpret information in tables, including timetables.
- To solve comparison, sum and difference problems using information presented in a line graph.

Success criteria

- I can use graphs to illustrate an event.
- I can pose questions and interrogate a graph to elicit further information.

Differentiation

Less confident learners

These children could work as group to write their report with an adult 'scribe'.

More confident learners

Expect higher level questioning.

Lesson 5
Oral and mental starter 73

Main teaching activities

Independent and paired work: First ask the children to produce some questions and answers to extract further facts and figures from their graphs. For example, What was the difference between the longest and shortest throw/jump? Therefore what is the range of this graph? Who had covered the most ground after five minutes? Whose heart rate was the first to slow after exercise?

Having done this they should use some of their facts and figures to produce a short, 'sports report' which they could present to the rest of the class. These could be displayed along with the graphs or maybe even recorded and turned into a multimedia 'sports programme' for other classes.

Progress check: Ask: *How are you comparing the different statistics? Are you using the language of difference and measures correctly? What was the time difference between your fastest and slowest times? Is this measured in seconds, minutes or fractions of a second? Have you thought about the superlatives often used by sports reporters that could be included in your own report?*

Review

Have a grand presentation of the sports reports and allow the class to ask further questions about the data. Review what they children have learnt through this activity.

■SCHOLASTIC

Curriculum objectives
• To solve problems involving addition, subtraction, multiplication and division and a combination of these, including understanding the meaning of the equals sign.

You will need
1. Check
Oral and mental starter
57 Mystery number

2. Assess
'A sporting problem'

3. Further practice
Oral and mental starter
46 It's all in a word

Mixed operation problems

Most children should be able to work out which operations to use to solve a practical problem.

Some children will not have made such progress and will require extra practice identifying the correct operation needed to solve a practical problem.

1. Check

57 Mystery number

Use the oral and mental starter to check the children's understanding of mathematical vocabulary and as a basis to discuss problem solving and unravelling information. Less confident learners will need reminding about some of the vocabulary.

- *Explain to me what this word in this problem means. Tell me the calculation you used. What strategy did you use? How will you check your answer? How would estimating help you to be accurate?*

2. Assess

Children should read photocopiable page 251 'A sporting problem' very carefully and decide on a way of working. Observe the choices that they make and the accuracy of their calculations. Confident learners will be able to comprehend the problem and make appropriate calculations to solve it. Other may have difficulty deciding on the important information and ways in which to translate the problem into a calculation. Record the outcomes.

3. Further practice

Use the oral and mental starter to practise the vocabulary of number and calculation and then encourage children to write their own word problems using the given vocabulary. In this way they will have practice in understanding how such problems are constructed.

Curriculum objectives
• To solve problems which require knowing percentage and decimal equivalents of ½, ¼, ⅕, ⅖, ⅘ and those fractions with a denominator of a multiple of 10 or 25.

You will need
1. Check
Oral and mental starter
51 Fraction problems

2. Assess
'Sale at Great Gardens'

3. Further practice
Oral and mental starter
50 Percentage pairs

Photocopiable sheets
'Match the percentage pair'

Using fraction and percentage equivalents to solve problems

Most children should be able to convert between fractions and percentages to solve simple problems.

Some children will not have made such progress and will require more practice in recognising or calculating equivalents and then using these to solve problems.

1. Check

51 Fraction problems

Add some simple percentage problems into the oral and mental starter and use it to establish how fractions and percentages are part of daily life and to provide children with the opportunity to solve such problems.

- *What is the equivalent percentage/fraction of this amount? How do you know? What knowledge do you use to solve this problem? Do you use fractions or percentages?*

2. Assess

As the children solve the questions on photocopiable page 252 'Sale at Great Gardens', observe how they make connections between fractions and percentages and how they calculate. Most children will understand how to calculate a sale price but some may forget to subtract the reduction from the original price. Record the outcomes.

3. Further practice

The oral and mental starter and photocopiable page will give children more practice in working out the equivalent percentages and fractions based on multiples of 10 and 100.

You will need
1. Check
Oral and mental starter
 Area calculator

2. Assess
A selection of rectangular items; lengths of rope or garden canes to create squares, rectangles and composite shapes; metre rules and/or tape measures

3. Further practice
Oral and mental starter
 Reversing area

General resources
Interactive activity 'Perimeter and area'

Calculating the area of squares and rectangles using appropriate measures

Most children should be able to use their knowledge of the formula area = length × breadth to calculate the area of rectangles, squares and composite shapes and to express this in metres squared or centimetres squared.

Some children will not have made such progress and will require more practice in calculating area and using the appropriate unit of measure.

1. Check
 Area calculator

Use the oral and mental starter to relate factor knowledge to the formula area = length × breadth. Confident learners will be able to find the area and also the inverse, working out the possible lengths of the sides from a given area. Observe those who are less confident, who can multiply the lengths together but who do not have a secure understanding of what area means.

- *How do factors help us to calculate area or to find all the possible lengths of sides? What do you understand area to be? What unit of measure do we use for area? How does it differ from perimeter? Why can area not be measured in centimetres?*

2. Assess

Encourage the children to measure and calculate the area of the items provided. Create larger composite shapes using garden canes or ropes and observe how the children calculate the area. Confident learners will be able to divide up composite shapes into the squares and rectangles and combine these to give the area of the whole shape. Record the outcomes.

3. Further practice

The interactive activity gives further practice in applying the formula area = length × breadth. The oral and mental starter gives practice in finding the lengths of sides from the area.

You will need
1. Check
Oral and mental starter
 On the line

2. Assess
'Walking holiday'

3. Further practice
'Blank axes'

Extracting comparison data from line graphs

Most children should be able to read various scales and interpret the information given on a line graph. Some children will not have made such progress and will require practice with reading information from a line graph, especially interpreting the information between points.

1. Check
 On the line

Use the oral and mental starter to observe how well children can estimate an unmarked position on a number line and relate this to reading scales where a value falls between two marked points. Observe how efficiently the children are able to do this. Some children will need extra practice to do this confidently.

- *Where is the midpoint? How do you know? What information can you use to estimate the value of an unmarked point on a line or scale? What can you do to help you?*

2. Assess

The children use the information on photocopiable page 253 'Walking holiday' to plot two lines on a line graph. Observe how they read the information between points on their graph and use it to make comparisons. Record the outcomes.

3. Further practice

For further practice with drawing and reading information from line graphs, distribute 'Blank axes' for the children to create their own line graphs.

Oral and mental starters

Number and place value

64 Place value elimination game

Write a five-digit number (such as 65,213) on a piece of paper and hide it from the children. Write the digits of your number on the board in a random order. Tell the children to ask questions to which the answer may be *Yes* or *No, higher* or *No, lower.*

For example: *Is the 5 digit in the tens column?* (No, higher.)

Explain that they have 20 questions to work out the position and place value of each digit.

73 Four operations

Ask a child to provide a three-digit number. Indicate the numbers 3, 6, 30, 5 and 8 written on the board. Ask the children to use only these numbers and any or all of the four operations to get as close as possible to the three-digit number. Less confident learners could use calculators. Ask the child with the closest answer to explain his or her calculation, so that everyone can try it.

Repeat, asking for a new three-digit number.

Measurement

65 Area calculator

Ask the children to remind you of the formula for finding the area of a rectangle. Draw some rectangles on the board labelled with their length and breadth measurements. Use mixed units as well as simple measurements, such as 5m × 6m; 3.5m × 200cm, and so on. Ask the children to calculate the area on their whiteboard and hold them up when you say: *Show me.*

75 It's a matter of scale

Ask the children to explain how they would solve the following:

- *A recipe gives an amount to feed two people. How would you change the recipe to feed eight people?*
- *A packet of sweets contains two mints for every three toffees. How many toffees would be needed for a packet of sweets that contains 12 mints?*
- *I use three onions to make 0.5 litres of soup. How much soup could I make if I used nine onions?*

Ask further similar questions.

66 Reversing area

Continue to explore area but this time, draw on the board rectangles showing the area not the dimensions. Ask: *If the area of this rectangle is 42m² what could the measurements of each side be? Could there be more than one answer? What if we used decimal numbers?*

Repeat with other areas such as 50cm² and 100m².

Statistics

67 Thirty days ...

Ask if any of the children have a strategy for remembering how many days there are in each month. Some children may know the old rhyme:

30 days has September,

April, June and November,

All the rest have 31 except February which has 28 days clear

and 29 each leap year.

Another strategy is as follows: Hold out a clenched hand in front of you with the four knuckles uppermost. The knuckles represent months with 31 days, and the spaces in between represent the months with 30 days or less. Start at the knuckle of your index finger 'January' (31), then the space between that and the next knuckle 'February' (28 or 29, ie not 31). Continue until you reach the knuckle of your little finger 'July' and then start back at the knuckle of your index finger for 'August' and carry on.

Extend the activity by asking questions that use this information such as:

- *What is the total number of days in June and July?*
- *How many more days are there in October than in February?*
- *Are there more days in the first three months of the year or the last three months?*

68 Pick your measure

Ask measurement questions such as:

- *What unit of measurement would you use to measure the amount of liquid in a bath? What about a drinking glass; a teaspoon; a bucket? Explain your choice.*
- *If you knew that a drinking glass held 300ml and a bath held 120 litres of water, how many glasses would it take to fill the bath? How did you calculate that?*

Multiplication and division

69 Speedy times

Ask quick-fire times tables questions such as: 5×3, 7 lots of 2, double 9. Ask the children to write their answers on their whiteboards and hold them up when you say: *Show me.*

Fraction

70 A fraction or a percentage?

Ask some simple fraction questions, such as ⅓ of 30 and ¼ of 24.

Then ask: *If we know ⅓ of 30 is 10, what is ⅔ of 30? How did you work it out?* (Two lots of ⅓).

Ask some similar questions such as: ⅕ of 25, ⅖ of 25; ⅓ of 27, ⅔ of 27; ¼ of 24, ¾ of 24.

Or ask quick-fire percentage questions such as: 10% of 30; 20% of 60; 15% of 40; 25% of 24; 50% of 32; 11% of 120. Ask children to show the answers on their whiteboards.

72 Doubling and halving

Start by playing 'Doubling around the room', with the groups passing on a number and doubling it each time. When you call *Change*, they change from doubling to halving. Start with 0.5, 1.5, 3.2, 3.1, 4.5, 0.7 or 1.2.

Repeat a few times with different starting numbers.

Oral and mental starters 71 and 74 continue on the CD-ROM.

A sporting problem

■ Use the information below. Write the calculations you use to solve each part of the problem.

Mr B has a problem. There are four different sporting events booked for the same day and he has the job of organising the transport.

There are three minibuses available, each carrying 18 people, and three coaches, each carrying 38 people. At least two adults must accompany each minibus or coach. There are 238 children in school that day. 56 are going to a football tournament; 27 have been invited to the school athletics event in the next town; 18 are swimming in the inter-schools swimming gala and 6 have been picked to try their hand at archery.

1. How many children will be staying at school because they are not involved in any of the sporting activities? _____

_____

2. How many adults would be out that day? _____

_____

3. How many minibuses or coaches should go to each event? _____

_____

I can solve mixed operation problems.

How did you do?

Sale at Great Gardens

Item	Original price	Sale price
Patio table and chairs	£300	
Garden swing	£59.50	
Bat and ball set	£15	
Shed	£278.98	
Spade	£35	
Tray of petunias	£6.80	
Rose bush		£12

I can use fractions and percentages to solve problems.

How did you do?

Name: _____   Date: _____

Walking holiday

Two friends went on a walking holiday. Fit Jim was very keen to cover as much countryside as he could each day. His friend, Slow Mo, was just happy to be out in the fresh air.

■ Plot the distance they cover in the day as a line graph on the axes below. Draw a separate line for each person.

	7am	9am	11am	1pm	3pm	5pm
Distance travelled by Jim	2km	10km	18km	24km	32km	40km
Distance travelled by Mo	0km	3km	5km	9km	9km	15km

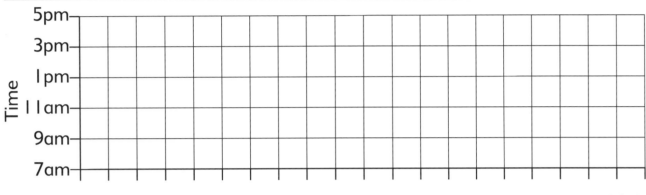

■ Now use your graph to answer the questions.

1. How far had Jim travelled by 8am? _____

2. What time do you estimate Jim left the hotel? _____

3. Estimate how much further Jim had travelled than Mo by 12 noon. _____

4. How long did Mo stop for lunch? How do you know? _____

5. How much later did Mo leave the hotel than Jim? _____

6. Jim walks at a steady 4km an hour. How long did he stop for lunch between

   11am and 1pm? How do you know?_____

   _____

7. Estimate the distance travelled by each person by 9.30am. _____

_____

I can interpret information from line graphs to solve problems.

How did you do?

Name: _____   Date: _____

Every picture tells a story

■ Using your imagination and your knowledge of graphs, think about what each of these graphs might be showing. Label the axes of each graph and give the graph a title.

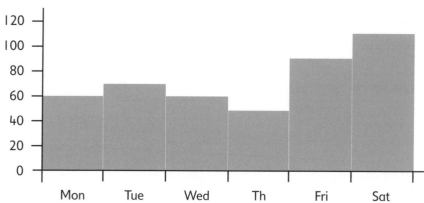

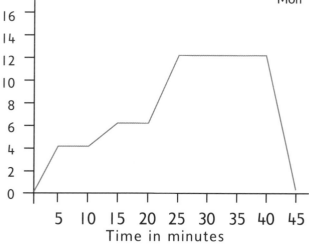

A graph to show contrasting

temperatures in _____

and _____

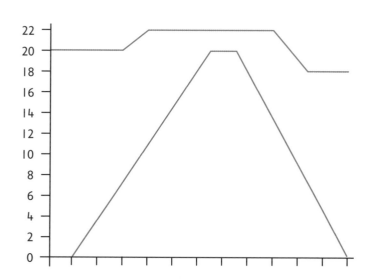

I can understand that graphs only have meaning with labels and titles.

How did you do?

PHOTOCOPIABLE

Vocabulary list

Number and place value

above/below zero, approximately, ascending, between, compare, decimal place, decimal point, descending, digit, estimate, greater than (>), hundred thousands, hundreds, hundredths, integer, less than (<), millions, minus, **negative number**, numeral, order, partition, pattern, place value, positive number, **Roman numerals**, round, sequence, size, ten thousands, tens, tenths, thousands, ones

Addition and subtraction

add, answer, approximate, calculate, calculation, counting back, counting on, decimal place, decimal point, difference between, digit, estimate, even, explain, formal standard method, hundred thousand, hundreds, hundredths, informal calculations, **integer**, **inverse**, jotting, method, million, minus, multiple, **numeral**, odd, ones, operation, partition, place value, plus, problem, reason, reasoning, round, significant digit, solution, strategy, subtract, sum, symbol, take away, ten thousand, tens, tenths, thousands, thousandth, total

Multiplication and division

add, answer, approximately, **area**, calculate, calculation, calculator, **composite number**, decimal place, decimal point, difference, digit, divide, divisible by, divisor, equation, estimate, even, explain, **factor**, factorise, hundred thousands, **inverse**, method, million, minus, multiple, multiply, **numeral**, odd, operation, pattern, place holder, place value, place, plus, predict, prime factor, prime number, problem, product , **quotient**, reason, reasoning, relationship, remainder, round, significant, solution, square number, square root, strategy, subtract, sum, symbol, ten thousands, thousands, total

Geometry: properties of shapes

2D, acute angle, acute, angle measurer, angle, anticlockwise, **bisect**, clockwise, degree (°), diagonal, diagonals, horizontal, including equilateral triangle, **intersect**, irregular, isosceles triangle, kite, names of shapes, obtuse angle, obtuse, parallel, parallelogram, perpendicular, polygon, protractor, quadrilateral, rectangle, **reflex angle**, regular, rhombus, right angle, right-angled triangle, scalene triangle, set square, side, square, symmetry, two-dimensional, vertical

Fractions

add, approximate, cancel, decimal fraction, decimal place, decimal point, decimal, **denominator**, difference, divide, divisible by, divisor, double, equivalent, equivalent fraction, estimate, **factor**, fraction, halve, hundredth, **improper fraction**, **inverse**, minus, mixed number, multiple, multiply, **numerator**, operation, **per cent (%)**, **percentage**, plus, product, proper fraction, quotient, remainder, round, subtract, sum, tenth, **thousandth**, total, unit fraction

Measurement

12-hour clock, 24-hour clock, am and pm, **area**, calendar, centimetres cubed (cm³), cubes, cuboid, day, days of the week, divisor, **factor**, formula, gallons, grams (g), imperial, measures: ounces, hour (h), imperial unit of measure, length, measure, measurement, metric unit, metric units of measurement and their abbreviations: kilograms (kg), litres, millilitres (ml); imperial measures: pints, minute (min), month, months of the year, **perimeter**, pounds, **scale factor**, **scale**, second (s), standard unit, stones; scale timetable, volume

Geometry: position and direction

coordinates, direction, line of symmetry, mirror line, motion, origin, position, reflection, reflective symmetry, **translation**, x-axis, x-coordinate, y-axis, y-coordinate

Statistics

analyse, axes, bar chart, bar line chart, calculate, calculation, chart, classify, comparative data, data, explain, graph, horizontal axis, information, interpret, label, line graph, maximum/minimum value, method, mode, pattern, pictogram, predict, problem, questionnaire, reason, reasoning, relationship, represent, **scale**, solution, survey, table, tally, title, vertical axis

Equipment list

Number and place value

Blu-Tack®; calculators; cards showing the numbers 256, 187, 387, 342 and 196; dice; dice marked +10, +100, +1000, −10, −100, −1000; internet access; number line which extends into negative numbers or bead string; 100 square

Addition and subtraction

calculation aids such as Diennes apparatus or bundles of straws (HTU)

Multiplication and division

access to ICT: internet; blocks or centimetre cubes; bundles of straws in tens plus individual straws; cake baking ingredients and equipment; calculators; counters of at least two different colours; dice; Diennes apparatus; hoops; newspapers giving exchange rates; spreadsheet software; straw bundles or bead strings

Geometry: properties of shapes

A4 card; coloured pens, calculators; Clixi or Polydron; glue; mirrors; plain paper; protractors/angle measurers (and a large scale version for board use or ICT equivalent); rulers; scissors; squared paper; square templates; 2D shapes

Fractions

blank cards, approximately 20 cards per pair; blank playing cards; calculators; card or commercially available fraction pieces; centimetre-squared paper; commercially available plastic fraction sets; counters; cubes; dice, fraction shapes; labels and items for a 'shop'; marker pen; multilink cubes or similar; up to 4 cakes

Measurement

a collection of items to measure known weights such as 50g, 500g and 1kg; a selection of bus and train timetables; a selection of containers; a variety of cubic and cuboid containers; a variety of equipment for measuring mass using a variety of scales: a top pan balance, a set of bathroom scales, a spring balance, electronic digital scales; a variety of items (or pictures of items) for children to match to appropriate measuring equipment; a variety of items that children might choose to pack for a winter holiday: jumpers, shoes, book, toothbrush; camera; capacity measuring equipment: jugs and measuring cylinders with a variety of different scales; centimetre-squared paper; chalk; clear plastic 1000cm³ cube containers; clock faces with moveable hands; coloured pens; Diennes apparatus; dry sand or water; food packaging displaying weight labels; internet; magazines; measuring equipment: rulers, metre rules and tape measures; metre sticks; paper; peg boards and elastic bands; newspapers; recipe books; rulers; tape measures; suitcase; wooden or plastic centimetre cubes or cubes that clip together: Multilink apparatus

Statistics

computers with graphing softwares: *Number box* or *Microsoft Excel*; sports equipment; squared paper; various measuring equipment: stopwatches, measuring tapes, trundle wheels, pedometers, sports heart rate monitors